"Get up kid ... you're in some deep shit."

Hmmm. Not exactly what I had in mind. But who was I to argue with Christ?

"Come with me, boy."

Slowly, things were coming into focus, and as I reached out to touch the hem of Christ's robe I noticed that he was wearing black, shiny combat boots with white laces. Peering through bloodshot eyes, I sluggishly raised my head to discover that either Jesus had enlisted, or there'd been a military takeover in Heaven. Either way, I was indeed in deep shit.

Everyone else was gone. All that was left of Ricky was one tennis shoe. I followed officer Jesus through the bushes and around the corner to the front of the house, to find a small crowd gathered around a fire truck. A long hose was stretched from the truck, down the street, and into the front door of the house next door.

Must have been a fire while I was asleep. Funny, I hadn't heard any alarms or smelled any smoke. "Did they put it out in time?" I asked.

The MP never even looked at me. "They're not pumping water in, kid, they're pumping water out. Guess you and your buddies had a good old time last night, huh? Yeah, sticking that garden hose in the mail slot of the front door and letting the water run all night was real fun, huh kid? Hope you're still laughing when your old man gets a hold of you."

"But ... but ... but ..."

"Yeah, 'butt' is right, kid. That's what your old man's gonna kick after I drag your happy ass home. Sure hope y'all can afford to live on less money, 'cause the military doesn't take kindly to dependents flooding an Officer's house. Probably gonna cost your old man a rank or two."

A rank or two? A rank or two! Deep shit was an understatement.

The Brat Chronicles

Michael Ritter

A Literary Road Publication

Published by Literaryroad.com
6523 California Ave SW, #193
Seattle, WA 98136
www.literaryroad.com

This is a work of fiction. Names, characters, places, and incidents either are the product of the author's imagination or are used fictitiously, and any resemblance to actual persons, living or dead, business establishments, events, or locales is entirely coincidental.

The Brat Chronicles
© 2005 Michael R. Ritter - Potty Chair Publications – Austin, Texas
Cover Illustration by Michael Ritter
1st edition printing - 2006

Library of Congress Control Number: 200693922
A Literary Road trade paperback ISBN: 1-934037-21-4

For Dad, Mom, Cyndy, Mark, Connie and Ruth; my wonderful wife, Barbara, for her unconditional love and support; and the friends of my youth who mean more to me with each passing day.

The Brat Chronicles

Michael Ritter

TABLE OF CONTENTS

Chapter One
GOING UNDERGROUND

It wasn't just a key. Oh, it looked like one, and you used it like one, but this was no ordinary key. It was a badge of independence, a license to ride in the fast lane, a ticket on the Babe Roller Coaster, a passport to cool.

Only a few kids were lucky enough to get the key. We all dreamed about it, bugged the shit out of our parents while pursuing it, and now I had it. The key that opened the door to freedom ... adventure ... romance ...

The Maid's Room. Man, I couldn't believe it! I was moving into the Maid's Room! No more listening to the endless fighting of my brother and sisters. No more entrapment at the dinner table, pretending to pay attention while my mom told me something for the umpteenth time. No more grilling about why I spend so much time in the bathroom. My childhood was behind me! I had reached the turning point! Nirvana loomed large on the horizon!

On the surface, there really wasn't much to it. A small, dark room with one window, an old radiator for heat, and access to the filthy bathroom used by the cleaning crew. Deep in the basements of the family housing units at Ramstein Air Force Base in Germany, the military had built single rooms that, in an earlier time, were used to house live-in maids. Each apartment had one, and while most people used them to store their old belongings, some bright parent eventually realized that the space could be used to store his pain-in-the-ass teenager.

Of course, many parents came unglued at the notion of their teenage sons and daughters having what were, essentially, their own apartments. Some went so far as to forbid their daughters from dating guys who lived in their Maid's Rooms, and the Officers' Wives Auxiliary Council, feathers ruffled, wrote a scathing article for *Stars and Stripes* that protested the "sordid activities" that were occurring in Maid's Rooms all over the base. After that article hit the fan, a lot of kids had to move back upstairs with their families; the only surviving Maid's Room dwellers were the really trustworthy or the really cool, or both ... a potent combination.

It was 1972, and I was loving life. I was almost seventeen, and about to start my senior year at Kaiserslautern American High, which was in the German town of Kaiserslautern (better known as K-Town), a few miles from Ramstein AFB. My old man had secured me a great summer job; my mom had finally given up hope that I was going to get a haircut; Nixon was ending the draft at the exact moment I was becoming eligible for an all-expenses-paid tour of Vietnam; and now the Maid's Room. Man, it just didn't get any better!

Through the open door of my family's upstairs apartment, I could hear my mother's last obligatory whimpering. "I don't know, Ray, do you think we're doing the right thing? I guess we are." She loved to ask my old man questions, and then answer them herself.

"Right," the old man offered. My dad's a man of few words. Good thing.

Suddenly, my little brother Mark, shakily balancing an armload of my records, came stumbling through my doorway. "I heard a kid got his wanger cut off by a German biker gang that had followed him back to his Maid's Room. Man, I'll bet you are gonna be so scared down here, by yourself."

"Hey watch it, you little jerk!" I snapped back, irritated by the invasion of my sanctuary. "Any of my albums get broken and you know what I'll do to that precious Star Trek model of yours."

Actually, my brother's a good guy. And even though he was as happy to see me go as I was to leave, we'd shared some good times and had often depended on one another when the old man's military career shot the family around the world. But at that moment, he was just an uninvited guest in my soon-to-be swinging bachelor pad.

"Nobody got his wanger cut off," I insisted, "and don't say that crap in front of Mom or I'll pound you! Man, if you blow this for me, I'll …"

"And give up having my own room?" Mark grunted as he dumped the records on my bed. "Are you kidding? I can't wait to finish moving your junk down here."

"Yeah? Well, it better all be here, too," I threatened, "every record, every poster …"

"And every Playboy?" He gleefully added.

Oh no! Somehow, in the frenzy of the big move, I'd forgotten to secure my secret stash of Playboy magazines! They were hidden in the back of the closet in the golf bag Dad had given me on my thirteenth birthday. "Now that you're a man," he'd said, "maybe you can appreciate a 'man's game'."

Yeah, I know … but he meant well.

I'd let Mark in on my secret, being that he'd have found it anyway. I made him promise that he would never rat on me, and that he would sit in the closet when he looked at them. But the shit-eating grin on his face told me that the latter promise had already been broken. The brother-bond of fear and intimidation had been challenged.

I raced up the stairs, shot past my mom, tripped over my baby sister, wobbled into the half empty bedroom and threw open the closet door. Much to my dismay, the bag was gone! Not just one Playboy, but the whole bag! I quickly decided that I'd have to kill him.

In a flash, I was standing at the Maid's Room door, my hands gripping the doorjamb. With the determination of Samson, and panting like George Foreman in the fifteenth round, I contemplated Mark's execution. But before I could ask my brother how he'd like to be remembered, he opened his mouth and uttered a word, just one word …

"Wanger."

I was screwed. If I unloaded on him, he'd tell Mom the story of Eunuch Boy, and I'd have to listen to every one of her "reservations" about letting me move down here. She might even cancel the whole deal!

"Okay, man," I growled, "where are they?"

"You let me have one of 'em and I'll tell you," Mark snickered.

"You give 'em back and I let you live," I bargained.

"You hit me and I tell Mom about the kid who got his …"

"You tell Mom and I kill you anyway," I promised him.

Mark sat on the bed and stared at me. I could hear the little wheels in his thirteen-year-old brain, spinning away. My only hope was that he was too stupid to figure out that he had me. It was like a game of chess, and he was about to make a critical move. Finally, he spoke, "And you still have to live upstairs."

Checkmate.

"All right," I whined, "which one?"

Mark leapt from the bed and excitedly declared, "February, 1971!"

Guess I wasn't the only one reaching Nirvana that day.

* * *

In the summer of 1970 my old man, Master Sergeant Ray Ritter, was transferred to Ramstein Air Force Base. That's right … at a time when the military was dumping troops all over Southeast Asia, Ray Ritter and family were gently deposited in an American suburb that just happened to be carved out of a forest in Germany. This wasn't the first time that Dad's military assignment had been fortuitous. He had enlisted in the Air Force in 1952, but was never sent to Korea. In 1966, Dad was presented with a four-year hitch in, of all places, California … a land of bronzed babes and hippie uprisings. And now, the new decade had brought my family an entirely fresh outlook that was, again, a world away from danger.

In California, the Ritters pretty much lived the "Brady Bunch" life, at a lower income level … really, right down to our groovy, striped bellbottoms. Even though an NCO's pay wasn't much, Dad worked a part-time job on the flight line every night, and Mom sold Avon to all the other sergeants' wives, so there was always enough money to ensure that the Ritter kids looked "so nice".

The impending move to Germany was met with a great deal of excite-ment at our house. We'd lived there once before, in the early sixties, and we kids had very fond memories of the experience. While Mom saw an opportunity to expose us to the cultures of Europe, and Dad breathed a sigh of relief that the assignment hadn't been Saigon, us kids were jazzed about living overseas for many reasons, some shared and some not. But one simple pleasure that we all looked forward to was Gummi Bears candy … not those waxy, tasteless things you can buy now at the 7-Eleven … real, thick, fruit juicy, bounce-'em-between-your-teeth-and-tongue Gummi Bears!

Then again, I had a much more urgent reason to want to beat it out of the country.

Living overseas as a military brat, you interact almost exclusively with other brats. But, when living stateside, military kids often go to school with "civilian" kids, and of course those kids have friends who go to other schools, and soon you get to know a whole network of kids.

It's a great deal, if you play it right. A guy can have one girlfriend who lives in base housing, and another who lives in the suburbs. The trick is to make sure they never meet one another. Fundamental to success, however, is having trustworthy friends who won't run their mouths off to their girlfriends about your "double-dipping". So in essence, the plan is flawed from the beginning since, with the proper motivation, any fifteen-year-old girl can get any fifteen-year-old boy to rat out his buddy. Therefore, it's always just a matter of time before one girlfriend finds out about the other one and you're dead meat. But hey, at fifteen, stupidity is a way of life.

In my personal drama, girlfriend "A" found out about girlfriend "B" because, in the heat of a five-minute hickey, best friend "C" told his girlfriend "D", who couldn't wait to rat out "E" (that's me). All of a sudden, the whole alphabet was involved, and football fullback brother of "A" was threatening to do some ass-kicking. So, just as I had prepared myself for a dateless life of looking over my shoulder, Dad came home with orders for Germany. Hell, Gummi Bears were just icing on the cake.

We left California via the standard, middle-class mode of transportation—the family station wagon. In 1970, every family with more than two kids had one. Our wagon had a far back seat that faced the opposite way; it was kind of cool to ride backwards because there was always some melodrama playing out in the car following us: moms screaming at kids, dads screaming at moms, kids screaming in general.

We were on our way to Iowa to spend the rest of the summer with my grandparents, while Dad went on to Germany to find us a house. That's one thing about the military—they're real hip on telling you where to go, but not too keen on providing a place to live once you get there. For a three bedroom apartment on base, we faced at least a year's wait, so Dad was dropping us in Iowa until he could find some German who was desperate enough to rent him a house in the village.

After battling through three days of bologna sandwich fights, countless rounds of "quit touching me!" and 437 choruses of "Let There Be Peace On Earth," the Ritter Platoon landed on my poor grandparents. There we stood—all six of us: Dad, Mom, Mark, Cyndy, the little girls, and me. Actually, there were seven of us, but my two youngest sisters were always referred to in the collective sense. I think by the time Mom gave birth to numbers four and five, it just became easier to start placing us into subgroups. The following week, Dad departed for Germany, and what would come to be known as the "what's wrong with Mike?" summer began.

Keokuk, Iowa. Named after Chief Keokuk. Home of the, uh … where people would come from miles around to see, um … world leader in the production of … named after Chief Keokuk. There was nothing to do … absolutely nothing.

My romantic difficulties notwithstanding, I'd loved living in California. Everything that embodied the late 1960s started, or ended, in California. In California, the times were most definitely a-changin'. In Iowa, the times were a-standin' still.

Realizing that I faced at least a couple of months with nothing to do but watch the corn grow, I could think only of the day when Dad would call, and we would be on our way to The Fatherland. I couldn't wait to say goodbye to McDonald's, and *guten tag* to bratwurst and beer.

The summer in Iowa was also the beginning of the Hair Wars. Actually, the Hair Wars were preceded by a series of skirmishes, dating back to the first time I'd seen the Beatles on TV. Like the Crusades, the

Hair Wars would go on forever, leave a lot of scar tissue, and produce no real winner. Quests rarely do ... it's the nobility of the act itself that is the true reward. And in 1970, in a world that cried "gimme a head of hair," I was determined to join the great challenge to the Establishment and grow my hair long—a soldier in the fight against social injustice, military imperialism, and political corruption. And besides, the girls really dug it.

My father's two-and-a-half month absence created a power vacuum ... and my first real opportunity to let my hair down, so to speak. My strategy had to be simple; I knew that even at half strength, the power of the parentcy is staggering, so it would be foolish to engage in a direct confrontation. No, this called for cunning, subtlety, guerrilla warfare. It wouldn't be enough merely to win a skirmish; lasting victory would depend upon my mother's total abdication, followed by her enthusiastic support.

All strong leaders have their weaknesses: money, power, sex, booze, dressing their pets in stupid little outfits, Jean-Claude van Damme movies—those preeminent priorities that precede all else. For Mom, it was the stamp of peer approval. Her family crest consisted of two crossed vacuum cleaner hoses surrounded by clusters of lint balls and adorned with a banner that read, "What Will the Neighbors Think?" While she never went so far as to cover the furniture with plastic, I swear we had wall-to-wall carpet that never saw a shoe print.

So, it was no surprise that Mom chose to view "the Sixties" through Audrey Hepburn glasses; she regarded it as a time when people were judged not by the color of their skin, but by the content of their closets. She loved the new "mod" clothes, and was young enough to have a genuine appreciation for the need of every generation to express itself. But while she understood and accepted the fashion savvy of bell-bottom pants and Nehru jackets, the idea that any son of hers was going to go out in public looking like one of those "longhaired druggies" was out of the question. No ... the only way that she was ever going to give on the "hair issue" was if she was sold on its social acceptability. I would have to alter her concept of the Bohemian—in other words, turn Charles Manson into Donny Osmond.

In the past, Hair War skirmishes had pitted my friends and me against the parental fortress, armed only with the stale "Jesus wore his long" argument. We may as well have been shooting ourselves, since that logic was always summarily dismissed by a simple "You aren't Jesus" response. So this time I had to carefully choose my allies. My grandmother was a screaming liberal from way back, who had supported every progressive cause since Woodrow Wilson's first stab at the League of Nations. She actually served as the president of the Keokuk NAACP—no small task for an old, white woman. But she was my mom's mom and, as it is with every generation, her support would only help to solidify my mother's anti-hair resolve. I needed someone whose opinion Mom unquestionably respected, whose very lifestyle was a shining tribute to stability, trust, and personal character. And I had the perfect candidate—my mom's Aunt Ginny.

My grandmother's sister, Aunt Ginny, was one of the original non-conformists. She never allowed a television in her book-filled house, grew her own vegetables, loved to engage in spirited political debate and, most importantly, Mom thought she hung the moon. Yes, Aunt Ginny was the ideal comrade, and group boredom quickly provided a golden opportunity, in the form of a road trip to her house. I used every minute of the two hour drive to draw up my battle plan. Each move had to be calculated ... there was little room for error.

A few props would be needed to help make my case, some squeaky clean examples of the "flower-power generation." I knew Aunt Ginny had two college-age daughters, and chances were good that somewhere in a TV-less house, there was a rock 'n' roll record or two. I only hoped their tastes ran more toward Paul Revere and the Raiders than Led Zeppelin. As we pulled into the driveway, my chest pounded with anticipation. I couldn't chicken out now. The time had come to make my stand.

There was always something tranquil and permanent about Aunt Ginny's house, which is very special to a military brat who's spent the better part of his life surrounded by government-issue furniture, in olive-drab apartments. The things in her house looked like they belonged there, each item wedded to the next, collectively creating the soul of the house. Sounds strange to say it now, but I know the karma of that house played a significant role in the events that transpired on that historic day.

We feasted on the traditional Aunt Ginny home cooking, and then retired to the living room to take several trips down memory lane. And suddenly I saw it, in the corner of the room, unobtrusively resting against a stereo speaker. My Holy Grail ... a Monkees album ... perfect. Who could ask for a better quasi-flower-child than Davy Jones?

"So, how are Susan and Becky doing in college?" Mom unwittingly opened the door. "Good thing you have such smart daughters, Ginny. You never have to worry that they'll drag home some refugee from a barber shop." And she promptly closed it again. "I swear," she continued, "these kids today. I just don't know what to make of them, Ginny. All I know is, the day this one (pointing at me) comes home looking like his sisters will be the last day he ever steps foot into my house!"

Now, it's hard to appear nonchalant when, before you've called your first witness, you realize your case is going up in flames. Davy Jones hadn't even been given a chance to take the stand, and I could already smell the foul odor of defeat. Still, I had to remain in control, cool … calm …

"I can't believe you wouldn't allow me in the house if I had long hair! That is so cruddy! Do you have any idea how shallow that is? You can't look at someone and assume he's a lowlife just because he has long hair! You gotta get to know him," I shrieked in a single breath.

"I wouldn't want to know anybody who looks like some of those hop-head weirdos I see on the news," Mom shot back.

"Weirdos, huh? Just because they have long hair. Well, what about Davy Jones?" I pleaded in the most innocent tone I could muster. It was a desperate attempt to salvage my plan. "He's got long hair. But you like him. I even heard you tell the little girls how cute you thought he was."

There … I had cast the bait. The connection had been proposed—long hair equals cute.

Mom reacted with a lengthy, thoughtful, parental pause; you know, those blips in time when the whole world stands still, the air leaves the room, your teeth grind, your forehead sweats, and you wish to God they'd say something, anything, just to break the tension. You don't know what they're going to say, and odds are it's going to piss you off, but still you wait with anxious anticipation, because maybe, just maybe …

"Well, you're not Davy Jones."

Augh! It still irks me to think about it. That was it. Turn off the lights, 'cause this game's over. She was never going to change her mind. It was hopeless. I looked imploringly at Aunt Ginny, silently begging for any moral support. Help me. It's time for the cavalry. This is your moment to save the day and strike a blow for freedom.

Aunt Ginny just sat there and continued with her knitting.

And then something happened that convinced me there are moments in life—rare, to be sure—but actual moments when your personal planets converge, and the light of lady luck shines right in your face. There I stood, in the middle of the room, alone in my darkest hour, clutching a picture of Davy Jones, when suddenly the back door swung open and in skipped Becky. Following closely behind was her boyfriend, a lanky, sandal-footed, love-bead-wearing, long-haired vision, in a "Remember Kent State" sweatshirt. "Hi, Ginny," he pleasantly greeted.

Great! He could talk!

"Sorry to be late," the vision continued, "after class, I got so wrapped up in a conversation with my students that I just lost track of time. I tell you, there's a fine group of young, dedicated social workers about to hit the streets. Ready to fight poverty and despair, full of hope and ambition. It's nice to think I had something to do with that. Oh, excuse me, I'm sorry," he apologized, extending his hand in Mom's direction. "You must be Becky's cousin. Please excuse my rant. I get pretty excited about my work."

I could only watch in amazement while Mom, her best "I can't believe what I'm seeing" smile plastered on her face, pretended she didn't notice the boyfriend's "ensemble". She reached out and stiffly accepted his handshake.

"Peg, this is Beck's fella, Jack. Jack Barclay," Aunt Ginny happily announced as she hugged her daughter. "He's a professor at the university. Remember? I told you about him when he spent last Christmas with us, and you said he sounded like the perfect guy. Smart, handsome, caring … the perfect guy."

To this day, I can still recall a faint blast of trumpets ringing in my ears. They were the chords of victory, with just a hint of Holy thrown in for good measure. Like the soundtrack from *Camelot*.

"And you were so right, Peg," Becky joyfully agreed, throwing her arms around Jack's neck. "He is the perfect guy! Mom loves him as much as I do."

Davy Jones hit the floor, and mentally, I was right down there with him. This seemed too good to be true, and it occurred to me that maybe Mom had really blown her top and knocked me out cold. Then I would be dreaming, and this would all make sense. I couldn't believe my luck! With Jack to point the finger at, there was no way that Mom's standard response, "Well, you're not so-and-so," would float. She had to face it— this guy had Aunt Ginny's blessing, and Aunt Ginny was Mom's favorite person, her "I only hope you grow up to be as good as" example. It was all I could do to hold back a maniacal laugh and a fast dance around the room, but I knew this was no time to get cocky. It's best not to taunt a caged animal, especially when it's your mother.

The next several hours were spent in conversation about the world, the country, each other; before we realized it, the time was almost one o'clock in the morning. Getting to know Jack had been great. I had actually forgotten all about my objective as he regaled us with stories of his exploits in the Peace Corps and the times he had spent protesting the war and fighting for civil rights. For me, at that age, in that time, he represented everything I wanted to be.

I had a hard time falling asleep—my mind was still racing from the excitement of the evening. I got up and went downstairs, in search of another hunk of Aunt Ginny's homemade bread. Inching my way through the darkened house, I could see light coming from under the kitchen door. When I swung it open, I found Mom seated at the table, pouring through an old, family picture album. She looked up, a little startled, then smiled and returned to her memories.

"Michael," she began, without raising her head, "you know, there are more important things in this world than whether or not you have long hair."

I sighed, unsure of where this was leading. "I know, Mom, but ..."

"So you can grow it out a little bit," she conceded. "But no longer than that Davy Jones character! And promise me you'll keep it clean!"

The next morning, we left on the return trip to Keokuk. Aunt Ginny moved a few years later, and I never did see that house again. But Becky and Jack tied the knot, and had a son. He's twenty-three now, and works as a lobbyist for the National Rifle Association ... guess it's a generational thing.

Chapter Two
NO MORE FOR ME, THANKS

"Ow! Damn!" If anyone ever asks, it does take more than one person to hang a parachute from the ceiling.

"Michael, are you okay?" Now, explain this to me. I was in the basement with the door closed and the Rolling Stones' "Jumpin' Jack Flash" at volume ten, and still, still Mom could hear me slam my thumb with a hammer. I say it's a sixth sense that women develop when they become mothers. Mom radar ... it's the only explanation.

"Yeah, Ma," I yelled up the stairwell. "Don't come down!"

For the better part of a week I'd been busy transforming a dingy Maid's Room into a teenage Taj Mahal. This was no staple-a-few-posters-to-the-wall job, mind you. We're talking major renovation. I'd painted one wall like a huge American flag which, except for my substituting the stars with a picture of Nixon and Agnew dressed as Batman and Robin, seemed to please my dad. Black lights hung in all four corners of the room, illuminating the fluorescent posters that covered the walls, and the ceiling was encased by an orange and white parachute. The room hadn't come with a closet, but the Air Force had provided an army green metal locker that looked really good after I painted a bright yellow peace sign on the door, and blanketed the rest of it with Playboy Playmate pin-ups (except for Miss February 1971, of course). I wanted to have lots of candles around to create the proper mood, but Mom swore I'd end up burning the building down, so I settled for those little white Christmas lights. When you wad a few strands of those suckers up, plug them in and throw them under your bed, man, the effects are really something.

From knee-level up, every inch of wall space was covered with something ... all except for a three-by-three foot bare space I'd positioned right above the bed. This was reserved for pictures of all the girls I would date while I lived in the Maid's Room. I thought the space adequate—if not a bit ambitious—and not at all in bad taste. Okay, maybe labeling it "Conquest Wall" was a little tacky.

And there on the nightstand, next to the lava lamp, was the pièce de résistance—a field phone that was wired from my room to the family apartment upstairs. A direct line of communication to the home front that allowed for a sense of security, but also served as a not-so-subtle way of saying, "Sure, come visit ... but call first."

"Hey, boy! … I catch you down here with my daughter and I'll wring your scrawny hippie neck! And keep that goddamn excuse for music turned down or I'll bust down your door and shove that stereo up your ass!"

I froze right there in the middle of the room, too terrified to turn around. God, the paint was still wet on the walls and already some irritated father was threatening me with bodily harm. Wait a minute! This was my castle, and nobody was going to threaten me in my castle! I clenched my fists, took a deep breath, and turned slowly around, prepared to confront the injustice that bellowed behind me.

"You are so easy!" It was my best buddy Sean, doubled over laughing in the doorway. "What were you gonna do, beg for mercy? Hey, Willie … you were right, he fell for it."

"Told you he would," came the reply from my other friend, Willie, who'd been waiting in the hallway. "Hey, check it out!" he continued as he looked around the room. "This place looks great! And there's the field phone! Man, are you lovin' life or what!"

Sean was one of the coolest guys I'd ever known. Not just hip cool, but cool-as-ice cool. The guy was a star athlete, had a black belt in karate, and a stare that would make Dracula blink. He had this "Clint Eastwood/Mr. Spock" deal going. You never knew what he was thinking. The quote under his yearbook picture read "wink and I'll do the rest,"

By contrast, Willie was a good ol' boy from Tennessee who still thought the South would rise again. A real "bacon grease, gravy and biscuits" kind of guy, he was the sixth Willie in a long line of Willies that stretched back to the Civil War.

"You jerk-offs! I knew it was you guys all along." Yeah, right, that's why my hands were sweating rivers.

"Welcome to the Maid's Room club. This calls for a celebration! Look what I five-finger discounted from my old man!" Willie crowed, pulling a pint of Southern Comfort from his jacket pocket. "It's cocktail time, fellas."

Some lessons in life come hard and some—like calculus—you never get. But the lesson that comes out of a bottle is one that almost everybody flunks no matter how many times they take the test. Drinking Southern Comfort was like taking the SATs, and it had been over a year since I last studied.

My first experience with liquor had been in California when I was thirteen. We used to camp out a lot when I lived there which, in reality, meant a few kids in sleeping bags behind the fence of somebody's backyard, giving us an excuse to run around all night creating general havoc. Harmless stuff, like peeling daisy decals off Volkswagens and sticking them over doorbells; putting frogs in car ashtrays and glove compartments; letting the air out of bicycle tires; trying to elude the MPs … stuff like that. If we were really lucky, there'd be a girls' slumber party going on and we'd go over and bug them for a while.

But on the night of September 16, 1968, things got a little rough.

We were doing our usual Friday night campout. Much earlier in the summer, my friend Ricky Boones had swiped a 16-ounce Schlitz Malt Liquor from his old man, and we were so scared of getting caught with it that we'd stashed it on the garage roof for the whole summer to allow time for things to cool off. Ricky and I decided that the statute of limitations on the Schlitz had probably run out, so we climbed up on the garage to retrieve our ill-gotten booty.

The trouble was, there were eight guys camping out—more kids than even a 16-ouncer could supply—and we didn't want to share our hard-earned treasure with any of them.

Camp outs always started late. First we'd run around with our girlfriends, or play a little football, or go to a movie, so it was usually around ten-thirty by the time we all started gathering at some predetermined spot to decide where we were going to toss our sleeping bags. Then, somebody would get drafted into running to the Snack Mart for cigarettes. Base curfew was midnight, so going to buy a pack of smokes involved the extremely hazardous business of hiding from patrolling Military Police, and serpentine through a minefield of built-in sprinkler heads which were near impossible to see at night and near fatal to trip over. We knew a kid who actually broke his ankle tripping over one of those babies in the dark. But we knew that the cigarette run was our only hope if we wanted to partake of our treasured elixir, so Ricky and I volunteered.

Our cigarette mission completed, we popped the top on the beer. Now, there's nothing quite like the taste of a warm Schlitz Malt Liquor that has been fermenting under the hot California sun for three months. It was awful, the worst thing I'd ever put in my mouth, really disgusting. So we did the only sensible thing and gulped it straight down, thus avoiding our taste buds altogether.

About halfway back, we saw the silhouettes of five figures coming towards us. It was a group of the "tough" kids … you know, those yellow-toothed, greasy-haired guys who wore the same pair of jeans to school every day, and whose sole accomplishment was the fact that they knew how to French-curl cigarette smoke. We always tried to avoid these pinheads at school, but well-roasted malt liquor has a way of building stupidity and, self-preservation being what it is, we asked them to come back to camp with us.

"Okay, man. We'll come with you. We usually don't hang out with wimps like you guys, but you look pretty cool, drinkin' malt liquor and all. Here, have a shot of this Jack Daniels we stole from Jake's old man."

We were so proud, standing there with our empty Beer Can Trophy, about to make the leap from Boy Scout to Hell's Angel. All we had to do was drink a little whisky, and how much could that hurt?

Needless to say, our sober buddies were impressed, though not amused, by our new found courage when we showed up with the rat pack in tow. So, as the rest of my friends did their best cool impressions, complete with appropriate hand and neck gyrations and the all-important "Gotta cigarette, man?" Ricky and I flopped down on our rolled up sleeping bags and began our little journey into the head spin abyss. The last thing I remembered was a voice saying, "So what are you pussies gonna do tonight?"

I woke up about six-thirty the next morning to the sound of heavy engines. The smell of stale vomit hung in the air, and cigarette butts spotted the trampled grass. A lone figure stood over me, his outline enveloped by the breaking sunlight. Oh, God! It was Jesus. I'd overdosed on stagnant malt liquor, and Jesus had come to carry me to Heaven! The figure raised his arms, and I waited for the soothing words that would ease my troubled soul and welcome me through the Pearly Gates.

"Get up kid ... you're in some deep shit."

Hmmm. Not exactly what I had in mind. But who was I to argue with Christ?

"Come with me, boy."

Slowly, things were coming into focus, and as I reached out to touch the hem of Christ's robe I noticed that he was wearing black, shiny combat boots with white laces. Peering through bloodshot eyes, I sluggishly raised my head to discover that either Jesus had enlisted, or there'd been a military takeover in Heaven. Either way, I was indeed in deep shit.

Everyone else was gone. All that was left of Ricky was one tennis shoe. I followed officer Jesus through the bushes and around the corner to the front of the house, to find a small crowd gathered around a fire truck.

A long hose was stretched from the truck, down the street, and into the front door of the house next door. Must have been a fire while I was asleep. Funny, I hadn't heard any alarms or smelled any smoke. "Did they put it out in time?" I asked.

The MP never even looked at me. "They're not pumping water in, kid, they're pumping water out. Guess you and your buddies had a good old time last night, huh? Yeah, sticking that garden hose in the mail slot of the front door and letting the water run all night was real fun, huh kid? Hope you're still laughing when your old man gets a hold of you."

"But … but … but …"

"Yeah, 'butt' is right, kid. That's what your old man's gonna kick after I drag your happy ass home. Sure hope y'all can afford to live on less money, 'cause the military doesn't take kindly to dependents flooding an Officer's house. Probably gonna cost your old man a rank or two."

A rank or two? A rank or two! Deep shit was an understatement.

I pleaded my case all the way home in the police jeep, "I didn't do it!" All the way up the walkway, "What do you think, I'm crazy?" Up to the moment my dad opened the front door, "It was some other guys!"

My dad stood in the front doorway. "Thanks. I'll take it from here," was all he said. I used to hate it when my parents stood in the doorway and made me slither past them to get into the room. I just waited for the hand up the backside of my head … their little way of helping me inside. But Dad didn't do anything and, for the longest time, he didn't say anything either.

"Dad, I didn't flood that house, I swear! Ricky and I were on our way back from buying some cigarettes …"

"Cigarettes?"

"Uh … yeah, and we ran into these guys who had some Jack Daniels …"

"Jack Daniels?"

"Uh … yeah. And they came back to camp with us and Ricky and I passed out "

"Passed out?"

"Uh-huh … and that's the last thing I remember. But I know I didn't have anything to do with that house being flooded."

Following a lengthy, parental, thoughtful pause, the old man spoke. "Okay, Michael, we'll see."

We'll see? The worst possible scenario. Now I had to live in limbo until it was all sorted out. It occurred to me to pray, but the thought of Officer Jesus was still fresh in my mind, so I opted just to go to bed and wait it out.

The next few days were the longest of my life. The Military Police came by that afternoon to hear my story, and attempted to get me to rat out my friends. Having passed out prior to the actual deed, I was really very little use to their case, and knowing this I held out for a good, oh, fifteen seconds before breaking down and giving them the name of every kid I'd ever known. Mom was going bananas. The "incident" was the talk of base housing, and she just knew everyone was thinking ill of her. I was restricted for life without parole.

On Monday, my dad was summoned to the Base Commander's office. While I never did hear what was actually said, I'm still alive, so I assume they believed my story.

What I mostly remember from the whole experience are the calm words of wisdom my dad shared with me upon his return. "If you ever do that again, Michael, I'll break both your arms." Both my arms. Can't argue with that.

Another two years passed. It was October of 1970 before I was again introduced to the joys of self-induced nausea. October's a big month in Germany, lots of carnivals and beer and food and beer and parties and ... you get the picture. Anyway, we were living in the village of Kindsbach waiting for base housing to open up. Dad had rented an old, drafty, three bedroom house from this elderly German couple, the Grossbergers, who lived in a small house in the back. The place had stone floors and, when the wind was blowing, the chill made it feel more like a crypt than a home. The Munsters would have loved it. Mom hated it. There were seven of us living in a place with one bathroom and a water heater the size of a postage stamp. I spent many early mornings shivering in a tub of cold water trying to get clean. All I really had to do was sit in it long enough to let the ice form on my body, and then break off the dirt with my hands. But it beat the hell out of Keokuk, and we were all together, so like many other military families before us, we just made the best of it.

One afternoon our landlords came by and invited us over to get acquainted. No easy feat since they spoke little English, and the only German we knew consisted of being able to ask where the bus station was. We were all sitting around their small living room smiling a lot, when Herr Grossberger brought out the first of several bottles of good German white wine. "Ve vill drink now, ya?"

"Sure, you bet," my dad replied. What a silver-tongued devil.

"Okay, you kids go out and play now," Mom said, "and stay out of the street." My siblings were more than happy to oblige. I, on the other hand, stayed seated. "Come on Michael, you too."

"No, no …" Herr Grossberger said, handing me a glass of wine. "Okay for him. Come drink." So, with international relations hanging in the balance, my mom had little choice but to give in, and we all clinked our glasses and drank to new friends. (I think that's what we drank to … after all, the guy was speaking German.)

The wine was real sweet, and went down real easy. All six glasses of it. Apparently, it's the German custom to simply turn your glass over when you have had your fill of wine. Being unfamiliar with this little practice, and wanting to take advantage of my parents' newfound tolerance, I decided to seize this opportunity to prove that I was ready to take my rightful place in the adult world.

I think it was right around glass number four that I began to feel all warm inside and, surprisingly enough, very comfortable with my hosts. I mean, this was really cool. Sitting in a German's house, slamming wine with my parents. Unbelievable. I loved this country! As Herr Grossberger filled my glass for the sixth time, it seemed like a good moment to open up the conversation and express a genuine interest in these good people, who were kind enough to invite me into their home and get me toasted on this great wine.

"So, were you a Nazi during the war?" I asked.

Now, there's a word that transcends all language barriers. Nazi. It just kind of hung in the air for a while, with no one wanting to claim it. You know, like a fart in an elevator.

Mom dropped her wine glass as she and Dad stumbled all over themselves trying to apologize for my insensitive behavior. I thought I was just being politely inquisitive. He was an old German, and for all I knew he might have known Hitler personally. "Aw, c'mon Mom. It's cool. We are all friends here aren't we, Herr Grossberger, old buddy?" I slurred as I stood up and put my arm around his shoulder.

"Okay, chief, time to go home," my dad broke in. "I think you've experienced enough culture for one afternoon."

I never did get an answer to my question. I did, however, get to watch Mom freak out for an hour and a half, which culminated in my being sent to my room for the rest of the night. At least she didn't make me take a bath.

I stood at the foot of the stairs that led up to my bedroom for the longest time. It wasn't because I felt as though I'd embarrassed my parents, or that I was dreading being sent to my room—when you live in a house with six other people any moment of solitude, even imposed solitude, is a welcomed experience. My legs simply refused to cooperate. It was as if the signal that went from my brain to my legs was on flashing yellow, and my whole body was stalled at a four-way stop. I just stood there gripping the banister, looking down at my feet and gulping for air.

"Come on Mister Grownup," my mom sneered, "get up those stairs."

Okay, okay, I thought to myself. I can do this. Just one step at a time. No way was I going to set myself up for an "I-told-you-so" lecture, so taking a deep breath, I bounded up the stairs. As I reached the top landing, I turned and looked back at my mom staring up from the bottom of the stairs. There, made it! Six glasses of wine ... ha! It would take more than six glasses of wine to ... slow ... me ...

Mom never saw it coming. Like a shot in the dark, the six glasses of wine and the two sloppy joe sandwiches I'd had for lunch came spewing out of my mouth and down the stairs like a volcanic eruption. There was vomit everywhere, clinging to the walls, dripping from the banister, pooling around my sister's favorite doll that had been left on the staircase. And I knew I was a dead man. Or at least I wished I was.

I spent the next two hours on my hands and knees with two buckets beside me, one filled with Pine Sol, and the other with residual puke. I'd clean a spot, get a whiff of cleaning solution, and throw up, think about the wine, and throw up, breathe, and throw up. Finally, my parents took mercy on me and let me go to bed. As I drifted off to sleep between waves of nausea, I swore that I'd never touch alcohol again.

I swore it again a year later as Willie, Sean, and I took turns throwing up in my trashcan.

Chapter Three
IN THE BEGINNING

Mom liked to leave little notes on my pillow whenever we had an argument about something. We'd have real screaming matches about the war in Vietnam; racial strife and protests that were happening all over America; the way I treated my family; the length of my hair; drinking milk directly from the carton; just about anything. It's said of children and parents that the acorn doesn't fall far from the tree, and while there were times I was certain my mom was a real nut, I have to admit that we share certain characteristics that often made life in the Ritter house seem like a scene from *One Flew Over The Cuckoo's Nest*. Sometimes the arguments would get a little harried, and usually when I felt I was losing the fight, I'd pull out my, "I didn't ask to be born" defense. She'd just counter with her, "I didn't ask for you either" retort. Neither of us would apologize to the other, not in person anyway, so I'd come home and find a note pinned to my pillow saying that she was sorry that we fought, but that she'd only said what she did because she "loved me so much and wanted what was best for me." It was actually a pretty good system; it gave us the night to calm down, so by the morning, we could just resume our normal life of staying out of each other's way.

Dad was the calming factor. Not that he'd get involved in any argument Mom and I were having; he'd just lay low until he'd reached his breaking point, and then tell us both to shut up. It worked every time. That's the thing about calm people, when they finally do blow up you know you've crossed the line and it's best to tuck your tail between your legs and beat it out of the house. Dad was definitely the disciplinarian, but he never raised his hand in anger. All he'd have to do is glare at us from under those dark, scowling eyebrows and mutter, "Damn it, I'm sick of this." That's when we knew it was time to cut our losses.

I don't remember Dad ever smacking any of us kids no matter what we'd done wrong. Wait, I take that back. Once, when I was in the sixth grade, I got a "C" on my report card, and Mom insisted that he spank me to drive home the fact that they expected better from me.

Dad grudgingly complied, marching me into my room and closing the door behind us. I was really nervous … I'd never been "sentenced" to a spanking before, and visions of woodshed tactics filled my head. Now, even though I was only twelve years old, I was already almost six feet tall, so the simple logistics of bending over Dad's knee for a spanking challenged some law of physics. Dad didn't say anything for a few minutes, just stood and looked out of my bedroom window. I sat on the bed feeling like a complete idiot and wondering what was so wrong with getting a "C" in the first place. I'm sure even budding nuclear scientists get the occasional "C" in grade school.

Finally, Dad broke his silence. "You know, Michael," he said softly, "I really hate having to go through this." Oh, no, he was going to give me the "this hurts me a lot more than it hurts you" speech.

"I'm sorry, Dad," I whimpered.

"Yeah, me too," he continued, as he walked over to the bed and sat down beside me. I prepared myself for the worst.

"You have no idea how much I ... don't want to spank you."

Huh?

"But, you know your Mom, if I don't go through with it she'll never give me a moment's peace."

I sat there for a moment, motionless, trying to figure out what the old man was thinking. Perhaps there was some room for negotiation. The more important thing here seemed to be Dad's desire to keep Mom happy, not the need to punish me for daring to be average. As I racked my brain for a possible compromise, Dad suddenly spoke. "Well, I guess I don't have any choice, Michael. Hand me that book on your dresser."

Now wait a minute, Pop, I thought, pleasing Mom is one thing, but smacking me with a book is something else!

I slinked over to my dresser, picked up the book, and handed it to Dad.

"Okay, chief," the old man said as he gently fingered the back of the book, "it's show time." As I closed my eyes in anticipation of tears, Dad continued. "When I hit this book, you yell out so your Mom will be satisfied, and I can go watch the news."

I opened my eyes and stared at the old man, a puzzled look on my face.

"Look, Michael," the old man continued, "I'm not saying it's okay to get a "C" on your report card—I just don't agree that it's a capital offense. I will tell you this though buddy, these grades will look a lot better next report card or I'll really have to hit you where it hurts."

Who cares about the next report card, I thought, just as long as I get through ...

"I'll take you down to the barber and have your head shaved."

My head shaved! I'd rather get hit with the entire set of encyclopedias!

Dad and I performed our "mini soap opera" as Mom, I'm sure, listened intently at the closed door. After a few rounds of him smacking the book and me letting out a whimper or two, Dad left the room telling me to "straighten up and fly right" because next time "will be a lot worse," I waited a few minutes before walking out to the kitchen where Mom was busily making dinner.

"Don't come crying to me, Michael," she said. "This is between you and your father."

Right. And we planned to keep it that way.

And so it went. My parents are like a balancing act ... Mom's the high wire, and Dad's the guy trying to get across it without busting his ass. I always felt just a little sorry for my old man as he tried to maneuver his way through a minefield of kids, while trying his best to keep Mom happy. It wasn't easy. It's said there are two kinds of people in the world, those whose glass is half empty and those whose glass is half full. Dad's an optimist ... half empty or half full doesn't matter to him; hell, he's just happy to have a glass. But Mom views life as an obstacle course, a series of hurdles that stand between her and a peaceful, happy life. To her credit, she never gives up, and the more barriers she encounters, the more determined she is to jump over them. And even though she makes anyone within earshot miserable while she runs the course, I think she secretly loves the challenge and thrives on the victory that awaits her at the finish line.

My folks are as different as night and day, but in some strange way that fact seems to be the cement that bonds them together. Dad was the tenth of fourteen children, and shared a bed with three brothers in a small, rundown house in East Peoria, Illinois. His was a staunchly conservative, Catholic family who believed in hard work and accepted life as it came. The family had no indoor plumbing for most of his life, so the simple act of taking a bath was a major accomplishment and, in a house with so many people, left little room for modesty. His father worked on the railroad and made very little money, so Christmas presents were limited to an orange, a few pieces of candy, and the occasional small toy or new pair of socks. Dad quit school and went to work when he was sixteen, to help out the family, so while his contemporaries were sitting around the malt shop sipping sodas, he was busy loading cases of Coke onto trucks. It would be natural to build up some resentment under those conditions, but Dad never did. That's just the way it was...griping about it wouldn't change anything.

By contrast, Mom had one brother who was ten years her senior. Essentially, she grew up as an only child in a nice, middle-class neighborhood in Keokuk, Iowa. Her father, Gentry Koch, was a draftsman at the local steel plant, and was as meticulous about his appearance as he was about his work. Her mother was a former school teacher turned housewife, who spent her many free hours trying to organize the city of Keokuk to fit her own vision of utopia. Mom lived a "Bobby-soxer's" life, running around with her girlfriends, dating the basketball team, and pretty much doing whatever she liked ... or could get away with.

My parents' planets converged one summer day in 1953. She was a Junior in high school and he had just joined the Air Force, in an effort to avoid being drafted into the Army. Dad was visiting Keokuk with a cousin of his when he spotted Mom sitting on a stool in the local drugstore. Actually, I'm certain she spotted him, and had one of her girlfriends set up the introductions, but it was love at first sight, whatever the details. With his long, slicked-back black hair, Dad had a dangerous Elvis Presley quality about him, while Mom's freckled face and good nature struck an innocent Doris Day chord. They hit it off immediately and, within a few days, Dad handed Mom his ring and asked her to marry him.

As the young couple wrapped themselves in Romeo and Juliet magic, a dark cloud was forming on the horizon in the shape of my grandmother. Although Mom was used to getting her way, this was one time when her mother was not going to sit idly by and let her daughter "make the mistake of her life." She insisted that my mom give the ring back and concentrate on finishing high school.

Dad was devastated. In a few weeks, the Air Force was sending him to Shemya, Alaska, for a year, and he just knew he'd never see his beloved girlfriend again. He left Keokuk and returned home to Peoria, throwing himself across his bed and crying for hours at the prospect of spending his life without the girl of his dreams.

But my old man was determined. He hadn't asked for much out of life, and he'd be damned if the one thing he really wanted was going to be denied him. Obviously, the only way to my mom was through her mother, so he spent his last free days endearing himself to his human barrier to happiness. Now, my old man is a charming guy ... not manipulative, but charming. He doesn't even realize how charming he is, which makes him all the more so.

Over those few short days, my grandmother realized that Dad was an honest, good-hearted soul who would rather cut off his arm than do anything to hurt anyone, and she gave her blessing to the marriage ... with a few stipulations. If this was true love it would stand the test of time, so she agreed that if the two of them still felt the same way when he returned from Alaska, she would not stand in their way. It was one of the happiest moments of my old man's life ... which was followed a few days later by one of the saddest, when he left his teary-eyed sweetheart and caught the train for the first leg of his journey to the frozen north, a thousand miles away.

While Mom spent her Senior year of high school spinning my old man's ring around her finger and dreaming of the future, Dad lived among the seals and walruses, pining for the day when he'd return home to the girl he loved. That day finally arrived. In September, 1954, Ray Ritter and Peggy Koch tied the knot and, with twenty dollars to their name, started laying the groundwork for what would become a family of seven, and a life filled with adventure and surprise. They must have been really anxious to get started ... I was born the following July.

Dad was transferred to Cannon Air Force Base in Clovis, New Mexico, where they encountered yet another hurdle. According to the military rules, Dad didn't have enough rank to qualify for base housing, much less base housing for a family, so they were forced to rent a small duplex off base.

Life in Clovis was substantially different from life in the Midwest: trees had been replaced by tumbleweeds, the green meadows supplanted by hard, red clay and, for the first time in their lives, they had only each other to rely on. Money was tight, but they supplemented their income by charging merchandise at Sears and pawning it for cash. It was rough at times, but innocence and determination make a powerful combination, and they settled into their little home to await the arrival of their first child ... me.

I was born on July 27, 1955, after putting my mom through delivery room hell for ten hours. It was not quite payday, so my folks had to borrow the eight dollars that the military charged for bringing another dependent into the world. They would be back two years later when my sister, Cyndy, was born. But they were doing better by then ... they had the eight dollars.

With the birth of my sister, we moved out of the small duplex and into an old, rundown, two bedroom house with a big porch. I was only two, so I'm not sure if my memory is real, or if I'm just recalling Mom's stories, but the place was covered with dog shit ... not the yard—the inside of the house. Mom and Dad gagged their way through the necessary scrubbing and disinfecting, and we settled in to what would be our home for the next five years. That house would witness three more trips to the maternity ward for the births of my brother, Mark, and my sisters, Connie and Ruth. Mom was only twenty-eight years old, and already the mother of five kids. I've always suspected that the sap of insanity runs through our family tree.

Life in the house at 321 Ross Street was ... challenging, to use a nice word. There were four kids crammed into one bedroom, with the ever-present baby's crib set up in my parents' room. I can still remember waking up to the sight of freshly laundered diapers hanging on wires strung across the bedroom, resembling a haunting by small ghosts, and scaring the crap out of me in the middle of the night.

I don't know if memories improve with the passing of time, but the house Mom still refers to as a real "rat hole", seemed a comfortable home to me. I can remember standing on the big front porch, eating Dad's infamous "fudge on a spoon" (the stuff never would fully harden), and watching Mighty Mouse through the screen door (yes, even in a "rat hole" we weren't allowed to eat in the living room). I remember Dad blanketing the area under the swing set with little white rocks so we wouldn't track dirt into the house (scraped knees healed on their own, it took time to clean floors). And I recall a pet rabbit that met its demise when Mom, insisting that it smelled too awful to play with, squirted it with room deodorizer (please, don't call the SPCA). But the event that clearly sticks out in my mind was the day the old man brought home new living room furniture.

Dad always harbored this dream of living on a ranch and driving a Cadillac with horns for a hood ornament, so when Mom got on a new furniture kick, he thought he'd surprise her with a living room ensemble that would take her breath away. He knew that Mom took us kids to a neighbor's house every afternoon to get out of the house for a while and enjoy some coffee and adult conversation. During one of these visits, he sneaked the furniture into the house and sat back, waiting for us to return home, basking in the glow of anticipation for what was certain to be an appreciative wife and family.

He must have heard us coming up the walkway, because he met us on the front porch. "Michael," the old man said as he took my baby sister from my mom's arms, "hold your little sister for a minute. I have a surprise waiting for Mom."

He put his hands over Mom's eyes and led her through the front door, guiding her to the center of the room.

"Ta-da," he sang, dropping his hands. "Are you surprised, babe? You always wanted leather furniture," the old man smiled. "Pretty nice, huh?"

There, in the middle of our living room, were three pieces of the coolest furniture I'd ever seen—a sofa and two armchairs covered in white leather. But the best part was, the arms of the chairs had saddles, saddles on them, and right on the middle of the sofa sat a big framed picture of a horse's head. We kids screamed with delight as we jumped up on the armchair saddles, kicking the sides of the chairs with our heels, and pretending that our living room was the Ponderosa. Mom just stood there with her hand over her mouth.

"I know, I know," the old man said, putting his arm around Mom's shoulders, "you're just too excited for words. It's alright, babe, it's nothing less than you deserve."

I'm sure Mom was wondering what she could possibly have done to deserve a living room that looked like it belonged in Dodge City ... but she hugged my old man, gave him a big kiss, and told us kids to quit climbing on her new furniture.

I rushed home from school the next day, anxious to strap on my official Gunsmoke holster and mount my faithful steed, but as I raced through the front door, it was obvious that the days of the Old West were over. The saddles had disappeared from the chairs, and the horse's head had been removed from the back of the sofa.

"What happened?" I asked the old man, who was standing in the kitchen eating a raw hotdog.

"Well, pardner," Dad replied, putting his large hand on my head, "there was a bank robbery last night and the sheriff sent out a posse to round the varmints up. But they were a few saddles short, so your wonderful mother volunteered the ones on our chairs. Life's like that sometimes, son, you have to give up something you really love for the greater good, and we couldn't have a bunch of bank robbers running around loose now, could we?"

Although I was only seven, I knew what the real deal was. Mom hated the furniture, and Dad "gave it up for the greater good". I was really mad at the old man for giving in, but with the passage of time, I came to appreciate that we live in a world of give and take, and even though the old man loved his all-too-brief ranch motif, he loved Mom more. Years later I asked him about the furniture and what had really happened, but all he would say was, "I can always get another sofa and chairs, but I'd never be able to replace your Mom."

I've always heard that you can't really miss what you've never had; so, since we didn't have much, I have very few bad memories of life in Clovis. There were the usual hassles that accompany an old, drafty house with wall-to-wall kids and very little money, but we took consolation in the knowledge that our situation wasn't unique, and everyone else we knew was trying to stay afloat in the same leaky boat. As I said, I was only a little kid, so trauma to me was running out of Sugar Pops cereal. I had adapted to the constant sandstorms that left inches of dirt on the sills inside the windows; a main course of fried Spam for dinner several times a week, and the addition of another kid every time Mom went to the hospital.

The first few years of a military career are the roughest. The Air Force expects a twenty-four-hour soldier; family concerns aren't their problem. It wasn't unusual for the old man to get a call in the middle of the night ordering him to report to the flight line. It was the height of the Cold War, and just a few years since the "UFO incident" at Roswell, in New Mexico. Mom was never sure if Dad was playing war games, going off to do battle with the Commies, or being sent to investigate an alien landing somewhere in the desert. He'd just get the call, ask no questions, kiss us goodbye, and walk out the door with his duffel bag. We never knew when, or if, he was coming back, but eventually someone from the base would call to let us know he was alright. Once he was sent to France, when we thought he was just down the road at the Air Base. Mom and the other young military wives would assemble, and pool their meager resources to make ends meet until "Daddy came marching home."

However, it was during one of Dad's few stays at home that something happened that would change the course of Ritter history, and unplug the baby machine that shared a bedroom with my old man.

Dad and I were in the front yard helping a buddy start his car by pouring gasoline into the carburetor. As Dad turned to answer my hundredth question, his buddy cranked up the engine, and the old man burst into flames. At first I thought it was a really neat trick, and wondered if he'd show me how to do it; however, as I watched Dad's buddy throw him to the rocky ground in an attempt to put out the fire, I realized that something was terribly wrong. Mom, who was watching from the kitchen window, ran out of the front door screaming as Dad rolled on the ground, flames licking his chest and neck. After what seemed like an eternity the fire was out, and Dad got back on his feet, patted his smoking shirt with his hand, and attempted to calm Mom down.

"It's okay, Peg," he said softly, "just singed my eyebrows a bit."

Dad was rushed to the base hospital, where they informed him that he had second and third degree burns from his stomach to the top of his face. As if that wasn't bad enough, Mom decided to make him a little more miserable by telling him she was pregnant with child number five. Mom wasn't too happy about it, and she informed her still smoldering husband that since he was in the hospital anyway, he should go ahead and get a vasectomy. Efficiency in the face of disaster ... that's my mom. Several days later, Dad came home from the hospital a changed man ... in more ways than one.

In 1962, the military must have decided that we'd had the pleasure of Dad's company long enough. He got orders for a year's tour of duty in Greenland, and we weren't invited.

The family went to live in Mom's hometown of Keokuk, while Dad took another unrequested, isolated tour of the frozen north. While my grandparents loved us, they weren't crazy enough to want to live with us, so Grandfather had secured us a small, two story duplex about eight blocks from their home. With a little help from anybody who'd offer it, we set up housekeeping, and embarked on our Dadless journey of waiting out the year until he came home.

It was one terrible year. Mom was alone with five kids, the oldest one being just seven and the youngest still in diapers. We caught every childhood disease from German measles to mumps to chicken pox. There was so much scratching, crying, vomiting, diarrhea, and general nastiness that my grandparents started taking us to their house in shifts just to give Mom a little time to recuperate ... and to rotate the mountain of soiled linens.

The two story deal had two bedrooms upstairs, where us kids slept. Right at the bottom of the stairs, on the floor, was a heating vent that was almost impossible to avoid. Winters in Iowa put 'the froze' in frozen and they last for months, so the damn furnace was on all the time. My baby sister Ruth was just learning to stand on her own. Mom would put her in one of those walker contraptions with the little plastic wheels that enabled her to scoot across the hardwood floors. It worked pretty well ... until she hit the heating vent. Those little plastic wheels melted, and fused to the hot metal, causing the whole house to smell.

One cold winter's morning, I got up from a near sleepless night and groggily crept to my Frosted Flakes breakfast, completely forgetting about the Dante's Inferno that awaited me at the bottom of the stairs.

Just as I was about to take the fateful step, Mom yelled, "Look out for—" Too late! The law that governs gravity had kicked in, and I stepped on the sizzling grate with the full weight of my left foot. Now I was tired and still half asleep, but it took only a split second for my brain to realize that my left foot had made a terrible error in judgment. Instinctively, I jumped up, landing this time with my right foot on the vent, making a matched set. I stood there, hopping like a dummy from one foot to the other … on the vent … until Mom raced over and pushed me off the thing, sending me stumbling across the floor. The grating had practically branded a waffle print on the bottom of my feet, and I sat on the floor crying as Mom spread ointment on the toasted flesh.

I slept with my tennis shoes on for the rest of the winter.

The only positive aspect of our year-long sabbatical in Keokuk was the chance to spend some time with my wonderful grandparents. Over the course of my young life, I had seen them only a few times, usually when Mom was popping out another kid, so my interaction with them had been limited to birthday cards and Christmas presents. Grandfather was an aloof sort of guy, dependable and kind, but not big on affection. Grammie was one of those people who carries the weight of the world on their shoulders. She was always concerned with making life better for the other guy, whether he wanted her help or not. Grammie made a point of letting us know how good we had it, usually by depressing us with stories of some of the unfortunate people who had crossed her path.

Grammie had been stricken with polio when she was three, but the leg brace she wore never slowed her down. Although she was a fine woman with a big heart, her compassion was somehow limited to people outside of the immediate family, and she never missed an opportunity to educate us about the "hard world out there." While she drove my mom crazy with her frantic mood swings, she really did bring a lot of joy to others' lives. To tell her "it can't be done" only served to strengthen her resolve, and I admired her determination.

My grandparents were deeply involved in local and national politics, and Grammie would take time out of every day to read the *Pogo* and *Li'l Abner* comic strips to me. We'd discuss what was being said between the lines, and it was due to her influence that I later developed a keen interest in drawing political cartoons.

Eventually, we got word from Dad that he was coming home, and that he had been transferred to Bremerhaven, Germany. We were all quite excited about seeing Dad again, but Mom was in double heaven. Wow!

Germany! Finally, the military life was beginning to pay off, and now this girl from Iowa was going to be given the chance to see Europe. But, nothing worthwhile comes easy.

Since this was our first trip overseas, we all had to be inoculated against numerous viruses, so twice a week for the next few weeks we drove to the nearest military base for a series of shots. The painful trips were always sweetened by stops at a hamburger joint with a huge playground, and knowing that I'd soon be seeing Dad again took much of the sting out of the needles.

A short time before we were scheduled to depart, I was put on a train to Clarksville, Missouri, for a visit with my Aunt Ginny. I was happy to get far away from the packing fray, and I'm sure that was the reason I was sent. At that time, Aunt Ginny lived above a small gift shop that she owned, so I spent my visit helping her in the store, playing with her piano, and enjoying the solitude and freedom that comes with being away from siblings for a while. After about a week, I boarded the train for the return trip to Keokuk, but within a few hours, the train broke down in the middle of nowhere, and all the passengers were loaded into taxis that would take them to their destinations. I was only seven, and I was traveling alone, so a large, friendly, black woman took me under her wing and accompanied me all the way back to Keokuk. I never knew who she was, and she declined to come in and meet the family, but I'll always be grateful for the kindness she showed a frightened little boy.

When I knocked on the front door of my grandparents' home, Dad opened the door. It was really him, Dad, and I hugged him with all my strength. I was happy to have the trip to Aunt Ginny's behind me, and excited about taking my first plane trip the next day; but more than that, we were a family again, on the horizon of a new life in Germany.

I had imagined that we'd be flying to Germany aboard a military transport, strapped into the cargo area of a B-52 or something, but that wasn't the case. To transport families, the armed services leases aircraft from the private sector so, as we boarded a Pan Am jet, I was thrilled beyond belief. "Look, Dad, a real live stewardess! Look, Mom, I can push this little button and my seat moves back and forth! When are we going to eat? When you flush the toilet, where does the stuff go? How does this stay in the air? Do you think they'll let me see the cockpit?"

The plane was full of military families, with kids outnumbering adults, three to one. Since our whole family of seven wanted to sit in the same row (which consisted of only six seats), my baby sister became carryon luggage and made the trip lying in a cardboard box on the floor between Mom and Dad. Now, it doesn't take long for a kid to get bored so, within an hour after liftoff, the aisles were filled with mothers corralling their screaming children, and discovering new ways to utilize the safety belts. My brother and I occupied ourselves by taking turns looking out of the window at the clouds below, and dreaming up disaster scenarios. "Wouldn't it be neat if an engine blew up and the plane crashed into the ocean and we got to get into one of those rubber boats and we could see sharks and maybe one of those giant squids like in that submarine movie?"

Just as things began to quiet down it was time to eat, and the plane again erupted with conversation as beleaguered stewardesses tossed plates of food at hungry passengers. With great anticipation, we each pulled down our food tray and waited anxiously for our turn to be served, imagining what wonderful culinary delights the Air Force had in store for us. Finally, it was placed before me ... a ham and cheese sandwich ... with mustard! Yuk!

"Mom," I protested, but before I could say another word, she yelled back across the aisle, "Just eat it, Michael." Fortunately, Mark and I had been munching on Tootsie Rolls so I wasn't particularly hungry, but I didn't want to get into trouble for not eating, so I stashed my sandwich in the airsick bag.

About three hours later, the plane hit an air pocket and took a sudden dive toward Earth. We weren't in any danger, but the unexpected jolt turned my stomach and I grabbed for my brother's vomit bag.

"No," he screamed, clutching the paper bag, "this one's mine! Use your own!"

Frantically, I searched for another receptacle to hurl into, but as the warm fluid filled my throat I had no choice. I grabbed my airsick bag and spewed out the remains of twenty-three, half-digested Tootsie Rolls.

Now the bag was already half-full of rejected sandwich, so it didn't take long to fill the remaining space, packing the small bag to capacity and causing vomit to drip down its sides and onto my hands. With chocolate drool hanging from the corners of my mouth, and looking pitifully to Mom for comfort, she leaned forward in her seat across the aisle and whispered, "Next time you'll find a better place to hide your sandwich, won't you?"

I slept through the rest of the flight, and when I awoke, we were landing in Frankfurt.

We gathered up our carryon luggage, including the box of little sister and, as we waited to leave the plane, the pilot's voice came over the speaker.

"Welcome to Germany, folks. Please keep to the right of the aircraft and someone will take you into the hangar for indoctrination."

Like immigrants arriving at Ellis Island, we milled around the large steel structure, searching for somebody—anybody—who knew what should happen next. Suddenly, a microphone clicked on with a loud "pop" and a booming voice echoed though the hangar.

"On behalf of the United States, President Kennedy, and the Government of Germany, welcome, and *guten tag.* I'm Major John Burger. I know you've had a long trip and are anxious to reach your final destination, so listen carefully to the instructions I am about to convey and we will process you through just as quickly as we can. All active military personnel report to the rear of the building, family members please stay with your belongings until your sponsor returns."

An hour-and-a-half later, Dad returned. "Okay, gang, we're on our way."

"To where?" Mom asked.

"Hell, Peg, I just go where they tell me to," the old man responded. "Let's get on the bus and see where we end up."

"You don't know where we're going? How can you not know where we're going?" she demanded.

"Well," Dad smiled, "isn't that the best way to get someplace we've never been?"

Thirty minutes on a bus, two hours on a train, and a taxi ride later, we pulled up in front of the olive-green apartment building that would be our home for the next three years. Mom made a quick survey of her surroundings, noting that the hospital was right across the street, and a playground was located at the end of the block. "Well," she sighed, "when the kids fall off the swing set, at least we won't have far to take them."

Each building had three stairwells, and each stairwell had six apartments, so there were eighteen families living in very close proximity. Bremerhaven is a port city, and large ships carrying Air Force, Army, and Navy personnel often docked there. The military provided everything from beds to pots and pans, so Mom immediately set her sights on getting the house in order, while Dad reported to the base. All I wanted to do was explore my new surroundings, and the hospital next door looked like a good place to start.

In the summer of 1963, remnants of Nazi Germany were still present all over the place, and the hospital was no exception. It was an oversized building, enclosed by a wooden fence that was made not with slats but with ten foot wooden poles placed about six inches apart. The U.S. Army had "acquired" the building after the war, but it still displayed the old German insignia—an eagle standing on a circle of leaves, its wings spread in a defiant manner. Only the swastika, which had once occupied the center of the circle, was missing, and you could still see the bullet holes made by the Allied forces when they removed it with a machine gun. Inside the hospital I discovered a snack bar, newsstand, barber and beauty shop, small grocery store, and what passed for a movie theatre ... all the comforts of home. The grounds were thick with crab apple trees, and a small cemetery and ivy-covered crematory were located at the back of the building. As I walked through the back gate, an old German man in uniform stopped me with a "Halt!" I froze in my tracks, certain I'd been caught by the last surviving soldier of Hitler's army.

"*Kommen Sie herein*," said the elderly man, waving his hand and motioning for me to come over to him.

I raised my hands over my head. "Don't shoot," I cried, "I'm an American."

The old German laughed, removed his helmet, and lit a cigarette. "So, American boy, huh? What are you doing here, American boy?"

"I'm lost," I cried, still holding my hands in the air.

"Vell," the old German said, exhaling a puff of smoke in my face. "I let you go ... this time."

As I ran home I could hear him laughing, and wondered if the Air Force knew there was an old Nazi living behind the hospital. I wasn't going to say anything to anybody ... that guy might find out where I lived.

Surprisingly, it didn't take long to settle into our new surroundings and adjust to apartment life. Actually, Mom loved it. We had three bedrooms and two baths, and the military was willing to let her paint the place any color she wanted, so she was as happy as a pig in a mud hole. We didn't have a car for the first year, so every other week Mom and Dad would catch the bus to the commissary, spend his paycheck, and take a taxi home. Mom would put together dinner menus to ensure that we wouldn't run out of food before Dad got paid again. Instead of buying sweets, she would make after school treats out of cinnamon, sugar, and Bisquick (which didn't taste all that great but was something to stick in our mouths, so both we, and she, were happy).

To make ends meet, Dad secured a part-time job as a projectionist at the movie theatre in the hospital, so we were able to go to the movies and get popcorn for free. It was great! From the comfort of the projection booth, I saw every movie from *Cleopatra* to *Thunderball*, and when the movie was over, I'd stroll the aisles looking for loose change that had dropped out of the patrons' pockets. Before long, the movie theatre became Mom's babysitting service. Whenever she had taken all she could from one or more of us, she'd send us to the movies with Dad, safe in the knowledge that he would watch us and keep us out of trouble.

But, things didn't always work out that way.

When Mark and I got bored at home, we'd climb the walls ... literally. We'd plant our feet on either side of the doorjamb, shimmy to the top, and perch like a couple of vultures waiting for prey to come into view. When one of our sisters would unsuspectingly walk through the doorway, we'd pounce on her, sending her crying to Mom. Then Mom would come storming into our room, spouting threats and trying to grab us, while we cowered just out of her reach, flattened against the wall in the bottom bunk bed. "Wait until your father gets home," she'd yell, and Mark and I would smile at one another, knowing that our punishment was going to be a trip to the movies.

Mark made a great little brother; he was so trusting, he'd let me try anything on him. I'd tell him to stand against the wall with his arms and legs spread apart, and I'd aim my dart gun to "see how close I can shoot these darts at you without hitting you," and he'd do it! Or, I'd tell him to stand in front of the swing with his arms sticking straight out at his sides, and I'd swoop toward him, catch him under the arms with my legs, and carry him up in the air. Of course, the return trip always resulted in Mark scraping his knees on the playground gravel, but he'd do it anyway.

So, we were sent to a "punishment movie," which turned out to be some romantic drama that got very boring, very fast. Mark and I started wrestling around in the projection booth and, while chasing him, I tripped on a cable and crashed into the movie projector, sending the reel flying. The audience immediately started yelling and throwing popcorn at the screen, as Dad frantically tried to untangle the climactic scene that had unraveled all over the floor.

I'd never seen my dad lose control before, but as I tried to help him, he looked straight in my face and growled, "Out ... take your little brother and get out." Not wanting to further test Dad's patience, and being too young to die, we scrambled from the room, searching for something exciting to do. We hung out at the snack bar, went outside and threw rocks, and kicked a can around the parking lot for a while. Then, Mark decided he needed to go to the bathroom.

As we entered the bathroom, I noticed there were bars on the window, and I came up with a scheme that would help pass the time, and might even be worth a few laughs.

"Mark," I beckoned, "I'll bet you this big nickel against your little dime that you can't get your head through the bars on that window."

"I could," Mark answered, "I just don't want to."

"What's the matter, are you … afraid?" I taunted.

"Afraid" is one of those words that will make any male, regardless of his age, do things that he normally wouldn't do. It's a challenge to manhood, and seems to know the way around that piece of our brain that dictates common sense.

"Okay," said my defiant little brother, "it's a bet."

Mark climbed up on the garbage can, hesitated for just a moment, and thrust his head between the bars on the window. "See," he said proudly, "told you I could do it."

"I guess you win," I smirked, "c'mon down and get your nickel."

But as Mark tried to retract his head, his ears hit the bars, and he couldn't move. "What's the problem, Dumbo?" I laughed.

"I'm … stuck, I'm stuck! Get Dad!" he cried.

There was no way I was going to drag my old man into this, so I went outside to the front of the window, thinking I could push him through.

Outside, as people were lining up to buy tickets to the next show, they began staring and pointing at my screaming little brother. I decided to play the role of worried big brother. "I begged you not to stick your head in there," I said in the direction of the crowd, "but you wouldn't listen."

"You made …"

"Seems like I'm always getting you out of trouble. Hold still while I push against you. Quit squirming, I can't get a grip on your head."

The more I pushed, the louder he yelled, until the lady who sold popcorn went upstairs and got my old man. I couldn't stop laughing … until I looked up and saw Dad staring at me through the window, holding his trapped son around the waist. "Having a good time, Michael?" he asked.

"I didn't make him do it," I protested. "Besides, I'm not in charge of him."

We tried lubing Mark's noggin with everything from popcorn butter to motor oil, but he wouldn't budge. Mark looked like a Frankenstein ice cream sundae, with yellow and black goop dripping off his head and creating a puddle on the sidewalk. "How 'bout we tie a rope around the bars and pull him out with a truck," said someone in line. "No, no," replied another helpful bystander, "that'll wreck the building. I think we're just gonna have to cut off his ears."

Mark started wailing. "Cut off my ears? Dad, please don't let anybody cut off my ears."

"Nobody's going to cut anything off you, Mark," the old man said, patting my brother's head. "Just give me a minute to think."

Finally, Dad called the Military Police who cut one of the bars, and freed my traumatized little brother from his trap. The MP's then proceeded to give my old man a lecture about destroying military property and being responsible for his kids, so Dad was not a happy camper.

Dad still had the second feature to show, so Mark and I slinked home without him. Mark's ears were red from all that pushing and shoving, so as soon as we walked through the door, Mom knew something was wrong.

"What happened to your ears, Mark? Michael, what happened to your brother's ears?"

I tried to stall. "I haven't seen them ... aren't they still attached to his head?"

"Don't get smart, young man," Mom said, cradling my little brother in her arms. "What did you do to your brother?"

"I didn't do anything to him," I stammered. "The little jerk got his head stuck between the bars on the bathroom window at the movies."

"How much did you pay him to do something stupid like that?" Mom demanded.

"That's right," I protested, "blame me. You know, Dad was supposed to be watching him, not me."

Mom surprised me with her reply. "You're right, Michael, I'm sorry for accusing you."

I felt really, really bad. Poor Dad. All he was guilty of was losing his temper a little bit, and I was trying to fault him for dereliction of duty.

"Well, you two go wash up and go to bed now," Mom said. "I'll just have a little talk with your father when he gets home." Oh God, one of Mom's "little talks." I'd rather face a firing squad!

Tucked safely in our beds, Mark and I lay silently in the darkness, waiting for the sound of the front door. Dad had no idea that he was innocently walking into a viper's pit, and I pulled the covers over my head in shame.

Finally we heard, "Peg, I'm home."

"I'll be right there," Mom responded as she walked toward the living room, closing our bedroom door as she went by.

This was going to be bad, I thought from my position deep under the covers. She never closes our bedroom door!

Mark and I both got out of bed and leaned against the door, trying to hear what was being said, and hoping Dad would still love us in the morning. Several minutes passed; then, suddenly, we heard a loud crash, like a lamp breaking against a wall.

I couldn't take it any longer! I flung open the door and ran into the living room, crying, "I made him do it, Mom. It's not Dad's fault. I told Mark to put his head through those stupid bars."

Dad and Mom were on their knees, picking up pieces of a broken plate from the floor. "Huh," Dad said, bewildered. "What's his problem?"

Mom stood up and walked over to me, gently grabbing my arms. "I know you did, Michael. Now don't you feel better for telling me the truth?"

"But if you knew, then why …" I whimpered, wiping my nose with the sleeve of my pajama shirt.

"Because I wanted to hear it from you," she explained. "It's important that you learn that even when you think you've gotten away with something, you never really do. It stays with you for a long, long time. Now you can just let it go and not worry about it anymore."

"What a nutty family," the old man muttered, as he sat down at the kitchen table to enjoy what was left of his dinner.

As I watched my little brother, snoring away in the bed next to me, I had to smile and feel a little sorry for him. I resolved, then and there, that I would try to be nicer, to quit taking advantage of him, and to let him know that I really did care about him.

And I wondered just how big my sister Cyndy's ears were.

In many ways, a military base is a little piece of America; even though we were thousands of miles away from the nearest McDonalds, we were surrounded by people who shared our customs. But venture off the base, and we soon realized that we weren't in Kansas anymore.

We loved to go to Spreckenbutal Park. It was close to base housing and smack in the middle of downtown Bremerhaven, so it provided an opportunity to mingle with the nationals, eat at the bratwurst stand, and drink in the "full German experience." Often, Mom and Dad would leave us at the playground while they roamed the park's perimeter, taking a few moments of solitude for themselves.

Now, a park in the States is a casual setting, where people don't really give much thought to what they're wearing. But in Germany, especially on Sundays, the people dress in their finest clothes and stroll down the cobblestone streets, arm in arm, stopping occasionally to shake hands and chat with their neighbors. Leave it to Germans to impose structure and tradition upon a simple walk in the park.

We viewed the whole procession as if it were a carnival sideshow, gawking with wonder at the parade of elderly, widowed, German women roaming the park in their black dresses and clunky high heels. By the same token, the Germans were having a field day whispering about Mom's hair curlers, and Dad's sporty, madras shorts. Of course, we spoke no German, so we didn't have an inkling as to what they were actually saying. But on one particular Sunday, actions spoke louder than words.

Mom decided to take us to the park, while Dad used the quiet time at home to finish some paperwork. Dressed in our usual Sunday afternoon casuals, we set out for the park; however, one by one, several cars slowed down next to us, and each time, a young man would ask Mom questions in German, attempting to coax her to the car. Mom would gesture that she didn't understand, but commented to us that she thought the Germans were very friendly, and was sorry that she couldn't help them. At one intersection, a car driven by a large German man pulled up next to us. He climbed out of the front seat, and walked toward Mom. "*Guten Tag*," he said.

Mom smiled and shook his hand. "Hello, there," she responded.

The German man seemed surprised that Mom was an American, but the confused expression on his face was quickly replaced by a broad smile, and he asked, "How many?"

Mom thought he was referring to her brood of kids, and answered, "Five."

The German's eyes widened. "Five? Only five?" he asked.

"Oh, five's plenty," Mom laughed.

The guy actually shook with excitement as he opened his wallet and took out a German five-mark piece. "Okay," he beamed, holding open the car door, "*kommen sie*."

"No, no," Mom chirped, "it's not that far. We'll walk."

The guy again looked very confused, and stood there with his hand on the car door. I was thinking about the treats we could buy with the five marks. After several moments, he sidled next to Mom and whispered something in her ear.

"WHAT!" Mom shrieked. "SEX? You want me to have ...! Oh ... Oh," she stammered, grabbing me and holding me in front of her. "Have you lost your mind?!"

I guess the guy thought she might call the police, because he quickly jumped back in his car and sped away, with Mom chasing after him, shaking her fist and yelling, "You filthy ... German, you."

We didn't make it to the park that day, but it was fun watching Mom tell Dad her story of being mistaken for a streetwalker. "Can you believe it, Ray? There I was, walking down the street, minding my own business ... and with all these kids! I'm telling you, Ray, it was just awful! And I thought Germans were so friendly."

Dad smiled and looked in my direction, giving me a wink. "Seems like he was trying to be friend—"

"It's not funny, Ray," Mom interrupted. "Michael, tell your father—"

"I understand, Peg," Dad said with mock concern. "I'd be offended, too. Five marks indeed! Hell, baby, you're worth at least five-and-a-half."

The "streetwalker incident" wasn't the only time a German man fell for Mom's charms. Now, I'm not the best judge because, after all, she is my mom, and even though I think I was born with an appreciation for the opposite sex, that doesn't include my immediate family. But, even though Mom had five kids, she was only in her late twenties and, compared to many of the other military wives, quite a looker. So, with all the disclaimers in place, and no need to refer to Sigmund Freud, I'll tell the story of Klaus.

As I've mentioned, field trips through Germany were a way of life for the Ritters. Dad bought an old, green, mini station wagon that was so rusty it had a tin can for a muffler. Still, it enabled the Ritters to be a "family on the go," and brother, we went. We traveled to Hamelin to see the Pied Piper, to Bremen to see the Town Musicians, to countless castles in Heidelberg, and to a huge zoo in Hamburg. En route to the Hamburg zoo, we crossed paths with Klaus, a round-faced German man in his early - thirties who adored President Kennedy, and said we reminded him of the Kennedy clan because Mom and Dad were so young, and had so many kids.

It was one of those chance meetings. We were lost, and Dad, like all men, never consults a map, so we stopped at a gas station for directions. Mom and Dad were "discussing" our situation when Klaus walked up and, in perfect English, gave us directions to the elusive zoo. He then said he didn't have anything else to do, and would be honored if we'd let him take us to the zoo and show us around.

Mom was ecstatic—our own personal German tour guide! Dad was polite, but it was obvious he didn't share Mom's enthusiasm. He's always been a little suspicious of overly friendly people, and didn't relish the idea of this guy tagging along with our family. But Mom was dancing on air, so the old man just "went with the flow."

The zoo itself wasn't all that memorable; I mean, a caged tiger is still a caged tiger, no matter what country it's sitting in. No, the real animal on the prowl was Klaus, and Mom was on the menu for dinner. We were young kids, so we just thought Klaus was being nice when he treated us to zoo souvenirs and chocolate; however, the old man's been around, and he knows an ulterior motive when he sees one. I honestly think Mom was oblivious to the situation because, as we were leaving the zoo, Klaus invited us to spend the night at his parents' house, and before Dad could utter a word, Mom accepted.

Dad fumed in silence as he followed Klaus through the narrow Hamburg streets. "This is just grand!" Mom said gleefully. "Imagine, Ray, we're getting the opportunity to spend a night in a real German house, with actual Germans! We've got to be some of the luckiest people in the world!"

"Whoopee," muttered the old man.

"Oh come on, Ray, it'll be fun. Don't you think so, Michael?"

"I dunno," I replied from my squished position in the crowded back seat. "I guess so. I'm a little worried …"

"Yeah, me too," interrupted the old man.

"I'm a little worried that they're gonna make me eat some awful German food, you know, sauerkraut and stuff like that," I continued.

"And what are you worried about, Ray?" Mom said, tugging on Dad's sleeve.

"Same thing … what this guy's feeding us," Dad mumbled.

When we arrived at Klaus' house, his parents met us with open arms. It was a lovely, large home, built in traditional German fashion, with painted stencil patterns running the entire length of the walls and wood inlays everywhere. Klaus' father had owned and operated a ship-building company before, and during, World War II, so the family had money— which I think made Dad all the more uncomfortable. We were given a tour of the grounds and shown to our rooms. Then we sat down to a feast of German delights that did include sauerkraut. "I thought you didn't like that stuff," I whispered to Dad, as he took a mouthful of the pickled cabbage and glared at Mom and Klaus, who were happily chatting across the table.

"I don't," the old man shot back.

"Isn't this nice, Ray?" Mom said, sitting back in her chair and sipping a glass of wine.

"Oh, yeah," muttered the old man, "wonderful."

We enjoyed a restful night, and were greeted in the morning by a smiling Klaus, who fed us a breakfast of hard German rolls, assorted jams, and fruit. Dad took bites between trips to the car; he was anxious to get back on the road. "Okay, all packed up, let's hit it," he announced, standing behind Mom's chair and putting his hands on her shoulders. "Thanks for the hospitality, Klaus, but it's time for me to take my family home, and leave you with yours."

Mom was nestled in the front seat of the car, a broad smile on her face, basking in the memories of the previous evening. "Klaus is so nice, isn't he, Ray? So polite, so thoughtful ... he'd make a good catch for some lucky girl."

"Preferably someone who isn't already caught," the old man replied, without looking at Mom.

"I was thinking of our babysitter, Babble. Don't tell me you're jealous, Ray. Why in the world would Klaus want an old, married lady with five kids?"

Dad scowled. "It's in their nature, Peg. Germans are always trying to take what isn't theirs."

Mom just laughed it off, but Dad failed to see the humor, and drove the rest of the way home without saying a word.

Several weeks passed. Then one day, there was a knock on the front door and there stood Klaus, his arms full of presents. He had dolls for my sisters, small bone-handled hunting knives for Mark and me, and flowers and chocolates for Mom, so we were all happy to see him. Dad just sat in his chair, arms folded across his chest, frowning.

"Well, what do you know, I was just thinking about you, Klaus," Mom said, shaking his hand.

Dad shot up in his chair. Klaus beamed.

"We have a German gal, Babble, who baby-sits for us now and then, and I think you two would really hit it off," Mom continued.

Dad sat back down. Klaus quit smiling.

"Yeah, Klaus," the old man smirked, "she'd be just perfect for you ... nice, cute, single!"

Mom sat on the arm of Dad's chair and slipped her hand into his. "Who knows, Klaus, maybe you'll get lucky, and she'll be the girl of your dreams, and you'll fall in love and start your own little family," she pleasantly remarked.

Dad smiled, gave Mom a kiss on the cheek and said, "Just like I did."

So, Mom arranged the big date between Klaus and Babble, and they were to meet at our house the following week. Babble arrived, looking pretty good for a woman with hairy, nylon-covered legs ... but Klaus never showed. No call, no telegram, nothing ... he just didn't show up. Mom was quite embarrassed. "I just don't understand it," she exclaimed, "he seemed like such a nice guy."

"Don't worry about it, Babble, the guy's a real loser," Dad added, consoling our wallflower babysitter. "Now, I've got a buddy at work who ..."

"Ray," Mom objected, "how do you know Klaus wasn't in an accident or something?"

"I don't think that Klaus does anything by accident," the old man replied.

We never heard from Klaus again. Sometimes, it's hard to know why things happen. Perhaps, certain people are sent into our lives for reasons we don't fully understand at the time, or maybe Dad was right, and Klaus was just a manipulative jerk. Either way, Mom and Dad seemed happier than I'd ever seen them, and I got a great knife out of the deal.

When Mom wasn't setting German hormones ablaze, she spent much of her time on a more mundane activity that absorbs the lives of military wives around the world ... the laundry. Washing is no small task when you have five kids, and you must vie with seventeen other families for washer space. The military had outfitted the large basements of each housing unit with about ten clothes washers, and each family was assigned a specific time to get its laundry done. God help the woman who didn't get her clothes out of the washer in time, because the person who had the following time slot would simply take the clean clothes out of the washer and heap them on the floor. This wasn't done to be mean, but wash time was at a premium, and if one person didn't comply with the schedule, it set everyone back. In keeping with its age-old tradition of doing most things half-ass, the military declined to provide dryers, so wet clothes were hung on clotheslines that stretched the length of the basement, and huge, hot air blowers attached to the wall pummeled the dripping laundry with heat. Since it was usually cold in Bremerhaven, fresh air drying was almost impossible, so we resigned ourselves to the fact that we were going to be wearing stiff underwear for the next three years.

Mark and I enjoyed playing hide-and-seek in the laundry room—it was easy to get lost in the maze of uniforms, linens, and diapers. However, with moisture evaporating from the clothes in steady streams of wispy, white smoke, the room was like a sauna, and by the time we were finished playing, the laundry was dry but we were soaking wet.

As with all hardships imposed by living the military life, Mom made the best of it. With my baby sister on one hip and the laundry basket on the other, she made the twice-weekly trip down the hard, cold, marble stairs that led to the laundry room. Although we were encouraged to recycle our clothes a few times before putting them in the dirty laundry, my brother took advantage of Mom's request and wore the same pair of lederhosen so often that the rear end of the leather, suspendered shorts became slick and shiny from continuous use. Mom loved lederhosen because she couldn't wash leather. She tried to get me to wear them too, but the 60s were blooming and, even at an early age, I knew what was cool and what wasn't. Let Mark wear them—he had no image to develop.

There were lots of little nuances to apartment living in Bremerhaven, but the one that used to drive everyone bananas was the fact that the front door to the apartment would lock the minute it was closed, and there was no way to get back in without a key. At first, Mom put the key on a string and whatever kid was going outside, had to wear it around his or her neck. That didn't work because kids tend to lose things, and the military police really resented being called on to unlock the door; so, Mom cleverly devised a system that would allow us to come and go through the front door without fear of locking ourselves out. She tied a rope around the front door knob, looped it under the door, and attached the other end to the handle on the inside of the door. All we had to do was yank on the rope and it would pull the inside handle down, allowing the door to swing open. No key, no muss, no fuss … no security. It never occurred to us that, with this system, anybody could walk in our front door—I guess Mom just figured we didn't have anything worth stealing.

But that was before she discovered the exciting world of Hummels—those little figurines of terminally cute kids holding umbrellas, or pouting, or playing with a puppy. I was told that these figurines were very expensive and were handmade by nuns in the Black Forest. I'm not sure if the nun part is true, but Hummels did increase in value, so Mom convinced the old man they were a good investment and, over time, my parents bought a few. It was at this point that Mom decided to give our olive-drab apartment a new look, and started collecting bits and pieces of German art. She became totally consumed with the idea of turning our place into a mini-Burchesgarten, but the art and the military-issue furniture clashed a bit, resulting in a home that looked more like a well-decorated bunker than the Swiss chalet she had envisioned.

There was no English-language television available in Bremerhaven, so the family would fill the entertainment gap with Mitch Miller records. Mitch's albums came with several sing-along music sheets which Dad would pass out, and we'd all sit around the living room singing songs like "K-K-K-Katy" and "Don't Sit Under the Apple Tree" until our throats were sore. Mom and Dad loved music, and we were raised with Frank Sinatra doing it his way, and Johnny Mathis crooning "Chances Are" at the top of his lungs. The house was always filled with music, everything from Marty Robbins to Nancy Wilson, but when the Beatles landed I had to reserve time on the record player, preferably when my parents weren't around. Like millions of other American kids, the Beatles changed my life. Oh, Elvis Presley was alright, I guess, and Annette and Frankie romping on the beach always gave me a thrill, but nothing could compare to the Beatles. I loved their cocky attitudes, the way they dressed, and most of all, their music. Man, the first time I heard "She Loves You" I knew I was onto something unique … wonderful … historic. Unfortunately, Mom and Dad didn't share my enthusiasm, so for two years I got up at four-thirty in the morning, closed the hallway door that led to the bedrooms and, by the light of the stereo, rocked in the early morning darkness, quietly singing along with John, Paul, George, and Ringo. I spent hours imagining myself in black, leather Beatle boots and long hair, running away from hundreds of screaming girls.

I was a member of the school choir, and one day our teacher broke the news that we were going to stage a concert for our parents. I teamed up with a couple of my buddies; we fashioned guitars out of cigar boxes and rulers, a set of bongos from a few oatmeal containers, and practiced mimicking our heroes, the Beatles. We decided to perform (she's got a) "Ticket to Ride," and rehearsed every day for a week—not merely the song, but the howling and the head shaking and the mannerisms of the Beatles as well. When the big day came, we all wore white, turtleneck dickies underneath red, collarless shirts, and set the auditorium on fire with our tribute to the Fab Four. We were definitely cuter than we were talented, but our performance was stellar enough for the USO to ask us to perform at their Saturday night talent show.

Man, we were in Heaven. This was it, the big time, and with visions of money and screaming girls dancing in our little nine-year-old heads, we set about expanding our repertoire and getting "She Loves You (yeah, yeah, yeah)" down to an art form. We discussed several names for the "band" but, since we didn't really play any instruments, settled on "The Golden Chords."

The big night finally arrived, and we showed up at the NCO Club, cigar-box guitars in hand, ready to take on the world. It was very exciting backstage, watching the other performers and one GI in particular, who was busily tuning a real, live, electric guitar. I'd never seen an electric guitar before, and stared in fascination as his hands danced their way across the metal strings. "What are you guys gonna sing tonight?" he asked, without looking up from his guitar.

"Who ... us?" I stammered, looking around the room.

"Yeah, you guys," he responded, glancing at our homemade instruments.

"'I Wanna Hold Your Hand,' by the Beatles," I answered.

"Not with these, I hope," he smiled, taking my El Cigundo guitar from my hand. "Tell you what ... I know that song. How 'bout if I just sit behind the curtain and play it, and you guys sing along." It sounded like a good idea, and we nodded our consent.

Before we knew it, the Master of Ceremonies was saying, "Ladies and gentlemen, put your hands together for that new singing sensation, The Golden Chords," and we ran onto the stage, to the sounds of applause and cheering. Now, there's a big difference between fantasizing a performance and actually facing an audience, and before our behind-the-scenes guitar player strummed his first note, my fellow Golden Chords, one by one, bolted from the stage, leaving me alone to face the nearly hysterical crowd. I probably would have joined my friends but I was too scared to move, frozen where I stood. Behind the curtain, our "band" had no idea that the group had disintegrated to just one "chord." and kept playing, but all I could muster was an "uhhhh". I sounded like Lurch from the Addams Family ... on a bad day! My buddies, huddled safely off-stage, stared at me with stunned looks on their faces, amazed that I hadn't joined them in their flight.

I closed my eyes and stood there shaking, unable to move. There was only one thing left to do ... sing, so I stuttered out the first words, "Yeah ... you ... got that something, I ... I ... I hope you understand."

Having chosen my course of action, I was determined to get through the song, and might have been able to pull it off, or at least earn points for not chickening out. But I was so focused on choking out the words, I hadn't noticed that our guitar player had stopped playing, and even though

I kept on singing, there is a good reason why we never heard the Beatles sing "I Wanna Hold Your Hand" a cappella. The audience erupted in laughter as I continued to force out the words, "I wanna hold your ha …ha … ha … hand." It was more than I could stand so I finally stopped, rigid with fear and humiliation.

I was certain I'd have to stand there until the audience got tired of laughing at me and left, when the Master of Ceremonies appeared on the stage. Smiling, he walked over to me and raised my arm in the air, like a boxing champion who'd just taken his opponent out in the first round. "Let's hear it for this kid," he laughed. "It took a lot of guts to stand up here. What's your name, kid?"

"M-M-Mike," I said, my eyes tearing up.

"Well, M-M-Mike," the MC continued, "you just stick with it, and I have no doubt that someday we'll all be seeing your name in lights."

As I crept from the stage the audience jumped to its feet, laughing, whistling, hooting, and applauding. And suddenly, a strange feeling came over me … a feeling of accomplishment, of courage, of … cockiness, just like the Beatles! With encouragement from the MC, I ran back on stage and took a bow, before the still-cheering spectators. What had begun as a nightmare had somehow developed into a dream come true, and I sauntered from the stage, my head held high, basking in the glow of stardom. It was the first and last time The Golden Chords performed in public. But I'll never forget the wonderful feeling of acceptance as my short-lived pop singer career came to an end.

My parents have always been supportive of whatever I decided to try, even when they suspected I'd either give up or crash and burn. They saw me through Boy Scouts (even when I was thrown out for not paying dues); trombone lessons (although I quit after two years of faking my way through band, by simply watching the guy next to me and following his lead); and various other endeavors that went nowhere and cost them money. I think they appreciated my willingness to experience new things, to take a shot at the brass ring, because to this day they still tell me, "The day will come when you look back on your life, and the biggest regret you'll have is knowing that you didn't do something because you were afraid. Better to try and possibly fail than fill your life with a series of 'what ifs'." Not that they didn't try to teach me the difference between bravery and stupidity, they just preferred that I find out for myself. And although I've made a lot of mistakes in my life, I've always appreciated the freedom they afforded me to make them.

Having said that, there are a few things that cross the boundary of "mistake" for which no excuse or good intention in the world can compensate. It was a lesson I'd learn the hard way and, I'm sorry to say, one that I've had to learn over and over again in the course of my life.

As I've mentioned, I've never had a big love for sports, which caused me a great deal of humiliation as a kid. I tried. I went out for the baseball and football teams, but I was motivated by peer pressure and a desire to impress the girls, so I was a team player only in the sense that I was wearing the same uniform as the other guys. My heart wasn't in it, and on those rare occasions when I was actually stuck out in right field, I'd end up dropping the one ball that was hit my way. Batting was even worse— I'd just stand there for the full count, hoping the pitcher would either walk me or, if I was really lucky, hit me with the ball so I could make it to first base. It was pathetic, and my pitiful efforts to become a jock only resulted in being labeled a pansy by my friends.

I was a nervous kid the whole time we lived in Bremer-haven. Oh, I had lots of friends, and even at the ages of eight and nine I was a hit with the girls. But kids have a way of being fickle, and more often than not, somebody was after me, or teasing me, or just plain mean to me. As a result, over time, I developed an attitude of mistrusting everybody, and doing whatever was necessary to get myself through another day.

In Bremerhaven, all students, regardless of age, caught the school bus at the same time and location. My general disinterest in sports, and my inability to play them, left me open to ridicule from not only my peers, but also their older brothers. Almost daily, I was called nasty names or subjected to effeminate gestures meant to impugn my manhood, and squash whatever prestige I managed to muster. I now realize that it was just kids being kids, but at the time, the indignity was almost intolerable. I had to find a way to make my life bearable, and I eventually discovered the one thing that transcends bad feelings, and makes friends out of former enemies ... money.

Mom was the Treasurer of the NCO Wives Club, and kept a small box of petty cash on the shelf in her closet. The box was small because the NCO Wives Club Treasury housed only a few dollar bills and some loose change. One morning, I crept into Mom's closet while she was busily getting my brother and sisters ready for school, pulled the small vault from the shelf, and stole fifty cents ... bribe money. I didn't think it would be missed, and justified my action by telling myself that Mom would rather make up the loss than see her son go through a daily taunting.

I left for the school bus early that day, ran over to the snack bar in the hospital, and spent half of my ill-gotten booty on five packs of Lifesavers, retaining twenty-five cents for future payoffs. I arrived at the bus station, and decided to make a preemptive strike. I started passing out the small, round candy to anybody who wanted one. The bribery continued for several days. Each morning I'd take another dip into Mom's treasury fund, and before long, fifty cents became several dollars. The taunts did stop, but I'd set a precedent that was beyond my ability to maintain, and my concern over being ridiculed was soon replaced by my anxiety over getting caught.

Eventually, the day I had been dreading arrived, and the NCO Wives Club assembled for its regular meeting. Mom returned home, extremely upset and embarrassed that almost five dollars was missing from the fund for which she was responsible. She asked me, point blank, if I knew anything about the shortage, and I told her "no". I was nine years old, a thief and now a liar and the combination ate at my guts in a way that was far worse than any amount of name calling ever was. But I didn't say a word.

The next day, when I came home from school, Mom was across the hall at the Stewart's apartment, having coffee. Frankie Stewart was my age and although he was sometimes friendly, he was more often the most egregious offender in my daily struggle to out-talk or out-run confrontations. Truth be told, I hated the guy, but his old man was a real hard-ass who would beat him with a belt so, more than anything else, I felt sorry for Frankie. Anyway, I was sitting at the Stewart's kitchen table trying to get Mom to come home, when Frankie came through the front door, a roll of Lifesavers in his hand. "Where did you get those?" his old man demanded.

Frankie looked at me, looked at his dad, and looked back at me, shuffling from one foot to the other. I just stared at him, my eyes pleading for mercy. Please, God, I prayed, please don't let him tell on me and I'll never …

"Mike gave them to me," Frankie confessed. "He gives them to lots of kids on the bus."

"What!" Mom howled, jumping up from her chair.

A chill shot up my spine and I shuddered. At some level I realized that it wasn't because Frankie had ratted me out; I knew, eventually, I'd get caught. No, it was worse than that. My arrest and trial were unfolding in front of the Stewart family, and the thought of the inevitable public execution made my whole body shake. The image of being blindfolded and fed that last cigarette, under the disapproving watch of strangers, flashed across my mind, and the disgrace I felt was far worse than the actual execution. To me, no punishment, no matter how severe, can equal the pain of public humiliation. Mom, on the other hand, never had any qualms about disciplining her children wherever she stood, so I knew I was facing embarrassment worse than death.

I looked at Mom, wondering what her reaction would be, and hoping she would opt to kill me in private. "And where did you get the money?" she growled.

"I ... I ... I found it," I lied.

"Oh," Mom continued, holding me by the arm, "you found it, huh? And just where did you find it?"

"You know," I answered, looking down at my feet, "here and there. On the sidewalk, at the movie theatre, under the cushions of the couch ..."

"... in my closet," Mom said, finishing my sentence.

It was a defining moment. There was no hard evidence linking me to the money box so, if I played it cool, Mom would never be able to pin her missing Wives Club dues on me.

"I don't know anything about that box of money in ... your ... closet," I stammered, trying to gulp the words back into my mouth.

"Uh-huh ... that's what I thought," Mom angrily replied, getting up from her chair and grabbing my arm, pulling me toward the front door.

"Looks like somebody needs to have a meeting with Mr. Belt," Frankie's father said, a smile creeping across his face.

"Oh, don't worry," Mom announced, shoving me into the hallway, "he'll think twice before he does anything like this again."

I went crashing through the front door of our apartment. Mom closed the door behind her, and the two of us stood there like sumo wrestlers sizing up each other, waiting for the first move to be made.

"I—" was all I could get out, before ...

"Don't say anything," Mom screeched. "Don't even try to say anything. I've had enough of your lying, Michael!"

"I—"

"What did I just say? Are you deaf? Didn't I just tell you not to say anything? If you say one more word, I'm going to—"

"I—"

"That's it!" She squealed, and lunged toward me, arms stretched out in front of her. I panicked and ran. I know, it's the worst thing a kid can do, but self-preservation took control, and for the next five minutes Mom and I played a game of cat and mouse as she chased me around the furniture, trying to grab me. At one point she had me by the leg, but I managed to break away and flee to the sanctuary of my bedroom, slamming the door behind me. I was cringing in my usual place, up against the wall in the bottom bunk bed, when Mom flung open the door, breathing like a mad bull, her hands gripping the doorframe as she scanned the room.

"There you are!" She bellowed through clenched teeth. "Come out of there right now, young man!"

"No way," I yelped.

Mom bent down so she could get a good look at me against the wall, shaking like a leaf. "I'm through playing with you, Michael!" She shrieked.

I stuck to that wall like a fly on a no-pest strip, while Mom made several attempts to pluck me from my sanctuary. I knew I was only delaying my fate, but I'd never seen Mom so upset. I figured I'd do better waiting it out and taking my chances with Dad.

"Okay," Mom said in frustration, "I've had it. You just stay there until your father gets home!" And with that, she stormed from the room and slammed the door.

I felt awful. It was bad enough that I was a thief and a liar, but the ramifications of waiting in my room until Dad got home were starting to sink in. Mom would have two hours to ponder my behavior—plenty of time to build up even more steam, leaving Dad little recourse but to powder my behind. Trying hard to see past my fear and remorse, I finally realized that it would be better for my health if I went ahead and took my medicine from Mom. I crept from my bunk bed sanctum, and slowly opened the bedroom door.

Mom was standing right outside the door, and before I could make it back to the safety of my bed, she grabbed me by the back of the collar and pulled me into the hallway. "Gotcha, you little shit," she barked.

I went limp, like a fish on a line that has given up the struggle.

Mom dragged me into the living room and tossed me on the couch like a sack of potatoes. She placed her hands against my shoulders to hold me down and, with her face three inches from mine, said the words that I'll never forget, "I don't like you, Michael. I have to love you because I'm your mother, but I don't like you any more."

I shook with fear, expecting a slap across the face, but it never came. Mom let go of me, and I jumped from the sofa. I stood there, anchored to the spot, and watched my mother as she slowly, almost casually, walked toward the kitchen. "Is that all?" I asked. "Can I go outside now?"

Mom stopped, but didn't respond.

"Did you hear me?" I squeaked.

Nothing.

"Okay, then," I cried, "I'm just gonna run away. Bet that'll make you happy, huh?"

Mom spun around and replied, "Okay, okay, you win, Michael …"

I smiled through crocodile tears.

"… let me help you pack your bags."

Mom turned me around and, with her hands on my shoulders, guided me back into the bedroom. She threw open my closet and started tossing clothes on the floor. "You'll need this, and this, and oh, yeah, you probably should take a sweater—it gets pretty cold outside at night. Now, you finish up in here and I'll go make you a few sandwiches for your trip. I wouldn't want anyone to accuse me of being a bad mother."

I stood among the tossed clothes, my mind searching for a way out of this predicament. "I don't have anything to put my clothes in," I yelled.

"Just use a pillowcase," Mom hollered back from the kitchen. "Oh, and I just stripped the beds this morning, so take one out of the clothes hamper … no sense in getting another one dirty. You're going to have to learn to fend for yourself now, Michael. It's a cruel world out there."

A dirty pillowcase! It was a pretty cruel world in here, too!

Alone in my room, packing my soiled pillowcase, I knew I didn't really want to leave. But what choice did I have? Mom had called my bluff, and the only way out of the situation seemed to be through the front door. I filled the pillowcase with all the necessities of life: jeans, t-shirts, comic books, and lugged my heavy burden down the hallway to the front door where Mom was waiting, a brown paper bag of bologna sandwiches in her hand and a big smile on her face. "Don't forget to write," she snickered, "let us know if you find work."

That's it? No tears, no "nice to have known you," not even a hand-shake?

"Michael …" Mom softly added.

Finally! I knew she couldn't do it. When push comes to shove, Mom always …

"… don't worry, I'll tell Dad that you're gone." And with that she closed the door, leaving me alone in the hallway.

I slowly descended the stairs that led to the front door of the apartment building, my bag thumping heavily against each step, my eyes brimming with tears. I couldn't believe this was happening. Outside, the air was cool, and thick, black clouds hung low in the sky. It looked as though my bad luck was holding; as soon as my heavy load and I hit the sidewalk, giant raindrops started pelting the cement entryway, leaving large wet spots that were quickly becoming puddles. I pulled my jacket over my head and sluggishly departed, dragging my sack behind me like a dejected Santa Claus, tears streaming down my face. Just at that moment, I heard the unmistakable clatter of Dad's old station wagon sputtering into the parking lot. "What's going on, chief," he said, climbing out of the car. "Don't you know it's raining out here?"

I dropped my pillowcase and ran to Dad, throwing my arms around his waist. "Mom threw me out of the house," I lied.

"Oh, really," the old man responded. "Just up and threw you out of the house, huh?"

"Yeah," I hesitantly replied.

Dad gave me a big hug and said, "Well, I guess she had a good reason. Sorry to lose you, son."

I couldn't take any more! I broke down and told Dad the whole story—all about the stealing, and the lying, and the reason for it all being my fear of my "friends". "I'm sorry. It was a stupid thing to do and I let you down. I made a mistake."

"No," Dad said calmly, rain dripping from the brim of his hat, "sounds like we made the mistake. We trusted you, Michael. You're going to have to live with what you've done, and we have to live with a son that we love very much, but can't trust anymore. Trust is a sacred thing, Michael. It's hard to get back once you lose it."

"What should I do?" I sobbed.

"Well," the old man smiled, "I wouldn't run away. I don't know how you'd ever find us … in California!"

California?

"The Air Force is sending us to California. Wouldn't be the same without you."

California! Suddenly, with that one word, my personal dark skies cleared a bit; temporarily, the spotlight would be focused elsewhere. I still had that trust thing to deal with, but at least Dad's news would get me back in the house.

I shadowed Dad as he opened the front door to our apartment. "Oh, I thought you'd left, Michael," Mom said, when she spotted me hiding behind Dad.

"We're all leaving," Dad chirped. "Pack your bags, babe, 'cause we're going to California."

Mom was so excited that she forgot about my misdemeanor, and even more miraculous, didn't gripe about the rain water that was dripping on her living room floor. She squealed with delight, and before Dad could say another word, she was already laying out her new life of year-long tans in the constant sunshine.

"Oh, Ray, this is so wonderful. Now we can visit Hollywood, and San Francisco, and swim in the Pacific Ocean, and, oh yes, we mustn't forget about Disneyland, and movie stars ... we're going to see actual movie stars ... why, I even read in the newspaper that Ronald Reagan is planning to run for Governor, but that's California for you, and I hear that there are orange trees in every backyard, and you can actually pan the rivers for gold, real gold! Oh, and I want to buy a freezer when we get there, Ray, because with all these kids it's wise to buy meat in bulk ... and a new car, we'll need a new car, and, oh my God, new clothes. We can't wear these same clothes in California, we'll melt. First thing we need to do is take a trip to Sears and ..."

Dad took me aside, leaving Mom to plan the next four years of our lives. "Things worked out pretty well for you didn't they, bud?" He said.

"Yeah," I beamed, "great!"

"I hear it's expensive to live in California," Dad continued. "Too bad you won't have any money to spend for awhile."

"Why ... what do you mean?" I asked.

"I'm going to pay back the money you stole, but you're going to reimburse me with your allowance until the whole five dollars is paid back. At twenty-five cents a week, it'll be Christmas before you see any more money. I think that's fair, don't you?"

I thought about it for a minute. I really had gotten off easy, what with Dad's news about California and not having to sleep outside and live off bologna sandwiches for the rest of my life.

"Well, what do you say?" the old man asked.

I grinned at Dad, thrust my hand deep in the pocket of my jeans, and said, "You want a lifesaver?"

Thinking back to the day when I stole the money, I've come to realize that my shame wasn't solely about abusing Mom's trust; it was also about my loss of trust in my family, my friends, myself. I'd lost sight of the qualities that make me who I am and, instead of appreciating and following my heart I had allowed others to define me. We live in a world that tells us how we should act, think, love. And, driven by an overwhelming need to be accepted, we all too often lose that which is most precious to each of us ... our souls. We follow others' leads, we conform, we do the "right thing" and smile through the sadness that screams from our spirit, as we try to please those around us. Like Cinderella's evil stepsisters, we try to turn that special shoe that was made just for us into one-size-fits-all. And while many of us manage to squeeze our foot into someone else's shoe, the pain eventually causes us to limp through life, never taking the opportunity to realize how special each of us is.

God intended for each of us to be individuals, to follow our own paths, to run joyfully through life, experiencing the wonder of the world while wearing our own shoes ... or better yet, without any shoes at all.

Chapter Four
AND IN THIS CORNER ...

"Nobody's better than you, and you're no better than anybody else." I can still hear my Grandmother drilling that into me. I never had any difficulty with the first part—I always just took that for granted—but the second part, all that "you're no better than anybody" jazz, well, that was a little harder to swallow. Of course, I knew what she meant. She was talking about an appreciation for various religions, ethnic backgrounds, upbringings, levels of economic status, stuff like that. No argument from me, Grammie. I'm with you.

But her mantra didn't take into account the qualities that define each of us and make us who we are. In high school, the admirable qualities included the ability to play sports, pick up girls, dance, be cool; these concerns transcended race, religion, and nationality. At that age, they were the things that linked people together, and the things that tore them apart.

Let's face it, how often does the head cheerleader date the president of the Chess Club? Never is how often ... not then, not now, not ever, never. The fact is we hang out with people we like. And more often than not, the people we like are, at their core, very much like ourselves. We share the same interests, disinterests, fears, desires, and general outlook on life.

Now, I'll grant you that "better" is in the eye of the beholder. I doubt that those guys who thought a good time was had by spending hours staring at a chessboard knew that they were a bunch of geeks, or that the cheerleading squad had any idea or, for that matter, even cared that everyone thought they were a bunch of airheads. The point is, the "best" crowd is always your crowd, because your crowd is made up of people just like you.

Why would you have it any other way?

In the civilian world, who you are is defined by the memories of your family, friends, and neighbors. For the rest of your life, you continue to carry every stupid thing you ever did, every fear you ever demonstrated, every failure you ever had, because there's always someone from your past who is ready and willing to recount them. I've always considered it the social equivalent of the burdensome chains that Marley's ghost lugged around in *A Christmas Carol*.

But military brats get to change their image every time the family is transferred to another base. It's great! You get a clean slate. You have the opportunity to rewrite history, and to be anybody you want to be. It's one big masquerade—super dork at one base, super cool at another. Of course, you have to have the ability to back up your claims ... a dork in a leather jacket is, after all, still a dork.

But sometimes this "redefining" takes place not because you've changed who you are, but rather because the people around you have changed their minds as to the worthiness of what you represent. I'll give you an example. As a kid, I was never too hot at sports. Even then, I had no real taste for organized anything, whether it was sports or religion or Boy Scouts ... whatever. If too many people are involved in something, chances are I won't want to be. Anyway, it was a real drag growing up in an environment where sports ability is everything, and little boys were expected to enjoy football, and know the names of all the guys who played in the World Series. I couldn't have cared less. My interests centered around two things, rock 'n' roll music and girls, neither of which impressed the peers of a ten-year-old. But a few years later, when these same friends discovered that girls are more fun to hold than a softball, I suddenly became a sought after commodity, a cornucopia of useful information, the guy to know. I hadn't changed ... my friends' perceptions of desirable qualities had shifted. And, after all, perception is everything.

We all try to manipulate others' perceptions of who we are; in fact, we spend most of our lives doing it. Yeah, I know, it sounds kind of fake, but let's look at the facts. Who behaves the same way with friends as they do with parents? And wasn't that you with a smile plastered on your face thanking the preacher for his inspirational sermon, even though you slept through half of it? Remember that "yes, officer, sir" routine you tap-danced through, the last time a cop pulled you over? See, like I said, everybody does it. Those who are really good at it become politicians, or evangelical preachers, or gynecologists, but most of us just develop the skill through required coexistence with people we'd rather not know at all. It's not easy ... it takes creativity, stamina, and real commitment, but it's a means to an end, and we each individually decide what our "end" is.

Now, don't get me wrong—I'm not saying that everyone is running around out there pretending to be something they're not. But in high school, it's a way of life. Your survival, your evolution to a higher plane, depends upon it.

I've heard it said that high school is the training ground for life. That sounds good, but it's wrong. High school is nowhere near real life, not human life anyway. It's more like Wild Kingdom, with kids traveling in packs, prowling hallways, establishing turf. There are the jocks, the dweebs, the brains, the fighters, the lovers, the druggies, the juicers—the list goes on and on. Separate and unequal ... and it's perceptions that keep them that way. But every so often, something happens that shatters our perceptions, causing people who couldn't stand each other to suddenly find themselves becoming the best of friends.

Friday night was the night in my life. Oh, Saturdays were cool, but they were generally date nights ... girlfriend, pizza, and movie evenings that featured a session of mild groping, and concluded with an "of course I still respect you" or two. But Friday nights were the best—at least they were for me. My "real" girlfriend lived off base, in a small town about 25 miles away. I'd see her all week at school, and on Saturday night, but not Fridays, boy. Friday nights were for me.

The truth is, I loved having a girlfriend. The stability, the familiarity, the always-have-a-date-for-Saturday-night factor. And I was, if I may say so, a great boyfriend. Considerate, thoughtful, sweet, polite to parents ... I'm telling you, a really nice guy. But I was a kid, man. I didn't want to be ... married, you know. I needed a night that was all mine ... for the good of the relationship, you understand. I mean, if I didn't have Friday nights to get the drinking, dancing, and carousing out of my system, well, there's just no way I could be such a swell boyfriend the other six nights of the week. As I explained to my girlfriend, I valued our relationship so much that I was willing to put myself through a night of debauchery once a week, to save her from my dark, slightly sinister side that would, if given the chance, ultimately destroy our love. Okay, well, she bought it. In fact, after a while I actually started believing it, and would become outraged when my girlfriend would question me about my Friday night antics.

So here it was, another Friday night, beckoning me from the darkness. As I stood and looked out the small window in my Maid's Room, at the shadows that danced across the streetlight-illuminated treetops, I wondered what adventures awaited me tonight. With my girlfriend tucked safely away, secure in the knowledge that whatever I was doing would only serve to strengthen our relationship, I needed no explanations. I didn't have to be the "boyfriend"—I could just be Michael. On-the-town, free-as-a-bird, your-place-or-mine, Michael.

Every Friday night, we would all converge at the Youth Center for the weekly dance. A local band, Dr. Pig, was always the entertainment. The members of this "swine" quartet were three military brats and this German guy who played the worst organ rendition of "Light My Fire" that you ever heard. Theirs was an eclectic repertoire, everything from The Carpenters to Grand Funk Railroad, but the music wasn't really the point of the dance anyway. It was a social gathering, plain and simple, a place to see and be seen. At the rear of the Center was the designated smoking area—a small, side room where only Juniors and Seniors were allowed. I guess the military thought you should wait until you were sixteen to start screwing up your lungs. We, of course, ruled that little enclave, and after a while only members of our group plus invited guests were permitted entrance.

Our group was known as the "Studs", and our female counterparts had dubbed themselves the "Duds". I have no idea why … I guess it just rhymed with "studs", which gives you some idea of the ingenuity of girls with whom we hung out. They were cute, but not terribly bright … which may explain why they hung out with us. Actually, we didn't come up with the name Studs—it was pinned on us by some other kids who really resented the high opinions we had of ourselves, and was meant as a put down. Nevertheless, we loved the name's implication, and promoted its use whenever and wherever we could. There was even an area at school where we used to congregate that bore a plaque designating it "Stud Corner," a warning to all that this was our space—better move along.

As a general rule, any group of people draws two emotions from outsiders—fear and envy—and we were no exception. There were a few kids that just chose to ignore us, but most of our contemporaries viewed our ability to get away with murder with both wariness and amazement. As I said, there were certain girls that were a part of our circle, but we never dated any of them. There was nothing in writing that governed our behavior, and I'm sure there were the occasional, secret make-out sessions, but generally, the relationships between members of the Studs and Duds were purely platonic. We were a bunch of kids who felt comfortable enough with one another to let our guards down and just be ourselves, and that feeling of freedom meant a lot to each of us.

Now, getting back to the subject of girlfriends, I had a "real" one, but I also dated a series of other girls who, for some reason, didn't seem to mind my short attention span and our limited interaction. I guess I didn't really care why they were willing to play second banana, but that very willingness to remain in the shadows sealed their fate. I mean, who wants to get serious about a chick who is satisfied with a game of grab-ass on Friday night, and doesn't mind that you spend your money and most of your time on some other girl? Not me. I had standards … low standards, to be sure, but standards just the same. It did bother me a little when, on Saturday night, I'd see one of my surrogates at the movie theater, and I'd always feel just a tinge of guilt as I cozied up next to my girlfriend. I wondered how they could respect themselves, although I've since come to realize it was me they didn't respect. I mean, who wants to get serious about a guy who cheats on his girlfriend?

One of my regular, Friday night flings was a girl named Sherrie. Actually, I liked her a lot. She was funny and cute, and had a real sense of self-confidence about her. Like me, she was a Maid's Room dweller, which provided some interesting late evenings. The only uncomfortable part about the whole deal was that her brother, Greg, hated me. Hated Me! He was constantly in my face about how I treated Sherrie. Luckily, his fear of punishment by the Studs kept him from openly venting his anger in any way other than under-his-breath mutterings. In a desperation move, he even tried to get his folks involved by insisting that I was a scumbag whom they shouldn't allow Sherrie to see. I had a real "screw you" attitude about the whole drama, and didn't pay him much mind. That was about to change.

I must digress a bit, to provide some background you'll need to fully understand the events that, for several people, made that night no ordinary Friday at the Youth Center. My girlfriend Pam, who lived off base, was my first true love. I'd pursued her relentlessly until she'd agreed to go out with me. We'd been dating for almost a year when a new kid moved to the village where Pam lived, and they started to ride the school bus together. His name was Bud, Bud Wankowski, and I considered him a real pain-in--the-ass. He lived with his dad—his Mom probably ran screaming into the night to get away from the two of them—and he displayed all the angst and anger one might expect from somebody whose evenings are occupied with nursing his old man through drunken stupors. Bud wore the same blue jeans, white shirt, and denim jacket every day. Every day. Pam said I should be understanding of his circumstances, and accept that he was actually a very nice guy. I was unsympathetic. I didn't care what his home life was like—to me he was just a greasy slime ball trying to move in on my girl.

One day, as Bud and Pam were leaving the bus together, I decided the time had come to stake my claim and make known my feelings about the whole situation.

"Look, asshole," I said to him, "I don't like this buddy-buddy deal you've got going with my girlfriend. Just stay the hell away from her, if you know what's good for you," I warned, backed up by the full force of the Studs. Bud didn't say a word, just gave Pam a look and walked away. And that, I thought, was that.

As the weeks passed, I noticed that while Pam and Bud had stopped walking together, they continued to share a seat on the morning bus. When confronted with this transgression, Pam told me there was nothing to worry about; however, boys being boys, and me being a jealous jerk, I again decided it was time to take some kind of action. I don't know what it is about teenage boys that makes them think life is like a scene from *West Side Story*, but words soon escalated into shoving, with the Studs solidly behind me, and Bud's friends equally committed to his cause. Fortunately for everyone involved, the "rumble" ended prematurely with the sound of the first period bell.

For whatever reason, Bud eventually stopped riding the bus. He had found a new girl to honor with his attention, and I felt totally vindicated until I found out who she was: Sherrie my Friday-night girlfriend! Of course, this pissed me off to no end, but delighted her brother who had been trying for months to stop her from seeing me. Regardless, I knew I'd won the real prize in Pam, and I proceeded to "interview" replacements for Sherrie.

So, it was another Friday night in Ramstein, and as I buckled the wide, leather belt that complemented my ever-fashionable, skintight, bell-bottom corduroys, an impatient voice from the other side of the Maid's Room door commanded my attention.

"C'mon, Ritter!" I opened the door to see Sean standing there. "Aren't you ready yet, man?" he questioned.

"Just a second," I murmured. "I broke a shoelace on my Adidas. What's the hurry? It's just Dr. Pig and the same bunch of people who are always there. Alright, let's see … comb, cigarettes, lighter, money … okay, I'm ready. Let's split."

A full moon lit up the night sky, and the faint sound of a police siren was wafting through the air. As we made our way toward Willie's place, I couldn't escape the feeling that this was not going to be an ordinary Friday night. I couldn't explain it … just a feeling.

Willie flung open the door to his Maid's Room, just as Sean and I were about to bang on it. "You're wearing your black cords tonight?" he yelped. "Man, I told you I was gonna wear mine … now, I have to change."

"Willie, you're worse than some girl," scolded Sean. "Who's gonna know? It's dark in there. No chick's gonna be paying attention to your ass, anyway. Just c'mon." But Willie would have none of it, and after a quick change into his maroon corduroys, we were off to the dance.

As we neared our destination, we could see the shadows of kids who were standing in front of the Youth Center. A thick cloud of cigarette smoke hung over them which, in the moonlight, created almost a mystical atmosphere. The only outside lights were the ones that encircled the basketball court, next to the Center. Sean, Willie, and I strolled past the crowd and through the front door. The music was deafening as Dr. Pig struggled through what sounded like a Black Sabbath tune, and the dance floor was bulging with the gyrating bodies of teenagers, trying their best to look cool for their dates. We crossed the dance floor, heading for our "private room" where the booths were filled with poker-playing Studs and Duds, ashtrays littered with the remnants of Kools and Marlboros. In one corner of the room was another group of kids—uninvited, I was sure—doing the same thing. We gave them a quick once-over and, having recognized a few of them, decided to let it go. We were feeling generous—might as well let them know what it's like to hang with the cool kids for an evening. But, just to make sure they remembered their place and realized this was a one-time deal only, Sean and I sauntered over to their table.

On a military base, everybody knows everybody else, so even though we didn't all interact on a daily basis, we pretty much knew who had "cool potential" and who didn't. The "leaders" of this group of trespassers were Rob Mathison and Tim Maxwell—not bad guys, just living above their station. "Hey, Rob," I said, "what gives? Not enough action out there with the pre-puberty crowd? I thought you only hustled fourteen-year-olds."

"Eat me, Ritter," Rob dryly replied, his eyes on his cards. "Hey, have you seen Wankowski? I hear he's on base tonight … looking for you."

"Me?" I quizzically responded. "What the hell does he want?"

"You," came the retort. "I think it has something to do with Pam and Sherrie. I dunno … he's wandering around here some place, with Greg."

"That pussy," I said, leaning over the table, directly in front of Rob's face. "Can't he take a hint? I swear, if I see him, I'll …"

"Don't tell me, man," Rob muttered, as he blew a smoke ring in my face, "tell him. He's standing right over there."

I turned to see Wankowski and his lapdog Greg parked in the doorway, staring in my direction. I've always believed that the best defense is a good offense—my one lesson learned from a half-assed attempt to appreciate sports—so I strode across the room to the door, Sean following closely behind.

"I hear you're looking for me," I confronted him. "What's the problem? You tired of living, or what?"

Wankowski stood his ground, but unexpectedly placed his arm around my shoulders and whispered, "Let's go outside."

I quickly jerked free, and snarled, "Screw you, man. You got something to say, say it!"

"Get him, Bud," barked Greg.

"Chew glass, pussy," I shot back.

Wankowski paused, brushed his long, blonde hair out of his eyes, and again put his arm around my shoulders. "Be cool, man," he appealed, "it's this Pam thing. Some of my buddies think I let you push me around. I'm under a lot of pressure to save face, you know. My reputation's at stake here."

"Screw your reputation," I screeched unsympathetically.

"Now listen, I've got a plan," Bud conspired. "Do you know how to fake fight?"

I knew exactly what he meant. A few months earlier, a kid had arrived at the base, whose father had been a movie stunt man before joining the military. This kid had shown everybody how to "fake fight" by slapping your hands together at the precise moment someone takes a pretend punch at you, and then grabbing your face, as if in pain. It was great fun, and a few times we'd even caused the Military Police to get involved when someone had reported that there were kids in the street, beating the crap out of one another. In reality, no one was getting hurt, and we all enjoyed a big laugh at the MP's expense.

I've never made any bones about the fact that I consider myself a lover, not a fighter, so this "fake fight" idea immediately appealed to me. It was a great way to resolve our differences, without tarnishing our own reputations or our friends' reputations.

Wankowski and I huddled in a corner of the room and discussed the terms, while Sean kept Greg at bay. We decided to make it a real extravaganza. We'd each "land" a few choice shots, then call it a draw and be on our way. We also agreed that we should stage our fearless little "passion play" in the most open, well-lit area available, so everyone could witness our virility. The answer was obvious—the basketball court. It was show time.

I began. "Listen, dick-wad," I screamed. "I've had it with your shit! Let's go outside and finish this, once and for all!"

"Just lead the way, asshole," Wankowski returned. "I've been waiting a long time for this moment!"

Amazing but true, the whole Youth Center was immediately solemn with heavy silence, as if the Pope was about to speak. Dr. Pig even suspended its hatchet job on "In In-A-Gadda-Da-Vida," leaving only the intense reverb from the bass guitar hanging in the air and throbbing in our ears. The big fight was happening! It had been brewing for months, and now Ritter and Wankowski were finally going to beat the hell out of each other. Alright!

The perimeter of the basketball court was literally lined with kids, hanging on the fence and climbing the backboard. Only the gladiators—Bud, Greg, Sean, and I—occupied the "arena," and no one but Bud and I knew what was really coming down. Sean was casting his best hard-ass look at Greg, who was jumping up and down like a poodle in heat, excitedly anticipating my painful payback for the terrible injustice I had perpetrated on his sister. Surrounding the court were floodlights that lent an eeriness to the whole event, as Wankowski and I continued to recite our "script".

"Okay, clown," I growled in my best menacing voice, "get ready to kiss dirt."

"The Studs suck," Wankowski spit out. "You walk around here like you own the place, thinkin' you're so cool."

"You wanna try and prove we're not?" I yelled back.

But before Bud could deliver his next line, the Director of the Youth Center, a huge, bouncer-looking-type guy, came charging through the gate to the basketball court. "No you don't," he bellowed, "not around here. You two idiots want to kill one another, do it someplace else."

Secretly relieved that an authority figure had entered the picture, I stuck my hands in the front pockets of my pants and, leaning forward on the balls of my feet, rocked back and forth in place, taunting my "opponent," "Saved your ass," I jeered. "You are so lucky."

A loud moan arose from the sea of spectators. "Let them fight," someone cried out, and soon the air was filled with a hundred voices, all chanting, "Fight ... fight ... fight!"

I looked around at the expectant faces, feeling like a knight who has just vanquished his greatest enemy. There was a definite hero story developing here; I could walk away, without a scratch, with my head held high, and milk this for months!

Sean must have decided that the crisis had passed, because his attention had been diverted by some blonde chick over by the fence, whom he was busily hustling. With my hands still thrust deeply in my pockets, I slowly turned around and, as I did, from out of nowhere, a fist came flying toward me, catching me right across the left eye and knocking me to the cement floor. In a flash, Greg was planted on my chest, screaming about how I'd mistreated his sister, and peppering my face with punches. I lay there, trapped and helpless, struggling to free my hands from my skintight pants pockets. I tried to avoid his punches by moving my head from side to side, which caused him to miss me several times, slamming his fist into the hard concrete. His hands started to bleed which, when he occasionally did land a punch, smeared my face with blood. I finally freed my hands, grabbed him by the throat, and wrestled him off me.

My only thought was, WHERE ARE THE STUDS?! Why was no one coming to my rescue? In true movie fashion, I'd expected to see the court fill with my buddies, racing to my assistance, the whole area erupting into a blur of bodies and a flurry of frenzied fighting. But, that only happens in the movies.

My mind finally registered an urgent need to get up, but just as I was struggling to my feet, Greg landed a punch that hit me so hard I actually saw stars, like in a cartoon where Popeye knocks Bluto across three continents. I felt pain, real pain, for the first time in my life, and as I slumped back to my knees I knew that this fight was over … and I had lost.

I lay there for what seemed like an eternity. I could hear sounds and make out a few shadowy shapes, but it was all in slow motion. Then, I felt someone lift me up by the shoulders and drag me off the basketball court. At last, I thought, the Stud's are making their move. But when I peered through my half-closed and very blackened eyes at my defender, I was stunned to see the face of Rob Mathison floating above me. "It's okay, man," he softly comforted, "just lie still for a minute."

The Studs and Duds encircled me, trying to make the best of a bad situation. "Did you see Greg's hands, man?" Willie heartened. "You really got him! They're all bloody and shit. Nice going, Mike."

"That's from the concrete," I dejectedly acknowledged. "He hit the concrete with his fists. I didn't do anything."

"It doesn't matter," Willie reassured, "everybody's gonna think you got the best of him. That's all that counts."

"Yeah, I guess so," I dubiously agreed, unable to look at anyone while I gingerly fingered my swollen eye. "It's just that now, everybody's gonna think that I'm a pussy, you know? If Greg hadn't gotten in that lucky punch ..."

"You'd still be out there, flailing around on the concrete," Mathison grinned, as he slapped me on the shoulder and stood up to leave. "But, who gives a shit? Is your whole world gonna end because a few jerks discovered that 'Mister Stud' is just another kid with a big mouth?" He lit a cigarette, turned, and headed back toward the Youth Center. "You think they didn't already know that?" he added with a chuckle.

I pulled myself up and limped away to my Maid's Room, leaving the Studs to ponder what had happened and draw their own conclusions. I lay on my bed, holding an ice-filled washcloth on my eye, and thinking about what Rob had said. Maybe he was right.

Much later that night, I returned to the Youth Center. The streets were empty, and the early morning was still, and thick with mist. I opened the gate to the basketball court, and shuffled slowly to the spot where, a few hours earlier, Greg and I had "made our mark." Fearful questions filled my brain. What would everyone think? What about my reputation? Would I still have the same luck with girls, now that my Achilles heel had been revealed? I envied Greg. He was safe at home, dreaming about his victory, while I stood here in the darkness, alone and troubled.

Without warning, my self-pity reverie was shattered when the back door of the Youth Center swung open, and out limped a short, old, German guy, pulling a bucket filled with soapy water and carrying a well-worn mop. Surprisingly, as he made his way over to the bloody stains on the concrete, he didn't seem startled by my presence, almost as if he expected to see me standing there.

Great, I thought, all I want is a little solitude, a few minutes to lick my wounds and feel sorry for myself, and I have to deal with this throwback to World War II.

"Sad, isn't it," he murmured softly, in perfect English.

"Huh? Oh, you mean the blood," I responded. "Yeah ... more than you know."

"No, no ... not the blood," the old German sighed, "the fight. Sad that people still fight. Fighting is always sad."

"Mostly because somebody has to lose," I whispered, my eyes fixed on the tarnished floor of the basketball court.

"Everybody loses ... in a fight, nobody really wins," he earnestly declared, while scrubbing the stained cement. "It's sad because we haven't found a way to appreciate people who are different from ourselves. We always come to blows, and never stop long enough to see …"

"See what?" I probed as I studied the old German's face.

"The beauty in the differences," he smiled. "The reward doesn't lie in winning or losing a fight; we win when we can appreciate the differences."

A car backfired in the distance, and I walked over to the fence to investigate. By the time I turned back around, both the German and the bloodstain were gone.

Walking home to my Maid's Room, I thought about the old German and what he had said, and I questioned if he'd actually been there at all. As I pondered his words, I began to realize their worth. Perhaps the common thread that ties us all together is that we are all different, and in those differences lies the key to real understanding. Maybe people are brought together by more than just attitudes and lifestyles. Perhaps alliances are born out of compassion, trust, empathy … and not always based on the way we look and act.

The days that followed weren't easy for me, but there were some blessings: I'd made a new friend in Rob, I'd learned humility, and I'd come to value what my grandmother had been trying to tell me.

Somehow, as time went on, the story changed and, since Greg's hands were so mangled, the perception became that I had won the fight. But I knew the truth, and eventually, it did set me free.

Chapter Five
GET A JOB, KID

Work. The original four-letter word.

Now don't misunderstand me. I've got as much Protestant work ethic as the next fella, it's just that I've never understood the concept of putting my efforts into making someone else money. Doesn't compute; it's like taking a girl to dinner and a movie, and then dropping her off at her boyfriend's house. He gets the dessert while I get to pay the tab. Wrong. Flag on the play. I want to see the rule book.

I've always thought of money in terms of what it could buy me. My allowance was five bucks a week, and five bucks equaled one pizza, two cokes, and maybe a Conan the Barbarian comic book. That was enough during the school year, but this was summer, the dating season. I had to have more money.

My dad was more than happy to oblige. Dad was the Supply Sergeant for Ramstein Air Base and, as part of NATO's 4th Allied Tactical Air Force, he had French, Canadian, and German soldiers working for him. He was always cutting some deal: A radio for a turkey, a footlocker for a motor scooter, stuff like that. I have no idea what he traded to get me this summer job, but the day after he told me about it, the family dog came up missing. Dad never did like that dog. Anyway, one day he came home and said he'd landed this great opportunity for me and two of my buddies, working for a German moving company. We'd be building crates and moving people out of their apartments when they got transferred back to the States. It would be a "learning experience."

I'd had jobs before delivering newspapers while dodging barking dogs in California, and cleaning tables and washing dishes at the Snack Bar last summer. But this sounded like real work, which was bound to be a drag. I was going to work for Germans, for God's sake! I could just imagine them screaming threatening orders at me ... *You vill build dis box and like it or I vill shmack you in der head*! Oh yeah, this was gonna be just peachy.

"It's 06:30 on a beautiful, sunny, Monday morning, and that was the Captain and Tennille singing "Muskrat Love." This is Private First Class Randy Peterson and you are listening to the Armed Forces Radio Network." I was already tying the shoelaces on my Adidas.

Rob and Willie would be here any minute, and we'd be on our way to the station, where we'd catch the train that would take us to Rottenstein and our prestigious new jobs. Sean was supposed to work with Willie and me, but he said getting dirty didn't fit his image. So, Sean had gotten a gig at the Commissary, bagging groceries for tips, and Rob took the job.

Rob was another Maid's Room dweller. His stepfather was about ten years younger than his Mom, and we all understood why. I don't know if it's a sin to lust after your buddy's Mom but, if it is, there are about fifteen guys who are destined for eternal damnation. The woman was a showcase for Frederick's of Hollywood, and nothin' says lovin' to a teenage boy like Spandex and spiked heels. Rob seemed oblivious to the situation, but he must have thought it strange that all of his friends had drooling problems.

BAM! BAM! BAM! "Get outta bed! Time to start our new careers in the moving business."

And so it began ... my summer of heavy lifting, smelly, sweat-stained T-shirts, and eight hours a day hauling tons of furniture down flights of stairs, with a bunch of middle-aged Germans who probably resented the hell out of my being there in the first place. Judging by the sounds coming from the other side of the door, Willie was just thrilled about it.

"Okay, okay ... I'm coming," I said, opening the door.

"Where's Rob? Man, isn't he here yet? I knew this was gonna happen, we're gonna be late for our first day at work," Willie whined.

"Will you be cool. He'll be here. Probably just had something to do first."

"Like what ... watch his mom get dressed?" Willie mused.

"Man, don't be saying that in front of Rob. I'd hate to start the day with him pissed off at you. Besides, he doesn't know we all have the hots for his mom."

"What? Is he blind? Have you ever seen her in those skin-tight stretch pants! Man, you can see the outline of her underwear, and she wears teeny, tiny, bikini underwear. Probably black ... all hot women wear black underwear. I mean, she's, she's ..."

"His Mom," I chided. "God! Do you have the hots for your Mom?"

"My mom's short and fat and only wears those baggy pants with the elastic waistband," he explained.

"That's not the point ... look," I choked, "would you want Rob looking at your Mom the way we look at his?"

"He'd have to be really hard up to ..." Willie thoughtfully replied.

"Man, are you trying to be stupid, or what? Just don't say anything!"

Suddenly, Rob came running into the room, out of breath. "Sorry, man," he panted, "my mom was getting dressed for work, and I had to help her—"

Willie and I froze, our minds considering the possibilities.

"—find one of her shoes," Rob finished, bursting our thought balloons.

Thankfully, my dad appeared before Willie could say anything really stupid. "C'mon fellas, daylight's wasting, train leaves in twenty minutes. How are you doin' Rob? I saw your Mother shopping at the B.X. yesterday. Tell her I said hello."

"Bet she was buying underwear," Willie whispered as we made our way to the car.

Dad dropped us off at the station and, after a thirty-minute train ride, we found ourselves standing in the village of Rottenstein. Now, there's a fine line between "quaint" and *Grapes of Wrath*, and Rottenstein was way over the line. As we stood on the platform of the dilapidated station, watching our train desert us, I wondered just what the hell my old man had gotten us into. Following an anxious ten minutes of waiting, a big, white truck came screeching up, stopping about fifteen yards from where we stood.

A cool wind blew the dust around our feet, as the early-morning sun cast eerie shadows across the ground between the Germans and us. Slowly, we started walking toward them. We'd walk a few feet and stop; they'd drive a few feet and stop. We'd take a few more steps, and they'd inch the truck forward. I felt like Matt Dillon, staring down some hombre who'd offended Miss Kitty. All that was missing was the soundtrack from *The Good, The Bad, and The Ugly*.

The truck door swung open, and one of the Germans climbed out of the cab. "Are you guys here to pick us up?" I asked. There was no response. I looked for support from Rob and Willie, but they just stood there, cemented in their tracks. "You know Sergeant Ritter?" I continued. Nothing. Maybe the guy didn't speak English.

"C'mon, man," Rob's voice cracked, "let's catch the next train outta here. This guy's a moron. Just tell your old man that nobody showed up and ..."

Then, suddenly, the big German man turned around, climbed back up into the cab, and had barely slammed the door shut when the truck lurched forward. It came to a quick stop right in front of us. Nobody moved. The door didn't open.

The truck sat shaking and growling like an iron beast about to devour its prey, dark smoke billowing from its exhaust. The door swung open, and we heard someone grumble, "Get in."

"Go on, man," said Willie, to no one in particular.

"No, that's okay man, go ahead," I responded.

"Come on, Mike," interrupted Rob, "your Dad got us into this."

"Hey man, no one forced you to take this job," I shot back.

"You're both a couple of pussies," Willie chimed in.

"Yeah? Well I don't see you jumpin' up there, you little ..."

"Get in," repeated the voice from deep inside the cab of the truck.

Hesitantly, and without looking up, we each climbed the step one by one and slid into the back seat of the cab. In front of us were two of the largest men I'd ever seen in my life. Even seated, you could tell by their mammoth arms and necks that these guys each weighed 250 pounds, easy. One had long, slicked-back, grey hair that had created a grease stain on the collar of his off-white shirt. The other guy sported a blonde crew cut and wasn't wearing a shirt under his overalls, revealing a large tattoo of an eagle on his upper back. A German flag pennant hung from the rearview mirror, the ashtray was crammed full of cigarette butts, and decals from various soccer teams decorated the dashboard. With each gear shift the truck lunged forward, and empty beer bottles were hitting our feet from under the front seat. Through the dust-covered front window, I could see that we were headed out of town.

The three of us just sat in the back seat, looking like prisoners on their way to the big house. "How do we know these are the right guys?" Willie said under his breath. "What if they're taking us out to kill us ... or worse!?"

Worse? I tried not to imagine what could be worse than being murdered.

Although it seemed like hours, about fifteen minutes later I could see that we were approaching a big metal building with a sign on it that simply read "Processing." Willie saw it, too. "Oh, God," he murmured as the driver slowed to a stop, "it's a meat processing plant. These guys are gonna turn us into bratwursts!"

"You already are a bratwurst," Rob said. "Look, I don't know what's going on, but we can take them. They'll get out first and, when they open the door to let us out, just kick them in the face and run back in the direction of the train station as fast as you can!"

Rob had obviously seen one too many cheap Kung Fu movies. There was no way three, skinny sixteen-year-olds were going to win in a fight against the Paul Bunyan twins. But it was the only plan available, and it beat being sent back to our families in a sausage casing, so we decided to go for it.

The two Germans had exited the truck and were standing next to the open door, waiting for us to get out. "Okay, guys, this is it," yelled Rob, as he jumped from his seat, "see you at the train station. HEE-YAAAA!" And with those words, he leapt from the seat in his best sidekick stance, hoping to catch at least one of our captors unaware. Willie and I bounded toward the open door and looked outside, expecting to see Rob at his martial arts best, kicking the crap out of these German slime-balls. But all we could see was a cloud of dust, accompanied by the low moaning of someone in a lot of pain.

As the dust cleared, it became woefully apparent that there had been a flaw in our escape plan. Rob was laying flat on his back in the dirt, and the two Germans were strolling toward the metal building, laughing. Willie and I hopped off the truck and walked over to our friend on the ground.

"Is it safe?" Rob coughed.

"Wow," he exclaimed, looking around, "did I get them both?"

"Hey you guys," a voice interjected from behind us, "what are you doing? We've got a lot of household goods to process today, and I don't have a lot of time to show you around. This stuff has to be loaded and on its way to Bremerhaven by tonight if it's going to make the transport back to the States on Wednesday."

We turned to see this short guy, wearing a brown, leather jacket and tan bell-bottom slacks, striding toward us. As he got closer, it was obvious that he was losing his hair, since he had resorted to using the creative "comb-over" method of hairstyling. Several gold chains hung around his neck, and he was smoking one of those new, long, brown cigarettes.

"Who's this clown?" Rob muttered, rolling over and leaning on one arm.

"Who cares," Willie joyfully replied, "at least he speaks English."

"Hey dudes, what's happening?" our new, snappily dressed friend inquired, as he thrust his hand in Rob's direction. "Let me help you up, brother. What a trip, huh? Should've warned you about that first step, it's a real bummer. Name's Dick, Dick Leasles, former PFC Dick Leasles. Everybody just calls me Slick Dick … especially the ladies. I run the show around here."

This was it … the thing worse than death. Having to work with a couple of missing links wasn't bad enough, oh no. We also had to have "Mr. Hip Geek ex-GI" here as our boss. There was often a feeling of animosity between GIs and us guys who were here on the family plan. Off-duty GIs were always parting their hair down the middle for maximum length, putting on their best plastic-hippie clothes, and trying to make time with our girls. They'd strut over to where we were sitting and lay their best groovy-speak on the girls, offering to buy them beers, and challenging our manhood. Admittedly, it seems kind of pathetic, but naturally we would feel obligated to protect our turf, and the trouble would begin.

The three of us followed our new leader into the furniture processing plant, with Rob whistling "I Wish I Were An Oscar Meyer Wiener", much to Willie's chagrin. "Well it could have been a meat processing plant," Willie protested.

Inside, the plant was humming with activity. Men operating forklifts were unloading huge trucks, while others were busily stenciling destinations on crates. Slick Dick ran the place like it was his empire. His eyes literally lit-up as he explained the nuances of the exciting world of furniture transportation. "You have to be very careful with dresser drawers. They have to be taped shut so they won't bang around during transcontinental shipping. And always make sure that everything has been removed from the dresser before you load it onto the truck. Think you guys can remember that?"

Gee, I dunno Boss, I thought. I remembered to put my pants on today, but this is real brain work. Loading furniture onto a truck … could be tricky … might take me two seconds to figure it out. What a potato head!

"But don't worry about that now," he continued, "because I want to put you guys to work actually building the crates themselves." He looked at us like he'd just handed us the keys to the city. We looked back like we didn't own a key ring. Apparently, building crates is the plum job of the moving business, because, as Slick explained, "I had to take some real heat from the German guys when I told them I was giving you the responsibility for the crate assembly. Most guys have to put in a few years here before they get to do that." A few years? To work their way up to crate-building?

Slick led us to a small office in one corner of the building. Behind the office desk sat a large, bearded man, busily writing something on yellow slips of paper. "This is Helmut; he's the foreman around here. He takes care of things when I'm not around. Helmut, these are the American kids I was telling you about. Be sure and put them to work."

Helmut didn't even look up. "Ya, ya," he sputtered, "I put them to work."

"Well, I gotta split, dudes," Slick announced as he made his way to the door. "My Mercedes is due for its 10,000-mile check-up today, and the mechanic gets real testy if I'm late. Good to have you aboard."

We stood before Helmut, heads slightly bowed, hands behind our backs, nervously waiting for the Commandant to issue our marching orders. "So, you look like smart American boys," he said without even glancing up from his paperwork, "smart enough to get the good job here. No heavy lifting for you boys, huh?"

Alright, let's hear it for Mr. Slick Dick.

"Gee," I sighed in my best apple pie voice, "I hope none of the other workers are upset because of the crate building thing."

Our American compadre, giving us the cakewalk job.

"No," answered Helmut, looking up from his papers, "not since you boys got stuck with it."

Yes sir, that Slick, what a ... stuck with it? ... big asshole!

"There are your hammers, boys," smiled Helmut, pointing to a large tool chest. "Follow me."

"Heigh-ho, heigh-ho," chirped Willie, "it's off to work we go."

Rob lit up a cigarette, and picked up a hammer. "Which dwarf are you, bratwurst boy?" he said with a smirk, "Queasy?"

"Look man," Willie shot back, "don't make me say something I'll regret."

"Too late," Rob replied, blowing small smoke rings in Willie's direction.

"Hey, guys," I interjected, "forget it."

Suddenly, Helmut ended the squabble. "No smoking," he yelled.

"Do you see anybody else smoking? See that sign? *Rauchen verboten,* it means 'smoking forbidden'."

"Yeah, okay, Field Marshal. See, I'm putting it out. Don't get your shorts all in a bundle," Rob sneered. "C'mon you guys, let's get this disaster on the road."

We followed Helmut as he headed toward the giant garage doors where trucks were being unloaded. Maybe it was a premonition, or a vision, or the fact that all the German guys were laughing and pointing in our direction, but as we walked through the work areas, I suddenly got that feeling I get when Mom says we're having liver and onions for dinner.

Helmut walked past the doors, past the trucks, and through the parking lot until he reached a small, dirty, white truck. "You," he said, pointing at me, "get in the truck. You other two sit in the back."

Helmut skidded across cobblestone streets for about six blocks until we came to a farmhouse. He turned onto a dirt road and jerked the truck to a stop in front of a wooden structure that leaned to one side. Right across the road, a skinny guy in waist-high rubber boots was shoveling scoops of what looked like dirt into a wooden wheelbarrow. Then I got out of the truck, and the stench hit me in the face like a skunk eating rotten eggs in an outhouse on a hot day.

I stopped gagging long enough to notice that Willie and Rob were glaring at me, their T-shirts pulled up over their noses. Helmut stood nearby. "You get used to it," he laughed. "This is the place where all the farmers bring their animals' shit to make into fertilizer."

Helmut swung open the creaky doors of the old wooden structure, and several hundred flies came buzzing out. Inside, the floor was covered with hay and residual cow shit, and large, flat pieces of wood were stacked ten feet high against the wall. "Here's the wood, and there are the nails," instructed Helmut. "I'll be back in six hours to pick you up."

"What time's lunch?" asked Willie.

Lunch? Who could think of eating? My appetite left with the flies.

"Eat whenever you feel like it," answered Helmut, walking back toward the truck. "Just have ten crates built by the time I get back. We're moving some officer out of base housing tonight, and we're going to need them."

"Hey Mike, have I thanked you yet for getting me this job?" Rob growled as he watched Helmut drive off.

"Look, man," I replied, "I had no idea we'd be working in a toilet."

"This really sucks," whined Willie.

However, we found the job of putting ten crates together is easy when there are no instructions to follow, and within three hours we were finished with our quota for the day. We spent the next three hours seeing how many flies we could smash with our hammers. Rob won the contest by killing 267.

The next morning, Willie called to say that Sean had gotten him a job at the Commissary, and he wasn't going to work with us anymore. Rob was delighted. "Good," he said, "I never liked that Willie anyway. He's always giving my mom funny looks, like he wants to screw her or something." I told him I hadn't noticed.

Helmut was standing at the station when we arrived back in Rottenstein. I guess he wasn't surprised that we'd already suffered one casualty because he didn't even ask about Willie. In fact, he didn't say anything except, "Get in the truck."

As we pulled up to the processing plant, I could see a man pacing in front of the building: he wore an Air Force uniform, and a pissed-off expression on his face. Slick was nowhere in sight. Rob and I got out of the truck and, before we took three steps, the pacing guy came running at us, screaming, "Are you the little bastards that put those crates together yesterday?!"

By now he was close enough for us to see the Colonel insignias on his uniform. "Those damn crates fell apart, and my stuff's all over the place!" he yelled. "Who the hell's in charge around here? These damn Krauts won't tell me anything."

"Slick is, sir," answered Rob.

"Slick? Slick who?' Hollered the Colonel.

"Dick," I replied.

"Who you calling a dick, boy?" Shrieked the officer.

"No, no," I quickly responded, "that's his name. Slick Dick."

"Slick Dick?! For Christ's sake, no wonder this place is a catastrophe! Well you tell Mr. Dick that my stuff had better be in tip-top shape when it gets to the States, or I'm going to come back over here and kick his ever-lovin' ass!" And with that the Colonel stormed over to his car and drove away.

Needless to say, our careers as crate-builders had come to an abrupt halt. My folks were disappointed that I'd lost my job after only one day. For me, there's nothing quite as bad as knowing that your parents are disappointed in you. I'd rather have a smack in the head; at least that pain goes away after a few minutes. But parental disappointment hangs around for a long time, gnawing at your guts, making you feel like a worm. I tried to explain that Helmut hadn't told us how to build the stupid crates, and that's why they'd fallen apart. But my excuses were met with shaking heads, heavy sighs, and raised eyebrows. I know when to give up, so as penance for my sins, I asked if there was anything I could do to make it up to them. My mom jumped at the chance, "How about getting a haircut?"

Nice try mom, maybe next time.

A few days later, my sister Cyndy came home with some great news. Cyndy had a summer job working at the base Personnel office, and had heard that two jobs were available in the warehouse of the Commissary.

Through some slip of the paperwork, she'd managed to place Rob's name and mine at the top of the "availability list." The jobs were listed as permanent but, hey, we could just quit before school started again in the fall. The pay was $3.25 an hour ... BIG money!

Rob and I worked with six other guys who had just graduated, and were earning money to attend college in the States. Well, five of them were college-bound; the sixth guy was the delinquent, 18-year-old, son of some Major who thought a job would keep his kid out of jail. This kid was always, *always* stoned. In response to any question, he'd tuck is neck back between his shoulder blades and peer through slitted eyes, shaking his head and giggling to himself, "Man … uh, oh, wow, man, uh …". A real space case. In fact, that's why we took to calling him "Space Child."

Every morning the milk trucks would roll in, and we'd slide cases of dairy products down a conveyer belt into the refrigeration unit. And every morning the truck would pull away, leaving a small mound of empty chocolate milk pints in its wake. Discretion was not part of our vocabulary, but it didn't seem to matter anyway. I mean, if they'd really wanted to, even Military Intelligence could have made the connection.

This experience taught me that there are two basic rules to follow when working for the government: "do what you're told" and "if anybody asks, you don't know anything." It's true... "I don't know who told me to do it" is an acceptable answer. As long as someone told you to do it, who told you wasn't important. The important factor was that you did not make a decision on your own. This way, no one was accountable for screw-ups, nor was anyone responsible for correcting them.

Truth be told, we spent a fair amount of time screwing off. Still, there were considerable stretches when we really worked our butts off to get the job done. Some days, ten or twelve trailer loads of everything from diapers to frozen turkeys would roll in, and we'd have the cargo unloaded and put away before we left for the night. And although it was hard work, I really enjoyed riding the forklifts and bullshitting with my workmates. Not to mention the fringe benefits.

Our creativity wasn't limited to the art of undetected milk pilferage. Quickly, we discovered that cases of Kotex make great hiding places. Rob and I spent hours building elaborate forts, connected by a series of tunnels made from huge boxes of sanitary napkins. Each tunnel led to a key "munchies" stash … if we had a craving for Sugar Smacks, we just crawled down the cereal tunnel; had a hankering for a Hershey bar, we slithered down the tunnel that led to where the chocolate was stored. And if we needed something to wash it all down, a quick shimmy to the juice aisle was all it took.

We'd been working at the warehouse for about a month, when one day we heard a lot of commotion coming from the supervisor's office. Peering over our fortress of feminine hygiene products, we could see six Airmen mulling around the loading dock.

"Wonder what's up," whispered Rob.

"Bet they're hip to our treating this place like a smorgasbord," I surmised, "and it's payback time."

Suddenly our supervisor emerged from his office and headed our way. He had a clipboard in his hand, and an Army officer followed like a shadow behind him. "Okay you guys," the supervisor yelled, "c'mon out. I need you front and center ... now!"

"Told you," I whimpered, sliding down behind a large case of maxipads. "It's our ass."

As we reluctantly moved to join our fellow conspirators, Space Child came scurrying past us, crawling down one of the tunnels like a hunted spider. "Hey," hollered Rob, "where you goin' Space?"

"Forget it, man," I said, "he's still looking for that pot he stashed in one of the tunnels last week. Let's climb on down and see what all the hoopla's about. And remember, no matter what, play stupid."

While everyone gathered in the open area that led to the loading dock to hear what our illustrious leader had to say, I spied Space Child peeking at us from behind a stack of "Cap'n Crunch" cases. Then, looking much like a gopher, he popped up from behind the baby food, then the canned green beans, then the pudding cups, until he finally settled at the very top of the warehouse where the cross beams came together.

"Okay," the supervisor began, "somebody's been stealing cases of cigarettes and selling 'em on the black market. So, these guys," pointing at the six Airmen, "are going to go through every inch of this place until we find out how they're being ..."

Out of the blue, a screech echoed through the warehouse, and everyone looked up to see Space Child hanging by his knees from one of the cross beams. "I know where the smokes went," he sang teasingly, "catch me if you can." And with that, he dismounted and disappeared into the labyrinth of tunnels.

"Get that little asshole," shrieked the Army officer. "I want him caught and brought to me now!"

The military contingency immediately flew into action, spreading out and running toward the storage racks. "There he is," bellowed their commander, "no, there he is ... over there. No, no, no ... over that way."

We froze, our eyes searching the stacks of boxes for glimpses of Space Child. I couldn't believe what I was seeing! Was this guy, jumping from rafter to rafter like Rocky the Flying Squirrel, the same guy who usually moved at a snail's pace? Suddenly we all started to chant, "Go Space

Child, go!" Even our supervisor had a smile on his face as he watched his doper employee evade the onslaught of fumbling GIs. Then, just as abruptly as he'd appeared, Space Child had vanished.

The warehouse became very quiet, as if everyone was holding his breath, waiting for Space to make his move. Then, like a skydiver exiting a plane, Space Child leapt from the top of Fort Kotex, waving his arms wildly in the air. "Over here," he hollered. "Come and get me. I'll wait right here for you."

"Well, don't just stand there playing with yourselves," shouted the Army officer. "Go get him!"

As the sea of khaki uniforms converged on Space's position, a low, rumbling sound filled the air. The GIs fought to retain their balance while, all around them, huge walls of boxes started to sway. Then, as if on cue, the cardboard walls began to crumble, falling in on themselves and crashing to the floor, taking the GIs with them. Ketchup oozed from shattered bottles, mixing with a menagerie of corn flakes, soap powder, syrup, and everything else imaginable, covering the warehouse floor like a thick, gooey, sticky carpet.

We spent the next several nights cleaning up the mess and disassembling what was left of our tunnel system. Work wasn't the same after that, and a few weeks later I quit to join my family on a camping vacation to Spain. As far as I know, they never caught Space Child, but later I heard he was safe and living in a youth hostel in Amsterdam. Or, someplace on the planet Mars.

Chapter Six
WITH SEVEN YOU GET CARSICK

It always started out with Mom...

"Okay, Ray, do we have everything? Travelers checks ..."

"Got 'em."

"...camera, suntan lotion, maps ..."

"Right here."

"... did you cancel the newspaper, make sure the stove was off, and ..."

"It's all taken care of."

"Okay, then ... head count ... Ruth, Connie, Mark, Cyndy, Michael ..."

"Here."

"Here."

"Here."

"Here."

"Where's Michael? Michael!"

"Yeah, yeah, here ... I'm here ... Damn!"

"You'd better turn that attitude around young man. This is our family vacation, and you will have a good time."

Family vacations. The Inquisition in a station wagon. Every year we all crammed into this closet on wheels and made our way to some destination that would, my mother insisted, bring us an "...appreciation for how other people live, and the rich history that makes us all part of the human race." She always said that ... even when we went to Disneyland and Knotts Berry Farms in California. The rich human history of Mickey Mouse and jellied fruit.

I guess I've never been big on mandatory fun, and family vacations were nothing if not mandatory. Once a year, all seven of us would crowd into the station wagon and tear around the countryside, stopping at every historical marker along the way. Mom had an eye for them. I swear, we could be driving through a rainstorm in the middle of the night, and she would spot that small sign on the side of the road, marking the spot where Teddy Roosevelt took a piss on his way to kill a bear. We'd all pile out of the car to see where one of history's greatest presidents relieved himself. "It's important, kids," she would say. "Take a good look. You may never pass this way again." And even though I'd somehow managed to live a fairly full existence without seeing the location of Teddy's outdoor pee, she thought it would enhance my life to stand on the very ground where a former president had marked his territory.

For me, family vacations were like a trip to the dentist … without the laughing gas. My continual bad attitude notwithstanding, they always began with the initial excitement of visiting some place new. But as soon as the newness wore off, we'd start the battle for space and solitude in an over-packed car, with seven people crammed shoulder to shoulder. The game of musical car seats would begin, as Mom set about rearranging us, trying to find just the right combination that would keep us from killing one another before we reached our destination. I would always "dibs" the far back of the station wagon … that seat that faced the other way where, in the packing frenzy, my old man had left one small space open for me. It was my sanctuary, a way to avoid the constant whining, and inevitable howls of "quit touching me!"

But the times I most dreaded, the one's that made my skin crawl, were when we'd stop someplace to eat. There was only one criteria when choosing a restaurant … it had to be cheap. My mom would call these eating establishments "rustic" or "colorful," but in reality, they were just cheap. I understood why … it's not easy feeding seven people on a Master Sergeant's pay. Whenever we had gone "road-tripping" through the States, we'd always stopped at little, local diners in the smallest of towns, to "soak up the atmosphere" along with some green slab of meat that was passing for hamburger. Now, it wasn't always that bad, and Mom made sure we got our daily allowance of the foods that were needed to "build healthy bones" but, when you're on vacation, well, let's just say it's amazing what passes for a recommended food group.

I have been called a picky eater … actually I've been called worse than that but, for the sake of argument, we'll stick with picky eater. I think I'm very easy to please … meat and potatoes are all I require. But my mom was always trying out some new recipe on us. And, while my brother, Mark, would eat sardines and peanut butter on a garlic roll if you put it in front of him, I had a real aversion to eating anything that smelled worse than my gym socks. I have a particular dislike for onions; actually, I avoid them like the plague. I would go on search and destroy missions through my mom's latest culinary concoction, seeking out those little breath killers, while my mom would stand by, insisting there wasn't "a single onion in there." There always was. But, after a time, my mom and I came to terms about my sensitive palette, and she just took a "this is what we're having for dinner, eat it or don't" attitude. One year I ate bologna sandwiches for dinner 179 times.

Eating road food was bad enough, but it couldn't hold a candle to the ordering ritual. Mom always tried to go through the motions of allowing us to order "whatever we wanted" (under $2.00). But she always ended up second-guessing our decisions, while the waitress stood by impatiently, wondering what horrible thing she'd done in a previous life that had caused her to experience the Ritter family's ordering ritual in this one.

"Are you sure you want chili, Michael?" Mom would interject. "It's a long ride until we stop for the night."

"Yeah, Mom, I'm sure."

"Doesn't it upset your stomach?"

"Yeah, Mom, I'm sure."

"I just don't want you to get diarrhea again like last time," she'd loudly whisper.

"I'm sure, Mom! I'm sure! I want chili, okay?!"

"Okay ... but it might have onions in it," her voice lilting.

"I'll have a grilled cheese and fries ... damn."

And the same procedure would start all over again with my brother and sisters. "I'm sorry honey," Mom would say to the waitress, "but it's important that my children learn to be independent, and think for themselves. It's a life lesson."

Before I go on, I want to say that I really do love my family.

My brother and sisters are the best, and my parents are always there to see me through the hard times. Individually, or maybe even a few at a time, we get along just fine. There were good times, times I'll never forget, when we'd all play games together, or sing together, or decorate the Christmas tree together. But, having said that, I couldn't stand eating in a restaurant together!

I'm sorry, but it was embarrassing, man. Somebody's milk always got spewed across the table, somebody always needed to be taken to the bathroom, somebody was always hitting somebody, or teasing somebody, or crying, or dropping food on the floor, or ... anything but eating. I would just stare down at my plate, pretending to be invisible. Who me? No, I'm not with these people. I was kidnapped ... yeah, that's it, kidnapped. HELP! Call the police!

But ... I digress.

Our latest venture into the world of mandatory fun was taking us to Barcelona for two weeks of camping on Spain's white beaches, and soaking up the warm Spanish sun. Dad had bought one of those tent-on-wheels campers, stuffed it full of K-rations (I loved the canned ham and eggs), sleeping bags, and everything else that Mom thought we might need, hooked the thing to the back of our Air Force-blue station wagon, piled luggage on the roof, shoved a few pillows and kids in the car, and we were ready to roll. My parents always had this "getting there is half the fun" philosophy (God knows what the other half was), so we took the scenic route to Spain ... through France and Italy.

France ... how can I say this ... sucked. All those clichés you hear about rude French people are true, and I think nothing expresses their bad attitude better than their public restrooms. They're a trip. The first time we had to make a "pit stop" in France, the old man pulled our circus over to what looked like phone booths on the side of the road. "Are you sure that's a bathroom?" my sister Connie asked. "It doesn't look like a bathroom."

"It's a bathroom," Dad replied, as he fumbled to open a road map.

"Come on dear, I have to go too," chirped Mom. "It will be a real adventure."

I think you can tell a lot about a country by its public restrooms. The Germans always had this God-awful toilet paper that rubbed your ass like a Brillo pad; the Swiss had very nice, clean, tidy facilities; and, the French had restrooms that just screamed, "Get out, we don't want you here!" I mean, they've really narrowed it down to the bare necessities—no frills, no niceties ... like a toilet ... just a hole in the cement with a footprint on either side of it, marking the position where you were to stand. I assumed there was some scientific research that went into the placement of these footprints, perhaps a graph that showed the optimal origination points to score a direct hit into the hole, with a minimum of pants leg backsplash, allowing, of course, for wind currents that could sweep under the stall from passing cars. But probably not. Either way, my mom was about to experience an aspect of multiculturalism that she hadn't counted on.

The rest of us waited in the car for my mom and little sister to return from what we hoped was a bathroom; and, a few minutes later, they came scurrying back to the car. My little sister was crying as she squished down on the back seat. "Okay, Ray," my mom said, as she reached back over the seat to try and comfort her soaking wet daughter. "Let's go."

Being a loving brood of siblings we all felt sorry for Connie ... for about thirty seconds.

"Augh ... Mom! Get her away from me!"

"Connie wet her pants ... Connie wet her pants ..."

Children are so understanding.

"What the Sam Hill happened back there?" Dad bellowed, as he tried to steer our caravan through the narrow French streets. "How come she's all wet?" And, as Mom covered Connie with a blanket in a vain attempt to get us to stop laughing, and set about peeling off my little sister's fermenting stretch pants, she explained about the "filthy French facilities" and how, in an effort to avoid exactly what had happened, she'd held Connie's pants back while my little sister squatted to relieve herself. It got really ugly from there, and I try hard not to envision it. But the end result was a wet, crying, little girl being jeered by her ever-unsympathetic siblings, as she watched her red stretch pants and soggy underwear get hung out the window, and listened to them flapping against the side of the car. I don't think anyone went to the bathroom again until we hit Italy.

While in France, we visited all the tourist hot spots: the Eiffel Tower, the Arc de Triomphe, the Louvre, stuff like that. But what really impressed me were the hookers. Not from personal experience, you understand ... I was with my family for God's sake; it's just that they were everywhere. Prostitution is legal in Europe, even government-regulated in some countries, so I'd seen hookers before. As a matter of fact, there were a few that worked the street that led to my high school. But they were old pros, and I do mean old pros. We called them "Hitler's Honeys," because a few of them looked like they'd been working the same lamp post since World War Two. In France, however, particularly in Paris, man, they looked like they came right off the set of *Irma La Douce* ... with shorter skirts. Yes sir, I was certainly gaining an appreciation for the French culture. Mom would be so proud.

It's true—all things must pass, and we finally bid a not-so-fond adieu to France, winding our way through the European countryside to the exciting land of good pasta, gondolas, and bona fide Catholic icons ... Italy.

It was closed.

Not the whole country, you understand, just the parts we wanted to see. The Leaning Tower of Pisa was closed for renovations; the gondolas weren't running due to flooding from the worst rainstorm to hit the country in twenty years; and, the Pope (yes, my mom actually thought we might "catch a glimpse of him") was out of town. The Road to Barcelona was beginning to seem like a bad Bob Hope-Bing Crosby movie. But my mom does not discourage easily, and decided we'd just check into an "authentic Italian hotel" for the night, go out to dinner, and appreciate exciting, romantic Italy by moonlight.

We drove around looking for the right place, one that just oozed with atmosphere, and found it in an old stone building with a flashing neon light that said something in Italian and "hotel," so we knew we were in the right place. The rest of the day having been somewhat disappointing, to say the least, my old man decided to "spring for the best room they have," one that would give us the best view of the street life below.

The room was dark and small, with one very large bed right in the middle. "There must be some mistake," my old man said to the bellboy, who just shrugged his shoulders and smiled a lot in response. "We can't all fit into this one bed," my dad continued, as the grinning bellboy held his hand out for a tip. "Am I getting through to you? Do you understand? There are seven of us," he said, holding up seven fingers to drive home the point. "Seven ... seven ... Christ, Margaret, this joker doesn't have any idea what I'm talking about."

My mom is from the old school that says anyone can understand English if you speak it slowly and loudly enough. "WE ... NEED...MORE...BEDS," she exclaimed to the now seemingly confused bellboy. "TO ... SLEEP ... MORE ... BEDS." Our Italian host let out a sigh, and went to a door in the corner of the room. Inside, was a small storage closet with two roll-out cots. "Here, more beds to sleep," he said in pigeon English, "all okay now."

"All okay?!" the old man shot back. "All okay...I'm paying ... what am I paying, I can't figure out this damn money. Everything costs thousands of lira ... well, whatever it is, it's too much for this hole in the ..."

"Gracias," (gracias?) Mom said, and handed the bellboy a tip. "By the way, where's the bathroom? WHERE'S ... THE ... BATHROOM? ... THE ... TOILET?" The bellboy opened the front door and pointed down the hall, where a large man was standing, dressed only in a towel wrapped around his waist. "Toilet there," the bellboy said, as he walked down the hall and got on the elevator. "Gracias," my mom yelled back.

"Well," Dad mused, "I know what the Italian word before 'hotel' on the sign means... 'stupid American.' We're at the Stupid American Hotel. Do you believe this...?"

"Oh it's fine, Ray," Mom replied, as she helped my little sisters out of their rain-soaked jackets. "It will be an adventure."

Right ... some adventure. The monsoon that blanketed the city left us Stupid American Hotel-bound, resulting in an "authentic Italian dinner" menu that consisted of potato chips, sandwiches, and some warm Kool-aid that had been aging in the car since we left Germany. Dad and I struggled with the foldout beds, while mom waited in line for the bathroom, under the disgusted gaze of several other guests, who watched as she crammed herself and my three sisters into the tiny facility. "We'll only be a minute," she chirped. Forty-five minutes later they returned to the room all cleaned up and "pottied," the line waiting to get into the bathroom now stretching down the hall and around the corner. "You know, Ray," she said, "Italians must put a lot of stake in their personal hygiene. We were tidying ourselves up for more than a half-hour, but when we came out I still heard a few people call us 'dirty Americans.' And you know I always make sure these kids are clean and washed before they go to bed."

"Don't worry about it," Dad responded, "they're just different from us."

The room was now wall-to-wall beds; Mark and I were in one, my three sisters were in another, and Mom and Dad took the smallest foldout bed for themselves. It was like the Waltons living in an efficiency apartment but, as I drifted off to sleep under the blinking gaze of the "Stupid American Hotel" neon light, I was just glad to be in a dry spot, between real sheets, in relative quiet. Because I knew what tomorrow would bring.

The rain ended with the dawn, and we packed up the wagon train in preparation for the trip to our final destination. Dad had just squeezed the last bit of luggage onto the rack on top of the car, when Mom came running out of the hotel. "I can't find Ruth Ann. Oh Ray, what if someone kidnapped her?! I've heard these Italians are all in the Mafia—what if they've taken her and are holding her somewhere for ransom?! My poor baby!" (Mom had only two speeds, "forward" and "panic.")

"I'm sure that's it, Peg," the old man replied wearily. "She's being held for ransom. Wait 'til her kidnappers find out that the only thing we could offer them in exchange is another kid." He looked around at the rest of us, "Any volunteers?"

As Mom was forming us into a posse, a large woman appeared in the hotel doorway holding my little sister in her arms. Ruth Ann was smiling, and eating what looked like a small, white apple. "The poor bambino was so hungry," the woman said with a laugh, "but she really like good Italian food." My mom ran over and snatched Ruth Ann from the woman's arms, and in an instant recognized that it wasn't an apple she'd been munching on, but a large clove of garlic.

"Oh, gracias," (again with the gracias) she said through tearing eyes, hugging my little sister. "We were so worried."

"I wasn't," the old man said under his breath, as he took Ruth Ann from my mom and, holding her at arms length, carried her to the car.

"Here," he said to the nearest kid, "put her in the back seat … and give her a mint or something, for Christsake."

Mom exchanged addresses with the large Italian woman, she was always exchanging addresses with whomever she met, and within a few minutes the Ritter caravan was back on the road, leaving a jet steam of garlic wafting through the air behind us.

Excuse me while I digress for a moment, but eventually it will become relevant to the story. My old man fancies himself a "Mr. Fix-it" kind of guy. The trouble is, he really doesn't know what he's doing. Oh, he can put something back together if he's right there when it falls apart, but since that rarely happens, he usually resorts to the age-old male trait of just winging it. You know, if it looks like it belongs there, even if the part doesn't fit, that must be where it goes. To hell with instructions or drawing up a plan—that's just a waste of time. He built a screened-in back porch once, using only a picture from a magazine for guidance. "I know what I'm doing … quit bugging me," were words I heard him say to my mom countless times. And he honestly believed it. He did know what he was doing, it was just that the thing he was trying to fix or build wouldn't cooperate. "Damn it, I know I cut this board the right length … damn thing must have warped overnight." We'd all stand around rolling our eyes at one another, safe in the knowledge that somehow he'd make it work, even if the end result only remotely resembled the picture in the magazine. "There you go," he'd say, proudly standing with his hands on his hips, gazing at his latest construction project with the same awe as a new father looking at his baby for the first time. And in his eyes, it was beautiful. Didn't matter that it looked like one of those funhouses with a slanted floor, so you feel like you're always walking at an angle, or that the screen door didn't close all the way, or that the walls weren't strong enough to support Mom's flower pots. Those were all things that could be "fixed later … after the wood settles … it'll be fine." He even built a picnic table and, although we'd have to hold our plates down to keep them from sliding off into our laps, he was happy, so we were happy for him. The important thing was he'd rigged another project together and, although it was imperfect to say the least, we were used to "making do" and appreciated him for trying.

Usually.

It was just getting dark as we reached the Spanish border, and the rainstorm we thought we'd left behind in Italy came upon us suddenly. The dirt road we were traveling became a sea of mud in a matter of minutes, and Dad was trying hard to concentrate on the narrow winding pathway that took us through the mountains. This was no easy task under the best of conditions, but lugging a camper behind a station wagon full of screaming kids made the job even more difficult. "Ray," my mom said, "maybe we should just pull over and sleep in the car tonight ... wait out the rain. This road looks pretty bad and ..."

"Horsefeathers," the old man replied as he tried to see through the rain-drenched windshield, between swipes of the wiper blades. "We'll be fine. We're only a couple of hours away from the campsite, and I want to make it tonight. Just relax, everything's under control."

"But the road is so bad, Ray ..."

"The road's fine ... just fine ... you know, kids, I remember this one time when I was driving to Keokuk to see your Mom and ... JESUS CHRIST!"

Mud splashed all the way up to the windows as Dad suddenly slammed on the brakes, bringing the car to a skidding halt. The road was gone! Not blocked ... not flooded ... gone! Before us loomed a thicket of trees that stood eerily against the dark, rain-swept sky, and for a moment I flashed on a Christopher Lee Dracula movie I'd seen the previous weekend. Mysterious shadows dancing across the hood of the car, the pounding rain against the metal roof, stuck out in the middle of nowhere. The perfect setting ... for horror.

We sat there for what seemed like an eternity, catching our breath, while at the same time wondering how the hell we were going to get out of this. Dad sat motionless, staring out the window, his hands glued to the steering wheel, his foot still pressed hard against the brake pedal. The rest of us looked like a bunch of store mannequins, our bodies frozen in fear, glazed eyes fixed on Dad, waiting for his next move.

"Well," the old man murmured in a low, almost emotionless, tone. "Looks like we're gonna have to find another way around."

My mom, who up until this point had the same deer-caught-in-a-headlight look as the rest of us, came unglued. "A different way!" She snapped. "A different way! We could have all been killed, Ray."

"But we weren't," my dad replied softly.

"I told you this road was no good."

"I know."

"So what are you going to do now?"

"Turn around."

My old man ... he never minces words. I just figured he knew Mom was going to be upset for a while and, after several years of marriage and five kids, knew there was nothing he could do about it except ride out the storm. So he gave in quickly, no defense, no counterpoint, just run the white flag up the pole from the start and get on with life.

And besides, in this case, he knew Mom was right.

Now, backing up a station wagon attached to a trailer is no easy task under the best of conditions. It had taken the old man thirty minutes to back it into our carport, for God's sake, and now he was going to attempt to do it on a hill, in a rainstorm, hubcap deep in mud. My mom held my little sister, Ruth, in her arms, my other two sisters and my brother huddled on the floor of the backseat, and I just sat in my little rumble seat, my eyes fixed on the old man. It all seemed to happen in slow motion, like one of those dream sequences in the movies, or that shampoo commercial with the two people running toward one another. The old man slowly, firmly, eased the gearshift into reverse. There was no trace of emotion in his face as he turned and placed his right arm on the backrest of the front seat, his left hand gripping the steering wheel, and pressed lightly on the gas pedal with his foot. "What do you think, Michael?" He asked. "We gonna make it back there?" Oh God, he was asking for my opinion … we were in trouble!

"I dunno," I stuttered in reply. "It's rainin' so hard I can't see very well."

"Well, roll the window down. C'mon now, I need your help here."

I rolled down the back window and, with every inch, more rain splashed against my face, soaking both my clothes and the backseat. "It's really dark, Dad."

"Can you see the trailer lights?"

I nodded.

"Okay, great. Now look to your right … go on, stick your head out the window and look to the right. Is there enough room for me to back this thing up and turn us around?"

I stuck my body halfway out the open window and looked to the right, but couldn't see anything through the driving rain.

"Well? Is it clear?"

I didn't know. I knew I didn't know, but yet, "Yeah, Dad, looks okay from here."

"Okay then, hold on to your seats. Here we go.'

I swear my heart stopped beating as the old man slowly backed the car down the hill, gently turning the steering wheel to the left. To my amazement, the trailer crept through the mud and turned to the right. It was gonna work! Alright! I looked at my dad who had just the faintest of grins on his face. The kind Superman gets when he's saved the day.

Dad had just about completed the tricky maneuver, when suddenly the back left corner of the trailer slammed into something. Dad didn't even turn around. "What'd we hit?" He said, in that low fatherly voice.

I didn't want to look. Perhaps if I didn't say anything he'd forget to blame me and somehow think it was his fault. Yeah, right. "Uh … looks like a tree, Dad," I stammered.

"Looks like a tree? Looks like a tree? How the hell did you miss seeing a whole damn tree?"

"Now, Ray," my mom interjected, "I'm sure Michael …"

"Wasn't paying attention as usual."

I felt like a real shit. I'd let the old man down, and probably marooned the whole family in the woods for life. But I really couldn't see through the rain; and besides, I wasn't the one who'd gotten us lost in the first place! So, it was his fault. I was just a passenger on the Titanic—he was supposed to be steering the ship. Easy to blame me, boy … that's it, no more Mr. Nice Guy. I was going to fight back. Yes, sir, it was showdown time!

"Sorry, Dad."

Okay, okay … so I'd left my nerve in my other pants.

"C'mon, then," Dad murmured as he opened the car door, "let's check out the damage, Michael."

"But, Ray," Mom said, tugging on the arm of his sleeve, "it's raining out there." Mom had a knack for pointing out the obvious.

"No kidding, Peg!" the old man shot back. "Maybe we should just sit here until it floods and hope it washes us back down the mountain! C'mon Michael!"

The trailer was resting against a huge tree. The back taillights had come unhooked, and wires hung limply, swinging in the monsoon-like wind that whipped rain around us like swarming flies on a garbage can. Through the fogged-up windows I could see the worried faces of my family watching us, as Dad and I pretended to know what we were doing. "Doesn't look too bad," the old man said. "Could have been a lot worse."

I looked up to see just what "a lot worse" could possibly mean, and gasped as I saw a cliff on the other side of the tree, that dropped so far down it was impossible to see the bottom through the driving rain. "Looks like this tree really saved our ass," the old man said, as he struggled to catch the swinging wires of the taillights.

"That's why I directed you to it," I replied, in a vain attempt to redeem myself.

"Yeah, okay …" the old man smiled, giving me that 'you're so full of shit' look. "Good work, Michael."

Mercifully, it suddenly stopped raining, and Dad and I spent the next hour-and-a-half hooking the taillights back up and maneuvering our water-logged caravan into position for the trip back down the mountain. Actually, Dad did most of the work—I just kind of supervised. I'm real good at supervising. Dad carefully reconnected the taillights as I shoved some clothes under the tires for traction. I don't exactly know how we made it, but at just about 3:00 in the morning our tires again hit pavement, and we parked the caravan on the side of the road, trying to get some sleep over the faint whimpering of Mom saying, "Those clothes will never be the same."

Somehow, I felt pretty good about the whole deal. Sure, I was caked in mud, tired, wet, and hungry, but we'd faced the situation head on and hadn't let it get the best of us. It was one of those father-son-bonding moments, and I couldn't help but smile as I drifted off to sleep.

We were up with the sun, and my mud-covered jeans cracked as I rolled out of the back window of the station wagon. What had looked like a deserted road at 3:00 in the morning, when we'd stopped to catch a few winks, turned out to be a major highway. And there I saw it, a sign from God. Well, actually a sign from the Spanish tourist bureau … "Happy Whale Campground - 10 kilometers." Alright! We were almost there! Only a few minutes from a hot shower, clean clothes, and several days of nothing to do but bake under the warm August sun. I turned to let my slumbering family in on the good news when I realized, by the moans and faint cry of, "Oh my God, Ray, I told you we should have stayed on the main road," that my mom was already busy trying to salvage the clothes I had used for traction. She had them laid out all over the car, and was busy scraping away at them like they were so many pieces of burnt toast.

Thirty minutes later we came over the top of a hill, and glimpsed the crystal blue water of the Spanish coastline … along with what looked to be several million people crammed into a stretch of beach the size of a large backyard. Our vacation site looked like a refugee camp, with tents and animals, and near-naked, out-of-shape bodies as far as the eye could see. That's one thing I've noticed about Europeans—they are not ashamed of their bodies … even when they should be. You haven't lived until you've seen a 300-pound, hairy woman in a string bathing suit, lumbering across the beach. There were people from every nationality scampering around like ants on a melted candy bar, each looking for the perfect place to make their campsite. The old man stood next to the car and stretched, flakes of crusted mud gently dropping to the ground around his feet. "Okay, gang," he yawned, "we're here."

Mom was beside herself with excitement. "Isn't it wonderful, kids?" She smiled. "Just look at that beautiful water out there. Betcha can't wait to get in it huh, Michael?"

Yeah, Ma ... just give me a bar of soap and an inner tube and send me out to sea. Anything to get this mud off me.

Two hours later, we had positioned ourselves on a small camping area, sandwiched between a German family on one side, and a bunch of Italian guys on the other. The Germans were busy smoking some sort of sausage on a small BBQ, and waved at us as we struggled to unload our caravan. The Italian guys, on the other hand, were busy playing grab-ass with bikini-clad blondes, so I don't think they even noticed the American invasion that was emptying onto the beach. Dad was busy trying to untie his famous slip-knot that held the luggage on top of the car, pretending to listen to my mom who was barking orders to us kids. "Cyndy, take Connie and Ruth and go find a bathroom. Mark, help your father get that stuff off the car, and Michael ... Michael, quit looking at those girls and take a walk down the road and see if you can find someplace where we can buy some water. Judy Johnson, you know, Carrie's mother, told me that we can't trust the tap water here. They were here last year, and Carrie got diarrhea so bad that she ended up spending half of her vacation sitting on the toilet."

Thanks, Ma ... much more information than I needed to know.

As I grudgingly walked through the campground, I couldn't help but notice that the trees seemed to hum, actually hum, as I strolled by. It was the weirdest thing. If I stopped, the humming stopped, but would pick up again as soon as I started walking. It sounded like an electric razor, you know, that low zzzzttt kind of noise—like a garage tube light on its last leg. I was walking along, staring up at the trees, when whump, I ran right into this Spanish fella who had stopped to tie the laces on his shoes, knocking him over into the dirt. Shit! I'd been here less than five minutes, and already I was about to start an international incident. "Oh, sorry man, I didn't see you," I stammered. "You okay?"

"Okay, okay," he smiled back at me. "American, right?"

"Yeah."

"I'm Juan," he said, extending his hand so I could help him up, "Juan

Sebastian."

"Michael. Call me Mike. Sorry about that. I was trying to figure out what makes the trees hum and wasn't watching where I was going."

"Bugs," Juan replied.

"Huh?"

"Bugs ... it's the bugs. The trees are full of them."

Bugs!? Mom will be thrilled!

I asked Juan about the bottled water deal, and he showed me the way to a little store just on the edge of the campground. It was more of a shack really, and inside the shelves were covered with all kinds of tacky tourist junk as well as the staples of life ... candy, ice cream, cigarettes, and water. The water came in huge, glass jugs that were covered with a kind of rope netting. They looked like a larger version of the rum jugs I'd seen in old pirate movies and, considering the dust that covered them, it was well within the realm of possibility that they had washed ashore sometime during the 1600s.

Everything in the store was a product of Spain. I'd thought that, given the international flavor of the campground, I'd be able to find a pack of Marlboros or Kools. But the only cigarettes available were these harsh, black tobacco, non-filter suckers, so I bought a few packs and a jug of water. On the way back, I asked Juan about the limited availability of imported products.

"Generalisimo," he said.

"Huh?"

"Generalisimo Francisco Franco," he continued. "Our president ... he doesn't allow many imported goods to come into the country. A lot of money can be made here selling American goods on the black market."

A lot of money!?

"But it means big trouble if you're caught."

A lot of trouble ... hmmmm ... money ... trouble ... money ... trouble ... money.

I was intrigued and, as I shifted the water jug to my other shoulder, asked, "Oh, yeah, what kind of money are we talking about here? And for what? Cigarettes, jeans, Spam...?"

"Yes," Juan answered, "all those things. But mostly Playboy magazines. You can get maybe twenty U.S. dollars for even a very old Playboy."

Twenty bucks for an old Playboy, Man, I wished I had my golf bag of magazines with me! I did have one issue stashed between my underwear and socks in my suitcase, so maybe...

"But," Juan continued, "if you are caught, you will spend some time in the Generalisimo's jail. He doesn't approve of any decadent material that would serve to corrupt his people."

"Corrupt his people?" I asked. "How in the world would a copy of Playboy corrupt his people? Afraid the jerking off would make the men weak and unable to fight off an invasion from ... Portugal?"

Juan laughed. "I know, it sounds stupid to me, too. But I just live here."

The water jug was getting very heavy, and I stopped to rest for a minute. Putting the jug down, I opened a pack of the Spanish cigarettes, and lit one of the fat, dark, cancer sticks, drawing the smoke deep into my lungs. I've never coughed so hard in my life! I really expected my entire stomach to come spilling out of my mouth. It was awful—like smoking dried-up horse shit, but without the flavor! Through my watery eyes, as I stood there hacking away, I could see Juan, doubled-over, laughing. Very funny, I thought. Wait a minute and I'll give you a real thrill by puking all over your feet.

"Not exactly smooth, are they?" I choked.

After several minutes of dry heaves, I picked up the water jug and we made our way down the dirt road to the campsite. "This is where I get off," I said, "that's my family down there. The guy struggling with the camper is my old man, and that butt you see sticking out of the car is my mom. She must be looking for something ... probably the one thing she forgot to pack. Anyway, I hope to see you again."

"Sure," Juan replied. "I'm camped just around the bend with a few friends of mine. Come by anytime."

"By the way," I asked, "how is it you speak English so well?"

"From American movies. Mostly Westerns; the Generalisimo approves of Westerns. Now, I have a question for you, Mike."

"Yeah?"

"What is Spam?"

Dad had just about finished getting the camper together but, as usual, there were a few "extra" pieces that didn't seem to go anywhere. "Not to worry," the old man said, "it'll hold."

"Michael," my mom's voice beckoned from inside the camper, "did you get the water? How much was it? Was the store nice? Is it close? Do you see your brother around? Where's your sleeping bag? Didn't you pack a pillow? Where's your suitcase? You did bring more than those ratty jeans you have on, didn't you?"

"Yeah ... not much ... it was okay ... not too far ... it's not my turn to watch him ... in there someplace ... I don't need a pillow ... I don't know ... and I like these jeans."

"Now don't be a smart mouth," she continued, sticking her head out of the camper, "you know I hate it when you won't give me a straight answer."

"I'll go look for Mark."

I combed the beach for over an hour looking for my wayward little brother. Mark had a habit of just wandering off, looking for adventure. The trouble was, he always found it, and it usually cost everybody but him some sort of problem. I'd just about given up on him when I noticed a small speck way out in the water, riding the incoming waves like an upturned soda can. As I walked closer to the surf, I could see my little brother waving from his inner tube. "Are you crazy?" I yelled. "Mom's gonna kill you!"

"Why?" He yelled back. "I'm fine."

"Because she's Mom, that's why. Get in here!"

Mark paddled his rubber vessel towards the beach and, as he approached the shoreline, tipped the inner tube over and body surfed the rest of the way in. "Man," he whined, "why can't she just leave me alone? I was having a great time."

"You've been out there for hours, man. She's worried about you. Everybody is."

'Were you?"

"Naw ... but then, I'm your brother. Don't expect too much out of me."

By the time we got back to the campsite, Dad had rigged up the badminton net and my sisters were busy flogging the air with their rackets, in vain attempts to get the birdie over the net. The air was thick with noise from the various camps around us: Germans and Italians and Spaniards and Norwegians and British ... one, big United Nations weenie roast! Then, suddenly, a loud siren shattered the moment, and everyone scattered into their tents and campers. We didn't know what was going on. An air raid drill? The Russians had invaded? An outbreak of some horrible disease? Generalisimo Francisco Franco had caught some guy with a Playboy?

Everyone except my family had mysteriously disappeared, leaving us alone at the campsite, looking for some reason to explain why. In the distance, we could hear a faint rumbling, like a very large truck coming in our direction; on the horizon, we could see large pillars of white smoke streaming into the air. Suddenly, a huge, dirty truck came roaring around the bend in the road, spraying something resembling white dust into the trees that surrounded the campsite. "What the hell?" the old man wondered aloud.

As the dust hit the trees, we realized all too late what was going on. Dark clouds of bugs poured from the treetops, heading right for us ... the only people stupid enough to still be standing outside. My mom had just enough time to let out a faint, "Oh, my God" before we were inundated by flying insects, swooping down on us like kamikaze pilots. My sisters screamed and made for the camper, mom jumped into the front seat of the station wagon, and dad—ever calm dad—walked over and picked up the badminton rackets that had been jettisoned by my sisters. He walked back over to Mark and me, tossing each of us a racket. "Let's have some fun," he said, through grinning teeth.

Mark and I just looked at each other, as we tried to ward off our unwanted guests. "What's he talking about?" Mark yelled. I wasn't sure. Maybe this was the last straw, and the old man had flipped completely out. I'd heard that people get really calm right before they go on a murder rampage. "Like this," the old man said, and WHAM, smacked the nearest dive-bombing bug with a badminton racket, sending it ricocheting against the side of the car. Alright! Game time! Dad, Mark and I spent the next fifteen minutes pounding darting insects into the dirt, and when it was all over, the three of us stood there proudly, surveying our kill.

Over the next few days we improved on the game, actually marking off a small baseball diamond and taking turns at bat; before long, other campers were joining us in a daily game of bug-ball.

At the end of the day's big bug bash, we had all settled in for a much-deserved quiet night's sleep when, sometime early in the morning, it began to rain again. It was kind of cool laying there in the camper tent, listening to the gentle rain pellet the canvas, and feeling all secure and comfortable in my sleeping bag. I guess it had been raining for a few hours when I awoke to see a large bulge in the roof of the tent directly over the spot where my folks were sleeping. The tent roof was so heavy with rainwater that it sagged within inches of my dad's snoring nose. As I lay there in the darkness, debating whether I should wake my parents or just take a chance that the weight of the pooling water on the roof wouldn't cause the tent to cave in, the canvas gave out, dumping gallons of water on my sleeping parents. My mom started screaming, "I'm drowning ... help me, I'm drowning," as the old man sat straight up with such force that his head went right through the opening in the roof of the tent.

My brothers and sisters were awake now, and we all laughed like a bunch of hyenas at the sight of Mom spitting out water, and Dad looking like the headless horseman, the roof of the tent down around his shoulders. "Ray," my mom sputtered, "I'm soaked! Absolutely soaked! I told you it didn't look like you were putting this tent together right, didn't I? 'It's just an extra piece' you said, 'nothing to worry about' you said. Well, now what do you have to say?!" Several seconds passed before the old man spoke, his head still protruding into the night air. "Looks like it's clearing up," he said with a laugh as he pulled his head back into the tent.

It was one of those moments that could go either way. We all knew the routine ... Mom would either just "go with the flow" and laugh with the rest of us, or we were all about to see Hurricane Peg rip through the tent, leaving no survivors. Silence gripped the darkness as we waited for the weather report.

"Well," my dad said softly, "look on the bright side, Peg. Now you don't have to worry about washing your hair in the morning." Oh God ... he'd made it worse! Now there was no way we were going to escape the Wrath of Mom!

Mom looked around the tent at us ... five sets of eyes shining in the darkness, all of us trying very hard to choke back the giggles; that same feeling as being in church when somebody farts or something, and you know it's gonna be your ass if you give in and start laughing. Mom just sat there on her soggy sleeping bag, peering at us through rain-drenched hair that hung dripping in her eyes. Uh-oh ... trouble. She was thinking, which was always more dangerous that just reacting, and we wondered what was going through that little Mom brain of hers. Without saying a word, she gently reached over and pulled the plug out of the old man's air mattress, sending it and him sinking to the ground with a kind of bphlurping sound.

"Look, Ray," she said, holding up the small red plug "an extra piece to your air mattress ... oh, well, not to worry." We all burst out laughing as we watched Dad's air mattress flatten out beneath him, and knew that a crisis had been averted ... the family unit would pull through again.

For the next several days we all just kind of hung out, exploring the campsite, splashing around in the water, getting a suntan, and slamming down several dozen Spanish ice cream cones that we bought from vendors along the beach. Mark made his daily inner-tube sail, even when his ankles got so sunburned that they became purple-swollen. He had to wear socks when he went in the water for the rest of the time we were there. I ended up trading my copy of Playboy to Juan for an official Matador hat (he said it was anyway); and spent most of my time cruising the coastline, having dreams of grandeur about the spectacular array of bikini-clad girls that decorated the white, sandy beach. (I never actually said anything to them, but fantasies rarely live up to reality, and I was gonna lie to my buddies when I got back anyway, so it didn't really matter.)

Before we knew it, it was time to go (I was officially sick of canned ham and eggs) and as we drove out of the campground, I looked back to see a few police cars parked at Juan's tent. "Michael," the old man said, "isn't that your buddy back there with all the police?"

"Yeah, Dad," I responded, thinking about the Playboy I'd traded him. "Guess it's a good thing we're leaving, huh?"

"Yeah," the old man replied. "I heard they caught him with a skin magazine. That's a big deal in this country."

"I wonder where he got something like that?" My mom asked.

"Yeah, I wonder," smiled Dad.

"Well," my mom continued, "it's a good thing we're leaving. A boy like that means nothing but trouble, Michael. I'm certainly glad you don't ..."

"Yeah, me too," I interrupted.

"Yeah, me too," the old man repeated.

I guess we were all just too tired to fight with one another, so the ride home was uneventful ... until we got back on the Autobahn, Germany's answer to the Indy 500. Every time the old man would signal left and try to change lanes, he'd end up cutting someone off, and we'd be lambasted with international hand gestures for "screw you." It was really annoying my mom.

"Ray," she finally said, "how can people be so rude? Aren't you signaling before you change lanes? You did hook the trailer lights back up, didn't you?"

Dad looked into the rearview mirror at me and, as our eyes met, I could tell we both knew what the problem was. He'd hooked the taillights back up alright, but he'd hooked them up backwards, so every time we turned left, the cars around us thought we were turning right. Cars were careening all over the highway, horns blaring, brakes screeching, and lots of other general motoring mayhem. I knew he had hooked them up backwards, and he knew that I knew.

"Well," my mom demanded, "did you hook them up or not, Ray?"

Dad shifted in his seat. "Well, I ..."

"They're cool, Mom," I said. "Dad and I checked them out before we left. You know how these crazy Europeans drive."

"It's alright, Peg," Dad said smiling. "It's all just part of the adventure."

Chapter Seven
THE GANG'S ALL HERE

Brrring … brrrring … brrrring … the field phone that stretched from my Maid's Room to the apartment upstairs was jumping off the hook … no doubt, Mom telling me that it was time to get up and start another year of school. What Mom didn't know was that I'd been up for hours, carefully selecting just the right clothes that would convey the image I'd cultivated over the past few years, clothes that would project a sense of reliability and neatness to my teachers, while letting all the girls know that a man of danger and excitement was lurking just below the surface, theirs for the asking.

I picked up the phone, "I'm already up, Mom," and promptly hung up again, without waiting for a response.

It was finally here … my Senior year of high school. I'd been looking forward to it for as long as I could remember, not as much for the freedom that lay at the end of the tunnel, but for the time that I knew would be one of the best of my life. I was entering that grey area between kid and adult, when a person gets to spread his wings and experience all the joys of a grownup's world while still retaining the security of living under his parents' roof.

My eventful summer had taken its toll: the "big fight" with Bud Wankowski, which had caused me to take a look at myself; my summer jobs, which had given me a fresh respect for what it takes to earn a living; and, our family vacation to Spain, which had produced a renewed appreciation for the tribulations of parenthood. They were all good lessons which, much to my surprise, had caused me to plunge head first into the deep end of the maturity pool and dog-paddle around for a while before panicking and racing to the comfort of the shallow water. The deep end had been foreign and a little scary, but it was exhilarating, and I knew, with the passage of time, I would return there. But right now, the one constant in my life that was more important to me than anything else was my life preserver, my support, the Studs and the Duds. They were, in a very real sense of the word, my kin, and now it was our Senior year, our time to rule, our chance to show the rest of the high school how it could be done. My girlfriend, Pam, had decided that my personality was "too volatile" for her to handle, so I was starting school wearing the date-bait moniker, and I couldn't wait to get the show on the road. There was no doubt about it, the Studs and the Duds were in the driver's seat now, and the weak of heart had better avoid the road.

Three weeks earlier, I had purchased a 1959, light blue Volkswagen Beetle from an airman who was being transferred back to the States. There was no driver's education class at our high school, probably because the military was anxious to prevent a bunch of American kids from wreaking havoc across the German countryside. But the old man called in a favor, and I got my driver's license without so much as a parallel parking test. In retrospect, it seems really crazy that my initiation to the world of driving took place on the German speedway known as the Autobahn, but at the time it was a ticket to ride, and I didn't ask any questions.

Learning the rules of the road was important, but my more urgent task was to transform an old VW Beetle into unique and stylish transportation. So, my buddies and I took my new car to an abandoned hangar to which Dad had access, and spent the time leading up to the first day of school turning a beat-up VW into what would become known around the base as the "Cream Machine." We pulled out the engine and replaced it with one from a smashed Karmen Ghia that we'd found at the junkyard; painted the car green with yellow racing stripes that ran across both doors, created "mag" wheels, with the use of some silver spray paint, and topped it off by decorating the driver's door with a large decal of a sultry, topless woman. I took some sticky, white shelf paper that Mom had around the house, carefully cut out the letters needed to spell "Cream Machine" and adhered them to the back window. Subtlety was not in my vocabulary; I was out to make a statement, a semi-pornographic statement to be sure, but a statement nonetheless. The car still ran like a '59 VW, but it looked good and, as we all know, an ounce of image is worth a pound of substance.

On the morning of the first day of classes, we had all decided to meet at the Youth Center and caravan to school—a parade of broken down cars filled with teenagers, who were themselves filled with joyful anticipation and far too many hormones. One last look in the mirror, a quick trip upstairs, and I would be on my way.

My brother and sisters were sitting around the kitchen table, slamming down Cap'n Crunch cereal and picking arguments with one another while Mom was busy throwing sandwiches and Hostess cupcakes into brown paper lunch bags. "My, don't we look hot-to-trot this morning, Michael," she grinned, from behind a small mountain of peanut butter and jelly sandwiches. "Planning on having a good time today?"

"Yeah, Mom," I grunted, "I may be a little late for dinner. Have you seen the hairbrush?"

"You're worse than a damn girl," Mom replied, wiping her hands on a dishrag. "It's probably in the bathroom, right where you left it."

It was … it always was. I had only posed the question to deflect any interrogation about why I'd be late for dinner. It was a preemptive strike; over the years, I'd gotten quite astute at taking a right turn around conversations I'd rather not have.

"What do you mean you'll be late for dinner?" Mom queried, as she followed me down the hall.

It didn't always work.

"You know," I said, brushing my shoulder-length hair, "first day of school and all. I'll want to sit around with my friends, compare notes, check out the new chicks."

"Now listen, young man," Mom interrupted, "this is your last year of high school and it's important that you make the most of it."

"I plan to." I smirked as I examined my reflection in the mirror, checking my face for blemishes.

Mom wasn't amused. "I mean study, crack a book now and then, don't do anything stupid that will cause any trouble for your father and me."

"That's the most important thing isn't it, mom," I shot back, as I walked into the living room. "You're just concerned about how you and Dad look, aren't you? Don't worry, I won't do anything to embarrass you. And if I do, I'll lie about my name."

"Oh, yeah," she said, pointing toward the front window, "like everybody doesn't know who you are. I can't believe you're actually going to drive around in that brothel on wheels out there."

"It's called style, Mom," I responded, "you should try it sometime."

It was a shot that landed way below the belt. You could call my mom names, question the way she raised her kids, even set her dress on fire, but never, ever, challenge her sense of style. She pouted. "I've got more style in my little finger—"

"—than I have in my whole body," I interrupted. "Yeah, I know this routine. Look, Mom, I don't have time to do this right now, so I'll just say you're right, I'm sorry, and I'll see you later tonight."

"Don't forget your lunch," she hollered, as I walked out the door.

Lunch? You've got to be kidding me!

I bounded down the stairs, through the parking lot, and jumped into the Cream Machine. The car hadn't come with a radio, but I'd rigged an old AM/FM cassette player under the front seat, so I turned on the morning tunes. This is going to be great, I thought, inserting the ignition key. Look out, K Town, Michael's on the move!

Rrrrrr … rrrr … rrrr … the car shuddered as the engine tried to kick over. C'mon baby, I thought, don't fail me now. Not today. C'mon baby, you can do it, you can do … my mental pleading was answered by a loud "pop" and black smoke billowed from the rear of the car. Aauuughhh!

I got out of the car, threw open the hood, and was quickly engulfed in a plume of smoke and gas fumes. Mad as hell, I kicked the rear bumper and cussed my decrepit, albeit highly-stylish, set of wheels. The gang would be converging at the Youth Center, while here I stood, up a creek without a paddle, on the first morning of what was certain to be the best year of my life. Shit!

"That's quite a style you've got going there, Michael," Mom laughed from the balcony. "Maybe you could just wear it to school." I ignored her, not an easy thing to do under the best of circumstances, and got back in the car, to ponder my predicament.

My pensiveness was shattered by a knock on the car window, and I looked up to see the smiling face of my sister, Cyndy, peering at me from the other side of the glass. "I'm on my way to the bus," she said. "Want to walk with me?"

Perfect, I thought, double humiliation...a broken down car, and walking with my sister to the bus. C'mon God, gimme a break here! But, as I sat on the sheepskin-covered car seat, which was shedding all over my new jeans, I remembered the best thing about owning a VW … they were very easy to jumpstart.

"I've got a better idea, Cyn," I sweetly smiled, as I got out of the car. "How 'bout I give you a ride to school?"

"On what, your back?" My suspicious sister asked.

"No … in my car. Just imagine how all your friends are gonna react when they see you drive up in the Cream Machine on the first day of school."

"They'll think I lost my mind over the summer," Cyndy responded, backing away from the car. "Besides, it's not even running, and … oh, no, I am not pushing you and this stupid car all the way to K-town, Mike. No way!"

"No, no," I chuckled, putting my arm around her shoulder, "I'll push us to that big hill that leads to the Youth Center. All I need you to do is sit behind the steering wheel and pop the clutch when I tell you to. When the engine kicks in, just hit the brakes, then I'll take over and drive you to school in style."

"I don't know," Cyndy said hesitantly. "Sounds kind of dangerous. I think I'll just take the bus."

I could see my dream of arriving at school in grand fashion slipping away, so I resorted to the tactic that always seemed to work on my good-hearted sister ... pity. "Okay," I whined, "I guess it doesn't matter if all my friends think I'm a loser. I don't really mind being laughed at all day," I continued, with my head bowed, dejectedly leaning on the car. "The important thing is that you feel safe."

"Oh, God," Cyndy sighed. "Alright, alright ... but I know I'm going to regret this."

"No you won't," I said excitedly, as I opened the car door for her, and bowed at the waist like the Queen's chauffeur. "Your chariot awaits, Madame."

"Chariot, huh?" Cyndy muttered. "I'd feel a lot better if horses were attached to this thing."

"Not to worry," I insisted, placing my hands on the front of the car. "Just put it in neutral, so I can turn it around."

"Where's the shifter?" Cyndy asked, checking out the steering wheel.

"There, on the floor, next to your leg," I responded, as I tried to hide my impatience.

For the next few minutes, the quiet morning was shattered by the sound of grinding gears, as my sister tried to shove the gearshift into neutral. "The clutch," I yelled, running around to the door, "step on the clutch. Damn, you're gonna kill my transmission!"

"Look, don't have a cow!" Cyndy yelled back. "I told you I didn't know how to do this! If you scream at me again, you can just ..."

"Okay, okay, sorry," I cajoled. "Here, let me show you."

Following a quick lesson on clutch/shift dynamics, I resumed my position at the front of the car, and gently pushed until it was facing the right way. I walked around to the driver's window to find Cyndy, her hands gripping the steering wheel, a look of terror on her face. A kind brother, a considerate brother, would have realized how frightened his sister was, and blown off the plan, but...

"Piece of cake, huh? You ready to get this show on the road, now?" I asked my scared-stiff sister.

"Uh-huh," Cyndy murmured, her eyes glued to the steering wheel.

"Are you sure?"

"Uh-huh."

"You're not nervous, are you?"

"Uh-huh."

"You trust me, don't you?"

"NO."

"Look," I coaxed, "all you have to do is sit there, and when I tell you to, throw the shift into first gear and ease your foot off the clutch. The car will do the rest. It's really simple, I promise."

Slowly, I pushed the Cream Machine down the street, and stopped at the top of the hill that led to the Youth Center ... my rendezvous point. In the distance, I could see the parking lot where my friends were waiting for me.

"Okay, Cyn," I hollered from my position behind the car, "this is it. Remember to hit the brake after the engine kicks in. Are you all set?" Through the rear window, I could see the back of Cyndy's head, nodding her readiness.

Ideas only become bad ideas in hindsight; but, even an idiot should realize that a plan which calls for an inexperienced driver to careen down a hill, with only the vaguest notion of how to work a car, isn't a very good strategy, still ...

"Here we go," I yelled, while giving the car a big shove, "don't forget to hit the ..."

The car flew down the hill like it was shot from a cannon—a green and yellow streak, wildly lurching all over the road, and sending dogs and small children running for cover. I listened for the sound of the engine, but heard only the panicked screams of my sister, which were fading with the rapidly increasing speed of the car. "The brakes!" I yelled, as I bolted after the car. "Hit the brakes!"

I chased my beloved car and screaming sister as Cyndy hurled down the hill like a ski jumper out of control, bouncing over potholes, and swerving to avoid oncoming traffic.

"The emergency brake!" I panted. "Pull the emergency brake!" But, Cyndy continued to rocket down the hill, and was quickly approaching the four-way stop that stood in her path.

Oh, God, I thought, please let her find the emergency brake before she gets to the intersection. Mom will be so mad if I get my little sister killed!

I stopped and shut my eyes, waiting for the sound of crushed metal, as Cyndy closed in on the intersection. To my amazement, she hit the cross-roads at just the right moment, making it through without even a scratch. The car hit the bottom of the hill, and began to slow down as it climbed the upward slope on the other side of the intersection. I watched in wonderment as Cyndy carefully took the turn into the Youth Center parking lot, and the car limped to a halt in front of my now-hysterical friends.

"Been giving driving lessons again, Ritter?" Someone laughed, as I jogged breathlessly into the parking lot. "Really trying to save on the gas, huh?"

I stumbled over to my car and found Cyndy inside, visibly shaken, her hands gripping the steering wheel. "Are you okay?" I gasped. "Why didn't you use the emergency brake?" Cyndy didn't say a word, as she turned and glared at my red, sweating face. "Well, why didn't you pull the emergency brake?" I repeated. "You could have wrecked my car, you know."

"Oh, the emergency brake," Cyndy calmly replied, while slowing releasing her hands from the steering wheel. "Is that what … this is?!" She bellowed, as she grabbed something that was sitting on the seat beside her, and thrust her hand through the open car window. And there it was, my emergency brake handle, with wires dangling from it like strands of spaghetti.

"You broke my emergency brake!" I yelled.

"I'll break your neck!" Cyndy shrieked as she jumped from the car, wildly waving the detached brake handle above her head. "I could have been killed! This car is a piece of junk! How could you …"

"I didn't know …" I cried, while trying to avoid being batted with the brake handle. "Besides, you made out alright. Next time, I'll …"

"Next time! Are you crazy?" Cyndy yelled, throwing the dismembered car part to the ground, and storming off in the direction of the bus stop.

"I'm sorry, Cyn," I hollered after her. "Don't tell Mom, okay?"

My friends gathered around my "D.O.A." car, laughing and making jokes. "Nice wheels, Mike," Rob chortled. "Just like the car Fred Flintstone drives. Who needs an engine … you've got one-sister-power in this baby."

I rode to school with five other kids, in Rob's '66 Volvo. I had to leave my smoking Cream Machine smoldering in the parking lot, and just hope this wasn't a sign of more trouble to come. After a fifteen-minute drive, we pulled into the student parking lot and, like clowns in a circus, piled out of the car. The lot was crowded with kids, busily scoping out the new arrivals, chatting with old friends who hadn't been seen since the previous June, and generally mulling around, like glassy-eyed cattle waiting to be led to the slaughterhouse.

Kaiserslautern American High looked more like a military outpost than a school. It had been carved out of the forest, and officially opened in 1953, under the name Rhine High. The name was changed to Kaiserslautern High in the early 1960s; it was the largest American high school outside the continental United States. Actually, the school was just a cluster of buildings, surrounded by a chain link fence with concrete posts, and topped off with barbed wire … kind of like Stalag 13 for teenagers. We were known as the K-Town Red Raiders and, in spite of the military atmosphere, had all the trappings of any other high school. So, as long as you stayed on campus, it felt like Anytown, USA.

My crowd, the Studs and the Duds, congregated just inside the main entrance, the best vantage point for sizing up our contemporaries as they walked down the hall in search of their lockers and first period classrooms. While we considered ourselves an exclusive club, we weren't averse to admitting new members who met the cool criteria. We had very specific standards for membership: long hair on the guys, signifying independence from parental control; short skirts on the girls, indicating the possibility of promiscuity, and anyone who looked like they might cause us a problem down the road. As the old adage advises, keep your friends close, and your enemies closer. Of course, anyone who stopped and tried to make conversation was eliminated immediately—we chose our friends, they didn't choose us.

I was sitting on a trash can, ogling girls as I took notes on potential date candidates, when a short man dressed in a pin-striped, red and black shirt and a paisley tie walked over and introduced himself.

"So, what's the score, Mike?" He laughed.

"Do I know you?" I asked, barely looking up from my notebook.

"The name's Dr. Fitzpatrick, Robert Fitzpatrick," he smiled, as he extended his hand. "I'm the new Guidance Director, just in from Berkeley, California."

"Glad to meet you, Doc," I said, shaking his hand. "How is it you know my name?"

"Oh," he continued, folding his arms across his chest, "I know all you guys: Rob, Willie, Sean, Tim, Paul, Lori, Valerie, Cissy, Jessie, Debbie— all the Studs and Duds. You guys have quite a reputation."

"Oh?" I beamed, loving the recognition. "Heard about us all the way in California, did ya?"

"Well, no," Dr. Fitzpatrick said as he smirked, "but, I understand you're the people to know here at K-Town."

"Maybe," I coyly replied, as I took note of a shapely redhead in a pink, plaid miniskirt bend down to pick up her notebook. "Depends on what you're looking for."

"I'm really interested in—"

"Just a minute," I interrupted, leaping from my garbage can perch. "I'll be right back."

I walked over to help the poor girl pick up her book. "Here," I smiled, "let me get that for you. Name's Michael ... you're new around here, aren't you?"

"Get bit, Ritter," the girl said coldly. "I know who you are ... you and all your egotistical friends."

"Oh?" I replied, stunned by her blunt response. "I don't recall ..."

"It's me, Charlene, the girl who sat in front of you in Algebra last year."

"Sorry," I grinned, "doesn't ring a bell."

"Metal mouth," she shot back, grabbing her notebook from my hand. "Remember now?"

Oh shit, I thought, it was her ... metal mouth. But, what happened to her braces, and how did she become so damn cute?

"Wow," I exclaimed. "Just like a butterfly."

"What?" she said, with irritation.

"A butterfly," I continued, "you left for the summer looking like a caterpillar, and now you've become a beautiful butterfly."

"Don't feed me any of your weak bullshit, Ritter," she said, taking a step back. "I'm not falling for it."

"I don't blame you," I said, shaking my head. "The horrible way I treated you ... well, all I can say is I'm sorry and I hope you have a great senior year."

"You know," she said, pushing her shoulder length hair behind her ear, "if you weren't such a jerk ..."

"I know, I know," I responded, and began to back away with my hands in the air. "Oh well, my loss."

"Well ... maybe not," she smiled, as she turned to walk away, "maybe not."

"Then, can I call you sometime, Charlene?" I yelled down the hall.

"Maybe," she said, without turning around, "but when you do, ask for Charlie. All my friends call me Charlie."

In the background, I could hear my buddies cheering my ability to snatch victory from the jaws of defeat. I turned around to see a smiling Dr.

Fitzpatrick, his hands in his pockets, rocking back and forth on the balls of his feet. "Now, what is it you wanted?" I asked.

"Never mind, Mike," he grinned. "Like they say, a picture is worth a thousand words. You guys better hustle over to the gym for orientation now. It was a pleasure meeting you, and I know I'll see more of you in the future."

"Who was that guy?" asked Willie, as we made our way to the gym.

"Never saw him before," I responded. "His name's Fitzpatrick, he's the new guidance counselor or head-shrinker or something. Seemed to know all of us, though. I wonder ..."

"What do you mean he knows all of us?" Willie demanded. "Are we in some kind of trouble? Man, I knew this was gonna happen."

"You knew what was going to happen?" Rob interjected.

"I don't know," Willie choked, "but, something's up. Why else would the guidance counselor be hanging around? I'm telling you guys ..."

"Don't worry," Rob snickered, putting his arm around Willie's shoulder. "We won't tell him about that fantasy you have about your mother."

"Actually, Rob," Tim chimed in, "it's your mom that ..."

"Shut up," Willie shot back, before Tim had a chance to finish his sentence. "You guys just wait, I've got a bad feeling about this."

"The only good feeling you ever have is when you're jerking off," Rob said, as we joined the throng of kids on their pilgrimage to the gym.

"Oh, yeah?" Willie sneered.

"Nice comeback, Willie," Rob smirked.

The din inside the gymnasium was deafening, as hundreds of kids waited impatiently for the administration to get its act together, and begin the series of boring "welcome back" speeches. One by one, the principal introduced the new teachers, who each felt obligated to tell us how happy they were to join our school.

When the time came for Dr. Fitzpatrick to take the podium, he provided the standard information: who he was, where he came from, how happy he was. Then he talked about his main interest—the behavior patterns of high school students. "I generally don't do this," he announced, "but, since you're all here, will the following students please report to my office tomorrow morning at 8:00 sharp: Rob Mathison, Willie Pickett, Sean Kincaid, Michael Ritter, Tim Maxwell, Paul Thompson, Valerie McKinney, Cissy Dobson, Lori Fisher, Jessie Kendall, and Debbie Montrose."

Suddenly, Willie's elbow was jamming into my side. "See," he loudly whispered, "I told you this was going to happen. Man, my mom's gonna kill me."

"Kill you for doing what?" Rob interrupted.

"I don't know," Willie said, leaning back in his chair. "Whatever I've done wrong."

"But, you're innocent," laughed Rob.

"I know," Willie responded, rubbing his eyes with the palms of his hands, "but of what?"

"You're a real basket case, Pickett," I said, getting up from my seat. "The only guy in the world who worries about something he didn't do."

"Maybe that's his problem," Rob snickered. "He's always worried because he never does anything."

"Well," Sean said calmly, "I ain't goin'."

"Yeah, me neither," added Tim.

"Aw, c'mon you guys," I urged, as we made our way through the labyrinth of meandering students, "what have you got to lose, besides getting out of first period? Let's see what the guy has to say ... could be fun. What do you chicks think?"

Jessie and Cissy were busy picking up the contents of Jessie's purse, which had spilled all over the floor. "I've got nothing to hide," said Jessie, as she crawled on her hands and knees to retrieve a lipstick that had rolled under a chair.

"I'll say," Rob leered, while attempting to see up Jessie's skirt as she reached for her elusive lipstick. "Wearing red today, huh?"

"Yeah," Jessie muttered from under the chair, "cherry flavored."

"I didn't know they came in flavors," Rob grinned.

"He doesn't mean your lipstick," Cissy retorted, pushing Rob out of the way, and pulling down Jessie's skirt.

"Asshole," Jessie yelled, getting to her feet and shoving Rob in the chest, which sent him tumbling to the ground.

"What'd I do?" Rob smiled, feigning innocence.

"You're such an asshole!" Jessie continued, glaring down at Rob.

"Is that all you think about? I'm gonna go tomorrow, just to tell Mr. Fitzpatrick what a pervert you are!"

"I'm not the one flashing panties all over the place," Rob protested.

"So, you do wear them?" Cissy smirked.

"Only on my head," Rob laughed.

"You see, you see!" Willie excitedly interrupted. "This is what I'm talking about. Just because Rob's twisted we all have to go tomorrow."

"Who you calling 'twisted', Pickett?" Rob shot back.

"You!" Willie yelled. "All you think about is sex, sex, sex!"

"Only with girls," Rob said sarcastically.

"Meaning what?" Willie screamed back.

"Let's just say that I've always wondered why you have so many posters of baseball and football players hanging in your room," Rob grinned.

"I oughta ..." Willie shouted, lunging at Rob.

"Give me your best shot, Pickett," Rob said defiantly.

I grabbed Willie while Tim held back Rob. "This is why that Mr. Fitzpatrick guy wants to see us tomorrow," Tim laughed, "because we get along so well."

"Tim's right, you guys," I said, struggling to keep Willie from getting himself killed, "we're supposed to be friends ... best friends. Studs and Duds forever, remember?"

"Okay, okay," Willie mumbled. "You're right. I'm sorry, Rob."

"I'll say you are," Rob smiled, as he gave Willie a playful punch.

Just as things were calming down, the Vice Principal, Mr. Francis Jones, came trotting over to our group. Mr. Jones was a balding, slightly effeminate man, with a pencil-thin mustache. "What's the problem here?" he demanded.

"Oh, hello, Francis," Rob smirked, as he freed himself from Tim's grip. "No problem here, Francis. Just a friendly disagreement."

"Yeah," Willie chimed in. "No problem here. We were just—"

"That's not how it looked from across the room," Mr. Jones interrupted, obviously irritated by Rob's familiarity. "I'm not going to take any guff from you guys this year."

"Guff?" Rob questioned, looking around. "Hey, Mike, you got any guff? No? How 'bout you Jessie, you got any guff for Francis?"

"Leave me out of this," Jessie whispered, as she fumbled through her purse.

"Sorry, Francis," Rob pushed the envelope, "we're fresh out of guff. Maybe you should check the lunch room—I think that's what they're serving today ... guff on a shingle."

"I'm not kidding around with you jokers," Mr. Jones said sternly. "This year you're going to treat me with the respect I deserve."

"That's what we're doing," Rob muttered from behind his hand.

"Look, Mr. Jones," I jumped in, "there's no problem. We were just wondering why Dr. Fitzpatrick wanted to see us tomorrow."

Mr. Jones folded his arms across his chest. "Guess you'll just have to wait until tomorrow, boys and girls," he smirked. "Have a nice day."

"We sure will," Rob shouted after Mr. Jones, as he walked away. "And you, too, Francis."

We spent the rest of the day attending classes, and meeting in the hallways to compare notes, but when Rob dropped me off at my terminally ill car that afternoon, I still had to wonder what tomorrow would bring.

Dad used his station wagon to tow the crippled Cream Machine back to the apartment. As we tinkered with the engine, I told him about the day's happenings, and my morning appointment with Dr. Fitzpatrick.

The old man was stretched across the engine and, between knuckle-busting tugs at the rusted bolts that held the carburetor in place, sighed, "I don't know about you guys, Mike. First day of school, and already you have to see the guidance counselor."

"Yeah," I replied, handing him a can of WD-4O, "Willie's all worked up about it. I dunno, seems like it might be kinda fun. I've never had anyone pick through my brain before."

"Except your mother," Dad smiled.

"I heard that," I laughed, "but she really picks at it, not through it."

"She means well, Mike," Dad grunted, as he finally loosened the last bolt.

"Yeah? Well, so did Hitler."

The old man stood upright, his knees cracking as he did. "Look, Michael," he moaned, "I want you to be nicer to your mom."

"She makes it real difficult, Dad."

"I know, I know, but you're no piece of cake to live with either," Dad responded, while wiping his oily hands on the pants of his uniform. "All I'm asking is that you not take everything she says so personally … let it roll off your back. Hell, Mike, you've lived with her for seventeen years now, you know how she is."

"I know that you have the patience of Job, being married to her for as long as you have," I said. "Besides, all she's gotta do is leave me alone and there won't be any trouble."

"She's never going to leave you alone; she's your mother for Christ's sake. It's her job to bug you—"

"But—"

"—and it's your job to treat her with respect."

"She's never happy with me," I protested. "No matter what I do, it's just not good enough. You remember last year when I was elected Vice President of the Junior class? I was so excited, couldn't wait to get home and tell you guys about it. I thought that, at last, Mom would put her obsession with my looks aside, and be really proud of me. But, do you know what she said? Why didn't you run for President? I couldn't believe it."

"She just wants you to live up to your potential," the old man sighed, shaking his head.

"She just wants me to live up to her expectations," I shot back.

"Are you going to do it again?" Dad asked.

"What?"

"Run for class Vice President."

"Yeah, sure," I responded, "why not? It's an easy job. All I have to do is plan parties, make a few pep rally speeches, and get a great picture in the yearbook."

"That's what your mother's talking about, Mike," the old man said, as he closed the hood of the car.

"What?"

"You could be President, take on some real responsibility, challenge yourself."

"Why?" I asked. "I'm happy. Doesn't that count for anything? Besides, I wouldn't get elected if they didn't think I could do the job."

"The job of planning parties?"

"Yeah," I responded, as I climbed into the driver's seat. "You should do what you do best, right?"

"But if you don't try new things, how do you know what you do best? Don't get stuck in a rut, Mike. You're a lucky guy, God gave you lots of talents. Mom just doesn't want you to waste them."

"Aw c'mon, Dad," I said, slamming my hands against the steering wheel. "It's not about wasting my talents … it's about Mom's need to control my life. I don't believe it doesn't bother you when she says that she doesn't want me to become just an Air Force Sergeant, like you."

"And why do you think she says stuff like that?" the old man questioned, resting his hands on the half opened car window.

"To bug me," I growled, "and to put you down."

"I don't feel put down," Dad smiled. "I feel lucky that a woman like your mom could love just an Air Force Sergeant like me. It hasn't been easy for her, you know."

"So I've heard," I quipped. "She reminds me of it every chance she gets."

"And, she wants you to have a better life, that's all. Just do me a favor, chief. Next time your mother starts riding you, remember that she thinks she's doing it for your own good. You may not think so, you may never think so, but you've got to accept her for who she is."

"Even though she can't do the same for me?" I huffed.

"The difference is," the old man smiled, "you aren't anyone yet."

I didn't respond—partly because I was pissed off, but mostly because I wasn't quite sure what Dad meant.

"Now, crank this baby up, and let's see what she does," Dad said, as he pushed away from the car.

I turned the ignition key and, after several attempts, the engine erupted and sent blue smoke billowing from the exhaust. "Push in the choke a little," Dad yelled over the noise from the rattling engine, and when I did, the car shuddered for a moment, then settled into a smooth rhythm.

"Alright," I shrieked. "Thanks, Pop!"

"No problem, chief," Dad said. "Just needed to adjust the carburetor. Hope you learned something, 'cause next time you're on your own."

Mom appeared on the balcony to call us in for dinner. "Got it running, huh?" She said, wiping her hands on her apron.

"Yeah," I beamed. "What do you think?"

Mom looked us both over and, without skipping a beat, said, "I think I'm never going to get those grease stains out of your father's uniform."

I looked at Dad, who was busily swiping his pants with a towel, trying to wipe off the stains. There, I thought, do you see what I mean? We spend hours out here working on the car, and all Mom can think about is the condition of your pants! No congratulations, no words of support, nothing!

As Dad climbed the stairs that led to the front door, he paused and turned to look at me, a broad smile on his face. "You see, Michael," he said, "she cares about me … just like she cares about you."

Amazingly, my car did start the next morning. I picked up Rob, Jessie, and Cissy, and the four of us set off for school, and our date with destiny. Rob was still hyped about what he saw as a way out of first period class, but it was obvious that his enthusiasm wasn't shared by the girls in the back seat.

"I talked to the Colonel about our session this morning," Cissy said, leaning on the front seat, "and he's not too hip about it." "The Colonel" was Cissy's old man, a pilot who had flown countless bombing missions over Vietnam, but who demonstrated his true spirit of patriotism on the front door of their apartment … a peace sign, inscribed with the words "footprint of the American chicken." I don't know whether or not it was at his insistence, but Cissy always referred to him as "the Colonel." Hers was a real "Gone With The Wind" family from South Carolina, who fancied themselves just a little better than everybody else. Her mother, Dixie, always lounged around the apartment in white, flowing, satin pajama, and smoked Virginia Slims through a long cigarette holder. Dixie's big claim to fame was her graduation from the same high school that Burt Reynolds had attended. Actually, I liked Cissy's mom because she really did sound like Scarlett O'Hara; but also, she was content with herself, and I've always admired people who make themselves happy and don't give a damn what the neighbors think.

"So, what's your old man's problem?" Rob asked, dusting off his pants where ashes had fallen from his Marlboro. "Afraid you'll say something bad about him?"

"There is nothing bad to say about the Colonel," Cissy huffed. "He just doesn't think it's proper for girls and boys to discuss private aspects of their lives with one another. He thinks it could lead to ... complications."

"Aw, Cissy," Rob smiled, taking another drag from his smoke, and blowing it her way, "we all know that you're still a virgin."

Jessie reached over and smacked the back of Rob's head, while shouting, "That's what she's talking about, jerk! You're such an insensitive asshole! How do we know that whatever we say won't be spread all over the school?"

"What makes you think anybody gives a shit?" Rob shot back, rubbing his head.

"Okay, guys," I interjected, "we're supposed to be friends, remember? People who trust each other."

Jessie popped Rob on the back of the head again, and said, "I wouldn't trust this guy as far as I could throw him."

"C'mon, Jessie," Rob smiled, "you know you can trust me. I never told anybody about your indiscretion with Cissy's boyfriend last year."

"What?!" Cissy roared at Jessie, "your what?!"

"He's lying, Cissy," Jessie protested, "I would never ..."

"That's not what Mike told me," Rob chuckled.

Rob was always pulling this kind of stuff ... he'd create controversy, then sit back to enjoy the fireworks. "I didn't say a word, Jessie," I grinned, "not even when I read about it on the bathroom wall at the Youth Center."

"Screw you, Ritter," Jessie pouted. "You know that's not true."

Rob and I burst into laughter, as Jessie tried desperately to convince

Cissy that she was innocent of the charges. "Tell her you made it up," Jessie insisted. "I'm not kidding, damn it, you guys tell her you're lying."

Rob and I exchanged glances, before I said, "Okay, we're sorry. It's not true."

"Yeah, that's right," Rob softly said, then turned abruptly in his seat and quickly added, "it was really written on the wall in the boys' locker room."

It took us the rest of the trip to school to convince the girls that we were just kidding around, and they really had nothing to worry about.

Okay, I'll go," sighed Cissy, "just don't tell the Colonel about it."

By the time we arrived, the rest of the gang—Sean, Willie, Paul, Tim, Lori, Debbie, and Valerie—were already waiting outside Dr. Fitzpatrick's office. As we approached the group, we could see Willie pacing the hall, still worried about why we were all there. Suddenly, the office door swung open, and Fitzpatrick's secretary motioned for us to come in. "Robert's running late this morning," she smiled, "but he said you should wait in his office, and he'll be with you directly."

"Who's Robert?" Willie asked.

"Fitzpatrick, you idiot," Rob responded, as he slumped down in an overstuffed chair. "Our host."

"Eat me, Mathison," Willie shot back.

"Sorry," Rob smirked, "I like a big breakfast."

Dr. Fitzpatrick's office was nice … nicer than I expected, anyway. His diplomas were hung on the wall, alongside Grateful Dead posters. And healthy, green plants were placed around the room. There were two sofas and two chairs, and a coffee table with a large bowl of M&Ms on it. We each took a seat, and didn't say anything for several minutes. "I still don't like this, Mike," Willie whined. "Sean thinks we should play it cool, and not answer any questions. What do you guys think?"

"The Colonel …" Cissy began.

"Forget the Colonel," I interrupted, "what did you expect from Mister Right Wing Babykiller?"

"He is not a baby kil—"

"Whatever," I continued. "The point is, we've been given a real opportunity here. Don't you guys see that? I mean, how often does a group of kids get the chance to speak their minds? We should go for it. If we can convince this Fitzpatrick guy that we're not a bunch of jerks, he'll let the other authority figures know, and it may just make our lives here a little easier."

"Like how?" Sean asked.

"Compassion, man," I answered, "compassion. If we can convince this guy that we're a bunch of misunderstood kids who have only the best of intentions, man, we're in like Flint. We can write our own ticket. He's handing us power on a silver platter—all we have to do is take it."

"Yeah," Rob interjected, "Mike's right. The name of the game is manipulation. Use whatever means necessary to get what we want."

"And what do we want?" Tim asked.

"Self rule," Rob replied, jumping up and down in his seat. "No hassles, no questions, no authority. We want to get to the point where, if we're seen walking down the hall, even the Principal won't ask what we're doing."

"Right," I exclaimed, "exactly. The way it is now, people are afraid of us, but that doesn't get us anything except resentment and hassles. If we can turn that fear into respect, then we can do what we want ... run the school."

"You're dreamin', man," Paul said, grabbing a handful of M&Ms. "There's no way this is going to be anything but the Doc trying to get into our heads. He's probably working on some paper, and we're the guinea pigs."

"I think Paul's right," Lori added. "Fitzpatrick's doing this for himself, not us."

"Of course he is," Rob shouted, sitting up in his chair, "but who cares what his motivations are? The way I figure it, there are eleven of us and only one of him ... the odds are in our favor."

"Well," Debbie said softly, "Valerie and I were talking it over, and we think we should just be honest and open and—"

"Suckers," Rob interrupted.

"How is that being a sucker?" Valerie protested.

"Look," I said, "Rob's just saying that we should answer Mr. Fitzpatrick's questions in a way that benefits us. If he asks us why we think the other kids resent us, just tell him it's because they don't understand what makes us tick."

"Hell," Tim mused, "I don't understand what makes us tick."

"The point is," I continued, "we hold all the cards, and we can make this guy think whatever we want him to think. If we do it right, we'll walk out of here with him believing that the Studs and Duds are the greatest thing since sliced bread."

"Where'd that come from?" Willie asked.

"What?" I said impatiently.

"Sliced bread ... where did that saying come from?"

"You forget," Rob grinned, reaching over and hitting my arm, "Hillbilly Willie comes from Tennessee ... they just eat the wheat raw; straight from the fields."

"Leave him alone, Rob," Valerie said, patting Willie on the shoulder. "At least he's not vulgar, like you."

"Vulgar? Moi?" Rob gasped, placing his hand on his chest. "You offend me, dear. It's not like I did this," he grinned, grabbing his crotch, "or, this," he smirked, sticking his finger up his nose, "or, even this," he simpered, raising himself up in his seat, and pretending to fart. "I just called him a hillbilly."

Suddenly, Sean jumped up from the couch and walked over to where Rob was sitting. He grabbed the arms of Rob's chair, looked right into Rob's face, and said, "If you don't cool it, I'm going to kick your ass."

"Lick my ass?" Rob stared back.

"Kick your ass," Sean growled, grabbing Rob by the shirt.

"Now stop it, you guys," Debbie yelled. "What if Dr. Fitzpatrick came in right now?"

"I guess he'd have answers to all his questions," Tim chuckled.

"And we'd blow our gig," I admonished, pulling Sean away from Rob.

"That's the point," Debbie said in frustration. "This isn't supposed to be a 'gig'. We should just be honest."

"Okay," Tim grinned, leaning back on the sofa, "I honestly think you're full of shit."

I couldn't believe this was happening. Our chance for respect was slipping through our fingers before Fitzpatrick had even entered the room. We were supposedly bosom buddies, friends, allies, comrades, and we were at each other's throats. Sean and Rob were arguing in the corner, while Willie and Paul tried to keep them from killing one another; Tim thought the whole thing was a joke; Cissy sat alone, shaking her head and mumbling to herself about how she should have listened to the Colonel; while Jessie and Valerie were consoling Debbie, who was upset about Tim's nasty remark, as Lori bitched at him for saying it. What should have been a united front was turning into disjointed hostility.

No one even noticed that Dr. Fitzpatrick was standing in the doorway, until we heard, "Wow, good thing I was only fifteen minutes late."

Embarrassment spread across the group like diarrhea in a baby's diaper, and we all took our places, over mutterings of "good morning" and "sorry". Rob was tucking in his shirt as he walked over to shake hands with Dr. Fitzpatrick. "Don't worry, Doc, we start every morning with a rumble. Keeps us young."

I'd be the first to admit that Rob sometimes excelled at being a jerk, but I had to hand it to him, the guy was fearless ... or stupid ... it's a fine line. Anyway, his comment broke the tension, as Fitzpatrick laughed and again apologized for his tardiness. "I would have been here sooner," he explained, as he pulled some papers from his briefcase, "but I had a hell of a time parking my car. There's something called 'Cream Machine' parked in my space. I'm glad you all decided to come. I know some of you are a little uptight about what we're going to do here, but I assure you that what transpires here will never leave this room. You have my word on it, as a professional and, I hope by the time we're finished, a friend. So, why don't we start with any questions you may have."

Suddenly, our rowdy group was transformed into a Sunday School class, and even Rob hesitated before asking the obvious, "So, what's the deal? How do we rate such special treatment?"

Fitzpatrick fingered his wide, paisley tie, sat back in his chair, and smiled. "Why don't you guys tell me why you think you're here."

"It beats the hell out of trig class," Rob chuckled, pulling back his long, wiry hair. "I'd rather walk into a beehive, wearing honey-flavored underwear, than go to trigonometry."

"That's not what he meant," Jessie said sternly.

"That's true, Jessie," Kirpatrick replied, "although I appreciate your honesty, Rob. I mean, out of all the kids in school, why do you think you guys were chosen to participate in this little experiment?"

"That's easy," Tim answered, "because we're the coolest kids in the school."

"Okay," Fitzpatrick smiled, "let's go with that. What makes you guys the coolest kids in school?"

"We just are," I responded.

"How do you know?" Fitzpatrick continued. "Did they take a vote, and you guys won? I really want to know. Tell me what makes a person 'cool'."

"You know," I stammered, "cool is ... well, cool. It's how you carry yourself, how you think, how you act ... it's an attitude, man."

"So, what you're saying, Mike," Fitzpatrick said, rolling a pen between his hands, "is that if one thinks he's cool, then he's cool ... right?"

"No, no," Tim jumped in, "it's not what we think of ourselves, it's what other people think of us. Just ask anybody, they'll tell you."

"What would they tell me?" Fitzpatrick queried.

"That we're cool," Willie responded.

Fitzpatrick tapped his pen against his lower lip. "Let's go at this another way," he said. "I want each of you to tell me what makes you so cool. Let's start with … you, Cissy. Tell us why you think you're cool."

Cissy thought for a moment, probably wondering what the Colonel would say, then softly replied, "Because I'm a cheerleader."

One by one, we each revealed our coolness factors to Fitzpatrick.

Rob: "I can drink a yard of ale without throwing up."

Tim: "My Fritz the Cat T-shirt, man."

Jessie: "I always date guys who are older than I am."

Paul: "I'm on the wrestling team. I can pin guys twice my size."

Valerie: "My clothes … not everyone can look good in a skirt this short."

Sean: "My hair … and karate. I'm a black belt in karate."

Debbie: "I've got my own phone."

Willie: "Uh, I don't know—I live in my Maid's Room."

Lori: "My folks let me stay out past midnight."

I thought about it for a minute, then admitted, "I have a way with the girls."

Fitzpatrick was busily jotting down notes, before tossing his pen and pad on the table. "Interesting," he mused. "So, a composite cool person has long hair, wears groovy clothes, likes sports, has limited parental supervision, is able to drink his friends under the table, and is very attractive to the opposite sex. Does that about sum it up?"

"Sounds good to me," Rob chortled, and we all nodded in agreement.

"And," Fitzpatrick continued, "anybody with all those qualities is cool."

"Yeah," I said, "but you don't have to have every one of them. I mean, I don't like sports, and Sean doesn't drink, and Cissy's parents want to know where she is every moment … but, we're all still cool."

"Help me out here, Mike," Fitzpatrick solicited. "If it's true that all of you don't share the same qualities, what makes you guys hang out together?"

"We're friends," I answered.

"Then, I guess the real question is," Fitzpatrick continued, "what is it that makes you all friends?"

It was a direct question and, judging by the silence that filled the room, no one seemed to have the answer. Finally, Cissy whispered, "We like each other."

Fitzpatrick leaned forward in his chair and folded his arms across his chest.

"We can depend on one another," I responded.

Fitzpatrick smiled, "That's a good word … depend. What does it mean to you?"

"That we'll always be there for one another," Sean volunteered.

"Yeah," Tim interjected, "I feel that way."

Depend … it was my word but, prior to blurting it out, I hadn't really given much thought to its meaning. As Fitzpatrick polled the room for definitions, I couldn't keep my mind from wandering back to a few weeks ago, and a situation when Dad gave true meaning to the word.

My parents always trusted me, even when I gave them reason not to, so I was able to come and go from my Maid's Room dwelling without "checking in." However, the events of the night of August 24th changed all that.

It began like any other Saturday night, with the weekly dance at the Youth Center. As I've said, I had a "real" girlfriend in Pam, but there were several other girls who were more than willing to fill in the gaps when Pam wasn't around. Jamie was one of those girls. She was a short, blonde cheerleader, two years younger than me, with a face that was nothing much to see, but a body that would cause a man to drive his car straight up a telephone pole. Grown men, mind you, people with kids her age. Anyway, we were having a good time on the dance floor, laughing and carrying on, when she asked if it would be alright to spend the night with me. Now, I'd spent a good part of my young life trying to convince girls to visit my room, but this was the first time I'd ever been involved in a preemptive strike, and it threw me just a little.

"Uh … sure," I stammered, while attempting to remain cool, "you could do that. But, don't you have to worry about your folks?"

"Not to worry," she cooed. "They think I'm spending the night with a girlfriend."

Self-preservation has always been an overriding concern of mine, even higher on the scale than sex, so I needed some solid assurance that our tryst wouldn't become public knowledge … particularly to her father, Major Wayne. As thrilled as I was at the prospect of spending the night with this willing, if not downright eager, young lady, it didn't hold a candle to my deep fear of getting caught.

"What if your folks call over there looking for you?" I asked.

"They won't," she assured me. "And, if they do, it's my problem, isn't it?"

No, I thought, it would be our problem. More than that, it would become my parents' problem. My brain was thrown into overdrive as neurons shot around inside my skull, like a computer searching for the correct solution to a difficult problem. Within a few seconds, my mind was filled with the image of that robot from the TV show Lost in Space, screaming "WARNING! ... WARNING!", and I knew this wasn't a good idea.

"Okay," I smiled, "I'll meet you at my Maid's Room thirty minutes after the dance is over."

I know, I know ... but, I never really liked that TV show, anyway.

I wanted to scream the exciting news to my friends but, even in my current state of euphoria, decided the best course of action was just to keep it to myself for the moment, and wait until morning to fill them in with all the details. No sense in pushing my luck.

The dance ended promptly at midnight and, to the surprise of my friends, I raced straight home, floating on clouds of lust, intrigue, and terror. Shoving open my Maid's Room door, I quickly set about creating the right mood, with a combination of candles, black lights, and the soundtrack from *Friends* by Elton John. Like a bride preparing for her first dinner party, I double-checked all the arrangements, making sure that everything was "just so" before I relaxed and settled in for a good time.

Time passed, and I began to pace the small room, checking my watch every few minutes, and wondering if Jamie was really going to make it at all. Torn between feelings of disappointment and elation, I hoped she would still show up but, at the same time, her tardiness provided me a certain amount of relief in the realization that, if she had chickened out, my fears about getting caught would go away. Just as I was about to give up, there was a soft knock on the door, and I opened it to find Jamie standing there, a broad smile on her face. "Thought I wasn't going to come, didn't you?" she chuckled.

Truth be told, my adrenaline rush had left me sleepy, and I had already accepted the idea that flying solo was for the best. Jamie's proposition alone would have been enough to keep me on a high for weeks, but now she was here, and there was no turning back. I swallowed my fears, and beckoned her to enter my den of iniquity. The evening taught me something I'd never known before, and it had nothing to do with exotic sexual positions. I learned there was a direct link between fear and impotence; I spent a good portion of what I'd imagined would be an uninhibited cruise on the lust boat apologizing for the first of what would be many times: "I'm sorry, this has never happened to me before."

She was a teenage boys dream come true ... ready, willing, and stripped down to nothing but her bra and pink panties, but my body just wouldn't cooperate. We tried everything, but the harder I concentrated, the weaker I became, until my fumbling got so pathetic that Jamie's own frustrations kicked in, and she finally acknowledged that she thought it best if she just left.

Terror filled my body ... double terror. In addition to the possibility that Jamie's folks would still discover her indiscretion, I also had to deal with my inability to perform and her disappointment, which had every chance of becoming the morning headline. So, with visions of private and public humiliation manifesting in my brain, I spent the remainder of what should have been a night in Heaven, staring at the ceiling and wondering what the morning would bring.

It was 6:30 the next morning and I'd just drifted off to sleep when my peace was shattered by a loud banging. Stumbling out of bed, I swung open the door and, through half opened, bloodshot eyes, I saw Willie standing in the doorway. "Yeah," I croaked, "what's up?"

"Man, you are in for it! " Willie loudly whispered.

"What are you talking about?" I yawned.

"Did Jamie spend the night with you last night?" Willie responded, his voice filled with both astonishment and apprehension.

It was one of those moments when time takes a holiday ... just sits back and grins for a long, lingering moment, so the full weight of panic can sink in while your heart tap-dances in your chest.

"Why'?" Was my safe and noncommittal answer.

"Because," Willie panted, "she told her parents she was staying at Sandra's house last night, but they called over there because some girl was hurt in a car accident after the dance, and they wanted to make sure that Jamie was all right."

"So, what makes her folks think she was over here?" I stammered, while nervously turning and walking back towards my bed.

"Sandra told them she was."

Have you ever had a moment in life when you could actually hear the sound of metal clanking, as if the door of a jail cell was closing behind you? The searchlight has found you, the dogs are yapping at your heels, there's no place to hide, you're caught and you know it. "Oh, shit," were the only words I could utter.

"Oh, it gets better," Willie continued. "Jamie's dad wants to see you and your dad, right away."

This is not happening, I thought. This is Twilight Zone stuff! Somebody wake me up from this nightmare! But I wasn't sleeping, and this wasn't a dream, and I knew my ass was grass.

Willie was kind enough to stick around, while I told my old man the whole story of the previous night (well, not the whole story, I had some pride left), which culminated with the words that no Master Sergeant ever wants to hear: "...and the Major wants to see you."

Dad was cool ... well, cool for a guy who's just been told that his son was caught screwing around with a Major's daughter. "Michael ... damn it, Michael, don't you ever learn? Jesus Christ ... alright, let's get this over with."

"Can I come?" Willie mistakenly asked. Dad's only response was one of his furrowed-brow glares that I had come to know so well. "Guess not," Willie quickly added.

Dad and I drove slowly over to Jamie's apartment, to face the music. Actually, it was my music—Dad had just been unwillingly drafted to lead the band. I drew comfort from the knowledge that, if Major Wayne tried to choke me or anything, Dad would be there to rescue me ... maybe. As we climbed the two flights of stairs that led to their door, Dad turned to me and said, "When this is over, chief, you and I are going to have a loooong talk."

Inside the Wayne's apartment, the air hung thick with anxiety and indignation. Jamie sat alone on the sofa, holding a box of Kleenex, as Mrs. Wayne showed Dad and me into the living room. Major Wayne, a drink in his hand and a scowl on his face, approached us from behind, scaring the shit out of me. "Sergeant Ritter," he bellowed, extending his hand, "I think we have a problem."

Dad shook the Major's hand, declined his offer of a drink, and sat down on the sofa next to Jamie. I took a seat across the room, while Major Wayne paced the floor, pontificating about trust and respect. His rantings concluded with, "I just hope she's not pregnant!"

"There's no way she's pregnant," I exclaimed. I saw the words leave my mouth, tried desperately to retrieve them, but realized it was too late.

Major Wayne glared at me with the kind of hate usually reserved for people like Hitler, or Oswald, or that woman who cut you off in traffic. "And just how the hell can you be so sure?" he demanded.

I was at the proverbial crossroads. I could tell the truth and expose my ineptitude, which would cost me my reputation but spare my dad and the Waynes any further worry, or I could lie and say we used "birth control," which could only serve to paint a more vivid picture of the previous night and, at a minimum, send Major Wayne into orbit.

"Because nothing happened," my old man interjected. "My son told me that he tried to take advantage of your daughter, but she didn't give in. You have nothing to worry about, sir. I can assure you that your daughter's integrity is still intact. Michael did wrong, to be sure, but he's my obligation and I'll deal with him. I'm only sorry that we had to meet under these circumstances."

It was a master stroke! With those few words, Dad had salvaged my reputation as a ladies man, taken responsibility for my actions, and gotten Jamie off the hook. Well, off the immediate hook, anyway, since we both still faced a laundry list of charges. But the atmosphere cleared with Dad's plea and, following several mini lectures from Major Wayne, we took our leave amid tidings of sorrow and understanding.

Dad and I rode home in silence, as I pondered what had just transpired. He had saved my ass, again, and I couldn't help the smile that crept across my face. But after giving it some thought, my elation turned to disgust … with myself. "Dad," I said softly, "don't you ever get tired of bailing me out?"

"Yep," Dad replied, without taking his eyes off the road, "I sure do …"

I hung my head in shame.

"… but, it's all part of the job," he continued. "You weren't born with a guarantee. It's not like I can take you back to the manufacturer."

"But, you would if you could, huh?" I said sheepishly.

"Doesn't work like that," Dad sighed. "It's a 'for better or worse' deal. Granted, I'd love it if you never made mistakes, but that's all part of the test. It's easy to care about someone who never screws up."

"Do you ever make mistakes?" I asked.

"Sure I do," the old man smiled. "All the time. I may have made one today. I don't know, Mike. I sure don't have all the answers."

"I guess not," I said, raising my head, "but you seem to learn from your mistakes. I just keep making the same ones over and over. It's like, I know you'll be there to bail me out, so in the back of my mind, even though I know I'm doing something I shouldn't, I also know I can count on you."

"I'm glad you know you can count on me," Dad said, "but you should also realize that I won't always be standing in the wings. It's one thing to make a mistake, it's a whole other deal when you know it's something you shouldn't do, and you do it anyway. It's a lesson you'd better learn, chief, or one of these days you're gonna get yourself into a pickle that will cost you a whole lot more than a few uncomfortable minutes with some girl's daddy."

Dad was right. I was seventeen years old and still depended on my old man to get me out of trouble. It was pathetic!

As we pulled into the parking lot in front of our apartment, Dad turned to me and said, "Okay, Mike, here's the deal. You are damn lucky, damn lucky that I don't take away your key and make you move back upstairs, and share a bedroom with your brother."

Please don't do that, I pleaded to myself. Anything but that!

"But," Dad reflected, "that would only aggravate your mom, so from now on, you have to leave the key upstairs when you go out and come in and pick it up when you get back home, so I'll know when you're in your room."

Not bad, I thought. I'll just check in at night and leave when I want to. All I'll have to do is return before Dad gets up in the morning.

"And," Dad continued, "I'll have an extra key that I'll carry with me all the time ... so, don't be surprised if you get a visit in the middle of the night. We'll just call it insurance."

Damn! Dad knew where to hit me so it'd really hurt! He was taking away my freedom. Still, given everything that had happened, I'd gotten off pretty...

"Oh, and one more thing," Dad smiled, as he turned off the motor, "for the next two weeks, you're in the house by 6:00."

"But that's the rest of the summer," I protested.

"Could be the rest of your life," Dad said calmly. "Don't push it."

My reverie was interrupted by shouts of, "Mike, hey Mike, you still with us?" It was Dr. Fitzpatrick, calling me back to the reality of the moment. "So, what do you think?" he asked. "What does it mean to 'depend' on someone?"

I hesitated for a moment, then responded. "When you really care about someone, and they care about you, then you can depend on one another." I looked around the room at my friends, who were nodding their agreement. "But," I added, "you should only depend on them to continue caring about you."

"Hmmm," Fitzpatrick mused, "go on."

"Well," I added, as I leaned forward in my seat, "I'm friends with these people because I care about them. They can depend on that, no matter what they do. But that doesn't mean I'm going to let them take advantage of my concern for them."

"Explain what you mean by that," Fitzpatrick urged.

"Let's say Rob gets in a fight and gets his butt kicked."

"Not very likely," Rob joked.

"As his friend, it's not my duty to go after the guy who kicked his butt. That's Rob's lesson to learn. My job is to be there for him when he's down. You know?"

"So," Fitzpatrick said, "I guess you would substitute the word 'care' for 'depend'. In other words, friends are people you care about rather than depend on."

"No," I responded, "I think the two go hand-in-hand. All these people can depend on the fact that I care about them. That doesn't mean I don't get irritated with them now and then ..."

"Not me," Rob laughed. "Say it isn't so ... you never get irritated with me, do you?"

"Honey," Jessie smirked, "we all get irritated with you!"

"Aw, Jessie," Rob smiled. "You know you love me."

"That's right," Jessie shot back. "I do love you. Even when you're a jerk, I still care about you."

"Exactly," Cissy agreed from her corner of the couch. "I mean, the Colonel can really piss me off sometimes, but I still love him. I'll always love him."

"Well," Sean chimed in, "I wouldn't say I love you guys, but I think Mike's right. I do care about you all. You're like ... family."

"Yeah ... like the Mafia," Tim laughed, as he walked over and stood in front of Rob. Lampooning Marlon Brando from The Godfather, Tim continued, "*Mi familia* ... don't mess with my family or we make you an offer you can't refuse." He grabbed Rob's face with one hand, "Sonny, Sonny ... look what they did to my boy."

We all burst into laughter, even Rob, who was rarely able to appreciate a joke at his expense.

"So, let's recap," Fitzpatrick said. "You guys are friends because you can depend on the fact that you care about one another, like a family does, right?"

"Si," Tim replied, still butchering the Godfather, "and nobody comes between us."

"That's right," Lori said with determination. "I can call Rob a jerk, but

nobody outside of this group had better, or they'll have to answer to me …
to all of us."

"For the record," Rob protested, "I am not a jerk! Why don't you pick
on Willie for awhile?"

"We're not picking on you sweetie," Jessie smiled. "You're just such
an easy target. What we're trying to say is, we'll always be there for you
… even when you're a jerk. We are a family."

"Actually," I interjected, "it's better than that. I didn't choose my mom
or dad, sisters or brother, but I chose to be friends with these people. In a
lot of ways, it's a stronger bond. We're all here because we want to be, not
because we have to be."

"It's like … we complete each other," Valerie smiled.

"Right," Paul agreed. "In our case, one plus one equals more than two."

"You mean, the sum is greater than the individual parts?" Fitzpatrick
probed.

"Uh, yeah," Paul answered, "I guess that's what I mean."

Fitzpatrick laughed. "In other words, you draw strength from one
another."

"Yeah," Sean declared, "as if we were somehow meant to be friends,
almost like we didn't really have a choice in it … destiny, or karma, or
something."

"I don't know why these particular people found each other at this
particular point in their lives," I cut in. "All I know is, they mean the world
to me. Wherever I go, whatever happens in my life, it'll always make me
smile when I remember the times I've had with these guys, and I thank
God for blessing me with such wonderful friends. I'm sure it's all part of
some big plan that I don't even pretend to understand. But maybe that's
okay. Maybe miracles aren't meant to be understood."

It was highly unusual for me to wax religious; I hadn't been to church,
other than the obligatory holidays, in several years. But, at that moment, I
actually felt some spirit come over me, some feeling that opened my heart
and, perhaps for the first time, helped me truly appreciate what it means to
look someone in the eye, to shake his hand, to value him, and to call him
my friend.

"That was beautiful," Cissy murmured softly, her eyes tearing.

"Yeah," Tim pensively added. "Heavy stuff, Ritter."

"I may just have to come over there and give you a big kiss!" Rob
teased.

The group was quiet for a few minutes, as we each reflected on what had been said. Fitzpatrick broke the silence, "Well, correct me if I'm wrong, but it seems you're convinced that to care, to love, to appreciate is cool ... and, if that's the case, I'd say you're one bunch of very cool people."

"Told ya," Tim grinned.

The hour was coming to a close and, as we readied ourselves to go to class, Rob posed the question we all wanted to ask, "So, Doc, why us— what makes us so special?"

Fitzpatrick opened the door to his office, as if he expected a hasty departure, but none of us were leaving until we got an answer. Our host deliberated for a moment and, as the hint of a smile crept across his mouth, replied, "You do. You make each other special."

The gang met with Dr. Fitzpatrick a few more times over the course of the next several weeks, sometimes as a group, sometimes the boys and the girls separately. None of us ever fully understood why we were called together in the first place—no report was forthcoming, no team of psychologists swarmed over the school, hooking us up to machines or flashing us with ink blot tests. But, every now and then, throughout my Senior year, I made it a point to pop in on Dr. Fitzpatrick, just to say hello ... and thank him for being so cool.

Chapter Eight
WHO WAS THAT MASKED MAN?

"Show me some I.D."—words every military dependent hears countless times a day. Those little, green, laminated cards were being flashed more often than a woman on a New York subway. The military is real keen on confirming ownership of its people, and required the hall pass from Uncle Sam be shown every time one of us entered the base. The Military Police, in their white hats and gloves, would stop us at the guard station, check our I.D. cards and, like St. Peter at the Pearly Gates, make sure we were on the "A-list" before granting permission to enter. It was a pain in the ass at times, but I have to admit a certain feeling of security in the knowledge that our boys in blue were busily keeping Ramstein Air Force Base safe from democracy.

But every September, security took a backseat to politics when the Air Force hosted its big Air Show and threw open the front gates to anyone who wanted to enter the base. The military would stage an "our guns are bigger than yours" extravaganza, and invite the German population to come for a firsthand look at why they lost the war. Jets screamed through the sky, tanks lined the flight line, and people of all ages and nationalities played on the instruments of destruction, like monkey bars in a playground. The display was really quite amazing, and I often wondered if any Russian spies were among the throngs of spectators, clicking away with microcameras while they gulped down good old American ice cream with tiny, flat, wooden spoons.

Attendance at the Air Show wasn't required, but most definitely encouraged, so I did my patriotic duty and joined the gawking hoards, strolling through the rows of armaments like shoppers at a flea market, hoping to pick up a great deal on a slightly used rocket launcher. I was busy listening to some airman explain the intricacies of an M-16 when I noticed Hank and two girls standing at the front of the hangar, motioning me to join them. I'd never been too fond of Hank. He was one of those really intense guys who took life way too seriously, but he was alone with two girls that I didn't recognize and, never being one to pass up an opportunity, I started walking toward them.

A beaming Hank met me halfway. "Hey, Ritter, how 'bout helping me out with one of these girls?"

Sounded like a reasonable request, and certainly the best offer I'd had all day, so I countered, "Maybe. Who are they? New kids in school?"

"No, man," Hank smiled as he placed his arm around my shoulder. "They're German chicks, don't speak hardly any English at all."

Hmmm … sounds like a fun date, spending the day teaching basic English to two German girls. Think I'll go back to the guy fumbling with the M-16.

"And they want us to go to a party with them tonight," Hank continued.

On the other hand...

"But, there's a rub." Hank laughed.

Okay, here it comes … I knew this was too good to be true.

"You have to pretend that you're somebody else."

"Who?" I indignantly responded.

Hank took a deep breath and whispered: "This guy who died last year."

Now, I've pretended to be a lot of things in my life, and I do have the ability to shovel bullshit with the best of them, but impersonating a dead man was a new role for me and I was going to need a little more information before committing to the part. "I dunno," I frowned, "don't you think they'll catch on when they see me breathing?"

"No, no," Hank continued. "They don't know he's dead. They just know he was in a bad motorcycle wreck last year.

"And …?" I pressed.

"And, we're going to tell them that you went back to the States for a year, you had plastic surgery, and now you're back."

Oh, this sounded like a good plan. What could possibly make them suspect our sincerity? Just because I don't look like the guy, or sound like the guy, or know anything about the guy...

"You know, Hank," I grinned, "the fact that they're German doesn't necessarily make them stupid. I know you speak fluent German, but I don't, so there's every possibility that this will blow up in our faces, and I'll be left standing there looking like an idiot. Maybe you should get yourself another boy."

"No, no," Hank insisted, "I already told them you were John—you know, the dead guy. It's gotta be you. Come on man, it'll be fun. All you have to do is nod your head a lot and agree with everything I say."

"I won't know what you're saying," I retorted, "and that's the least of my problems with this plan."

"Aw, c'mon Mike, show some balls. Just play along and who knows, you might get lucky. John had a thing going with the tall blonde," Hank added, as he pointed and waved in the direction of the two girls.

"What!" I exclaimed, "John had a thing going with the blonde? Have you lost your mind? There's no way she's gonna buy this."

"She already has," Hank assured me, "and she told me she can't wait to pick up where the two of you left off. Just look at her, she's gorgeous."

I couldn't argue with that, and since the quickest way to a teenage boy's brain is through his pants, my reluctance quickly evaporated and I agreed to help Hank with his little charade.

As we approached the girls, I could hear them hurriedly whispering. Hank made the introductions. "John," he began, which caused me to glance around, already forgetting who John was. "Oh, John," he continued, jamming me in the side with his elbow, "this is Ingrid ... and I'm sure you remember Gerta." Gerta was a truly breathtaking girl, with shoulder-length blonde hair and deep brown eyes. She smiled and said something in German as she reached forward to give me a big hug.

I didn't respond. How could I? I had no idea what she was talking about but, judging by the look on her face, it was obvious that I should have. I gave Hank a confused squint, and he quickly said something to her in German. "What's up?" I whispered.

"Not to worry," Hank smiled, "I just told her that, as a result of your accident, you've lost all memory so you can't remember how to speak German."

"John spoke fluent German?" I shuddered. "Not a good detail to leave out, Hank. And besides, how is it I remember English?"

"Be cool," he responded. "She's buying it."

And from all indications, she was. Gerta's sympathy grew as Hank recounted my various afflictions resulting from the "accident"—loss of memory (which covered all lack of knowledge about everything); loss of all my hair (which, I guess, sufficiently explained how it had gone from blonde to brown); and, drastic face reconstruction (which seemed to please her immensely ... this John guy must have been a real bowser). "But, you okay now?" she asked, in broken English.

"Oh, yeah," I lied, "all the scars have healed."

The four of us strolled around the Air Show for the next few hours, examining the weapons of mass destruction while "remembering old times." I spent the majority of the afternoon nodding my head and smiling like an idiot, until the girls indicated that it was time for them to go home and prepare for the party.

"Okay, then," Hank said in German, "we'll see you tonight."

This flimflam had disaster written all over it, and as Hank and I said goodbye to the girls I knew I was buying a first class ticket on the Hindenberg.

I'd known Hank for a few years, and initially, we were pretty good friends. The summer before we were Juniors, he another kid named Jack and myself got heavily into the rock opera *Jesus Christ Superstar*. We spent hours at Jack's house, listening to the album and playing different parts. I focused on the role of Judas—I saw him as a sympathetic and greatly misunderstood character—while Hank insisted on starring as Jesus Christ and, as I would come to discover, the role of martyr suited him all too well. However, shortly after school started, I began hanging around with Sean, Willie, and the rest of the gang that would evolve into the Studs, and rather than join in on the fun, Hank chose to resent my newly-forged friendships.

Besides Hank's need for attention, the guy was also just   too ... intense. He was one of those "know-it-all" guys who would spend hours trying to convince someone of something that they really didn't give two shits about in the first place. Eventually, it got to the point where we'd go out of our way to avoid him. Athletically, Hank was a talented kid, a school star in cross-country running who seemed to be happy with himself. But he spent so much energy convincing us that his opinion was always "right" that, over time, it cost him his friends. Hank's dad was a strict disciplinarian, and his mom was a large German woman who paid more attention to her prize poodle than she did to her son. So at some level, I understood why Hank pontificated about everything ... no one was listening to him at home. Still, my compassion notwithstanding, he got on my last nerve, and our friendship could never outweigh my annoyance. We continued to be cordial to one another, and often attended the same parties, but I would be hard-pressed to call him a friend. He was more like a skin rash that hangs around so long that eventually you get used to the irritation.

Anyway, Hank appeared at my Maid's Room at 6:30 that night. Since my car, the Cream Machine, was again sporting a "DOA" toe tag, we walked the short distance to the bus stop and caught a ride to the village of Gruenweld where the party, and the girls, were waiting.

"This is going to be great, Mike," Hank beamed, as we climbed into the bus.

"I don't know, Hank," I stammered. "I've been giving this a lot of thought, and we're taking a real chance here. I mean, we're going twenty kilometers from the base to a party full of Germans, we're depending on this damn bus for transportation, and I have to pretend to be some dead guy all night … come on!"

Hank found two seats in the back of the bus and, plopping down in one of them, immediately began his counterargument. "Quit saying you have to pretend to be a dead guy. He's not dead, buddy," he continued, smacking me on the chest. "He's right here. You're John tonight. Hell, you can do anything you want, 'cause it's not Mike making an ass out of himself, it's John. Besides, you've got amnesia, remember? If someone asks you something about the past, all you have to do is hold your head, apologize, and say you don't recall. Get it? It's the perfect caper."

"Uh, Hank," I cautioned, "if John gets into trouble, it's still Mike who's gonna get his ass kicked!"

"What trouble?" Hank argued. "Stop anticipating the worst, man. It's going to be a cakewalk. I guarantee you that before the night is out, you'll experience things you've never even dreamed of."

Hmmm … things I've never even dreamed of, sounds … inviting. Still, I've had some pretty horrible dreams in my life—even a recurring one, where I'm hiding in a small crawl space in a closet, holding my breath, trying desperately to avoid being discovered by an army of Nazis. Really! I had that same dream at least once a week, always waking up just as the Nazis were throwing open the closet door. I shuddered just thinking about it, and hoped it wasn't a foreshadowing of events to come.

It was eight o'clock by the time we arrived at 727 Hinklestrasse in Gruenweld. Only half of that time was spent on the bus; an additional thirty minutes passed while Hank continued to sell me the fantasy that everything was cool, and I had nothing to worry about. I still wasn't convinced.

After several rings of the doorbell, Gerta opened the door. She looked great and, for the moment, my fear and intimidation took a backseat to that cure for all teenage angst … lust.

"Hello, John," she smiled, giving me a big hug, "come, come." Gerta motioned for us to follow her into the house and down a short flight of stairs that led to the basement, where the party was in full swing.

The stairs emptied into a dark room lit only by the glow of black lights, and reflections from the multitude of Day-Glo posters that covered the walls. David Bowie's "Space Oddity" was blaring from the stereo speakers, and the floor was littered with people who were passing around several joints, happily getting stoned. Through the cloud of burnt-rope-scented smoke that hung thickly in the room, Gerta managed to hold the short attention span of her guests just long enough to introduce us. After a few polite nods from some of the participants, the pot orgy continued unabated. Hank and I grabbed a comer of the floor and sat down, as our hostess scurried off to get us drinks, leaving us adrift in a sea of stoned Germans. "Isn't this great?" Hank jubilantly cheered, his dropped-jaw stare darting all around the room. "It's like ..."

"Sodom and Gomorrah?" I muttered.

"Well," Hank paused, "I was going to say Playboy after Dark, but I think I like your analogy better. Yeah ... Sodom and Gomorrah! That's cool! It's biblical, man, like *Jesus Christ Superstar*. Remember when we used to play the shit out of that record? I always liked the Jesus role, but you really got into that Judas guy, didn't you? How'd that song go that he sings about Jesus ... 'Every time I look at you I don't understand ...'"

"' ... why you let the things you did get so out of hand,'" I completed the lyric.

"Right!" Hank exclaimed, the irony soaring right over his head. "Yes, sir, Sodom and Gomorrah. The last big wing-ding before ..."

"God wiped 'em out," I reminded him.

Gerta returned with two glasses of red punch and, planting herself next to us, proceeded to fire a flurry of questions at Hank, which he, in turn, translated for "John"—me. Between gulps of the sweet-tasting juice, our verbal ménage a trois continued for some thirty or forty minutes before Gerta excused herself, saying she'd be back in a moment with someone who was most anxious to see me again.

"See," Hank grinned, and he drained the drink from his plastic cup. "Nothing to worry about, Mike. You're in like Flint."

As I sat in the corner, breathing in the mind bending fumes, a general calm washed over me. What had I been so worried about? Gerta was either really dumb, or was so taken by my winning smile and charming disposition that she didn't mind that we were trying to pull one over on her. I chose to believe the latter but, either way, it didn't matter. Chances were, I'd never see her again and, assuming I could remember anything in the morning, I'd have a hell of a story for my buddies. Everyone was having a good time, especially Hank, who was involved in a heavy conversation with Gerta's dachshund. No, the dog wasn't talking ... not to me, anyway. But Hank seemed deeply engrossed in regaling his new fleabag buddy with tales of romantic conquests, happy that, for once in his life, his audience didn't roll its eyes and try to make a break for the door. The Beatles' White Album filled the small room with liquid music and, closing my eyes, it seemed I could actually see the notes dancing on the puffs of joy smoke that hung in the air, like marshmallows floating on some wondrous sea of tranquility. My mind drifted with the sounds and smells of laughter, music, beer, and marijuana, which invited my inhibitions, like the rest of me, to take a break from reality.

Then suddenly, like a shriek splits a still night, the song "Revolution Number 9" erupted from the stereo speakers, shattering my serenity and introducing yet another new experience to my already fragile psyche ... paranoia.

In a flash, my brain went from tiptoeing through the tulips to running smack into a big, sticky spider web. The Beatles' anthem to chaos had always been a little disconcerting to me, but in my current mind-altered condition, it sounded like Muzak playing on the down elevator to hell. Creepy, bone-chilling ... Nazi stuff!

As with beauty, terror also lies in the eye of the beholder, and my eyes started beholding a scene that scared the shit out of me. What had been a nice little trip down the road to Never-Never Land was immediately transformed into a ride on a demonic Tilt-A-Whirl—without a seatbelt.

We've gotta get out of here, Hank," I panicked, "this place is full of Germans, man!"

Hank suspended his one-sided conversation with the dog, and glanced up at me. "Yeah, so? What did you expect ... Japanese?"

"Oh, man," I mumbled out of the corner of my mouth, "Japanese! I forgot about the Japanese! Sure, of course, these are Nazis, the Japs can't be far behind! Oh, God, Hank ... oh, God ..."

"Man, what's the matter with you?" Hank slurred. "Nazis? They're just a bunch of German kids, man. C'mon, John, get a grip. Man, this is some great punch."

"John? Who's John?" I dimly questioned.

"You are ... remember?" Hank muttered through gritted teeth.

"Me? I'm Mike. Jesus, Hank, don't you recognize me?"

"Tonight, you're John ... the dead guy ..." he reiterated.

"Dead guy?" I whimpered, jumping to my feet. "I don't want to be a dead guy, Hank! C'mon, let's get out of here before the Japanese show up, and find out we're really Americans."

"What Japanese?" Hank laughed, as he rubbed his eyes with the palms of his hands. "There are no Japanese, no Nazis, just you and me and John."

"Well, let's find John and get the hell out of here," I yelped.

"You're John," Hank insisted.

"Oh, yeah... good, then we don't have to look for me. Now c'mon, Hank, let's go."

Hank slowly climbed to his feet and, laughing hysterically, placed his hands on my shoulders. "Okay, man. One more time. You're here pretending to be John. You had a horrible accident and you had plastic surgery, so Gerta, remember Gerta, she thinks that you're John. She invited us to this party," Hank continued, his legs beginning to sway, "and that's all there is to it. Now will you cool it! Have some more punch."

I took a long drink from the cup. It was all coming back to me now, Gerta ... the Air Show ... dead John ... oh, yeah ... the big scam, and as my memory made a pit stop back at my brain, I started feeling a little better about the situation. "That's right, Hank," I grinned. "I'm John. The masked man. Like the Lone Ranger, huh?"

"Right," Hank said, as he slumped back to the floor, "like the Lone Ranger."

"Revolution Number 9" had ended, and a haunting melody by Quicksilver Messenger Service soothed my pounding ears. As quickly as it had vanished, an ambience of peace, laughter, and good times again bathed the room.

Abruptly, out of nowhere, Gerta appeared, accompanied by a tall, skinny guy, dressed in a shiny pink and red shirt. "John," she smiled, taking my hand and speaking in her best pigeon English, "Fredrich ... remember Fredrich?"

I, of course, didn't have a clue who this joker was but, assured of my anonymity from behind my Lone Ranger mask, quickly replied, "Sure, how's it hangin', Freddie?"

Bad move ... really bad move.

"Then you remember that I was the one going with Gerta when you stole her away from me," Fredrich rebuked, in perfect English.

Okay ... this was not shaping up well. No sir, not at all. My options had boiled down to either a potential punch in the face for something that I, Mike, had never even done, or a full confession. I looked to Hank for support, but he was blissfully asleep on the floor, curled up with the dog; so, I decided to try faking my way through it.

"Oh," I stammered, "that Fredrich. Sorry, man, I thought you were this other guy I used to know by the same name."

Unhinged, I tried to connect telepathically with Hank ... *Wake up,*

Hank. Get me out of this mess, Hank. I'm gonna kill you, Hank ... but he just lay there, a slumbering compost heap.

"Gerta told me about your accident," Fredrich continued the torture, "and about the plastic surgery. I didn't know doctors could make you taller now, too."

Taller? Another little detail that Hank had forgotten to tell me. I was at the end of my rope, the scam was unraveling ... forget it, this game is lost, throw in the towel and head for the showers. And then it hit me ... my recurring nightmare was coming true. I was trapped by the Nazis, who were throwing open the closet door. I kicked Hank, and he jumped to his feet in a Kung Fu stance—he was always pulling that Kung Fu crap, like he was Bruce Lee about to stave off a hoard of angry Chinese.

"What," he yelled. "What's going on, Mike?"

Mike?! Swift move there, Hank. Should we start running now?

Gerta smirked, grabbed Hank by the collar of his shirt, and laid into him with a barrage of German that, from the tone alone, told me we were in real trouble. The only words I understood were "John", "Mike", and "LSD".

"You what?" Hank screamed. "You put LSD in the punch?"

"Ya," Gerta laughed, putting her arm around Fredrich, "the joke is on you."

Amazing thing, the human body. It reacts to situations in exactly the way that the mind dictates. I'd never even thought about taking LSD ... it was one of those scary, heroin-type drugs that causes daughters of talk show hosts to jump out of windows, and I just knew it was only a matter of time before I'd flip out and attempt to dive down the toilet, or something equally as stupid. My stomach flip-flopped as fear gripped my body; all I wanted was to get out of there before I made the situation worse by puking all over the floor.

"I think I'm gonna throw up, Hank," I moaned, leaning against Fredrich and holding my stomach.

"Go ahead, Mike," Hank roared, his words filled with venom. "Serve these guys right if you barfed all over them."

Strange ... we were running the scam on Gerta, pretending to be some dead guy and all, yet somehow, Hank was the one who was incensed, jumping up and down and screaming about how he'd get even.

"Can we just go now, Hank?" I pleaded.

"Sure we can, Mike," Hank persisted in his rampage. "I don't want to be around these, these ... sour krauts any more, either!"

We stumbled through the multitude of laughing Germans, crawled up the stairs, and escaped into the stillness of the dark, cool night. The LSD was now in full swing, and as I looked up at the star-punched, black sky, I could feel the earth below my feet spinning on its axis. Now, chances were good that it was actually me doing the spinning, but my sense of wonder exceeded anything I'd ever experienced and I stood motionless, drinking in the universe, momentarily forgetting my plight.

Hank was still highly pissed off. "Do you believe that?" he bellowed. "They drugged us, man. How could anyone take advantage of another person like that? I ought to report them to the police, teach them not to mess around with us again."

"Uh, Hank," I replied, my arms wrapped around a streetlight in an attempt to hold myself upright.

"Yeah, what?" he fumed.

"I just wanna go home. When's the next bus supposed to get here?"

"Well ... here's the thing ..." Hank stammered.

Uh-oh, here it comes ... don't say it, Hank, don't even think it.

"... there isn't another bus. We're gonna have to run back to the base."

The absurdity of the evening swept over me, and I broke into uncontrollable laughter. Let's see ... I'd made a fool out of myself, been thrown out of a party, was tripping on LSD, and had no way home. Run? Sure—why not?

Hank's mood lightened. "You're taking this better than I expected," he sighed with relief.

"I've got an idea, Hank," I said, between bursts of drug-induced hysteria. "Since I'm the Lone Ranger, how 'bout you pretend to be my trusty steed, Silver, and carry my ass back to the base. Hi-ho, Silver, awaaaaaay!"

Hank wasn't amused, which seemed only fair because neither was I. It was just past midnight—my, how time flies when you spend most of the evening lying on the floor—and I was supposed to "check in" no later than 1:00 a.m., my punishment for previous offenses. So I was, in a word ... screwed. But, facing my old man was the least of my worries. While it was just barely possible that I might be able to hobble the twenty kilometers home, there was little chance that I could uproot my supportive streetlight and take it on the road with me, so a plan was an absolute must.

Hopefully, this plan would involve neither the Military Police nor a mob of angry Germans brandishing torches and chasing me down some moonlit, cobblestone street, like they did to Frankenstein's monster.

Hank sat in the gutter, his head in his hands. "I'm sorry, man," he quietly said, "this is all my fault."

Even in my LSD-induced stupor, I found myself shocked by Hank's display of remorse. Here was the "I'm never wrong" king, admitting for the first time in recorded history that he, Hank, might actually be wrong. Somebody check the temperature in Hell.

I was born with the defect known as a kind heart, so within a few minutes, my ire diminished and was replaced with compassion and empathy for this guy who had gotten us both in way over our heads. "C'mon, Hank," I said, still clutching my incandescent life preserver, "you gotta get a grip, man. How could you have known that Gerta was planning to make suckers out of us, that there'd be LSD in the punch, or that we'd miss the last bus and be stranded out here in the middle of nowhere?"

There, that ought to make him feel better.

"Oh, man ..." Hank sighed, wiping his eyes with the sleeve of his shirt, "you're right ... it's not my fault ..."

Good ... now maybe we can concentrate on...

"... it's really your fault," Hank spat.

So much for compassion. "My fault? How is any of this my fault?" I volleyed.

"Because you blew it, man. You freaked out about Fredrich ... should have just kept your mouth shut."

Is it me? Am I the crazy one here? Did he just say what I thought he said?

"Yeah," Hank moaned, holding his stomach as he stood up. "I should have known better than to involve a chicken-shit like you."

Chicken-shit?! I released my grip on the streetlight and lunged at Hank, hitting him squarely in the chest and sending the two of us crashing onto the hard, cement sidewalk.

"I don't believe you," I shouted, "it was your stupid idea. You're the reason I'm in this mess in the first place!"

Hank jumped to his feet and, for the second time that night, struck his infamous Kung Fu stance, breathing heavily and glaring at me with pure hatred in his eyes. "C'mon, Ritter," he bellowed, "give me your best shot."

From my position on the ground, I rolled over on my side, looked up at Hank, and burst into laughter. "Now what are you gonna do," I grinned, "beat me up? Oooo, I'm so scared of you, Hank. Please, oh please, master Hank sir, don't beat me," I taunted. "I'll be good."

"You're not worth it," Hank scowled, turning his back to me.

"Screw you, Ritter."

"You're not really my type, and besides, don't you think it'll upset your little doggy girlfriend?" I jeered. "You seemed so happy at the party, laying on the floor together. I wouldn't want to step on any ... paws."

Hank stopped dead in his tracks, his fists clenched at his sides. Under normal conditions, I would have been afraid for my life; the guy really did have a few loose screws, and there was every possibility that the LSD screwdriver had finished the job and removed them altogether. However, my present condition being anything but normal, I was still laughing when he turned around. His face, beet red with indignation, was contorted like a character from a Tex Avery cartoon.

"Okay, okay, Hank," I snickered, raising my hands like a white flag, "if it's so damn important to you, you can be right. I'll be dead John ... the Lone Ranger ... even a chicken-shit if it'll make you happy ... tell you the truth, I don't really care. I just want to get the hell out of here and get back to the base."

Hank slowly walked over to my seat on the ground and extended his hand, offering to help me up. I clutched his arm and, as I teetered to my feet, Hank smiled and said, "Okay, Lone Ranger, Tonto will get us home."

As we trotted down the narrow, cobblestone street, I turned to Hank and grinned, "I'll give you this, Hank," I panted, "you said that tonight I'd experience things I never dreamed of ... well, you got that part right, anyway. You sure as hell got that part right."

The route we traveled was a winding, two-lane road that was sprinkled with tiny villages, and blanketed on both sides by clusters of trees. For most of the trip, our only source of light was the glow of the deep orange-yellow moon that hung low in the dark firmament, and the silent stillness of the night only served to amplify the sound of our sneakers, pounding against the concrete as we loped along the shadow-strewn avenue.

Three-and-a-half hours later we arrived, panting and wheezing, at the woods that encircled Ramstein Air Force Base. Home ... we were almost there! The trouble was, we had no idea how to actually get "there". We knew that the base lay just beyond the woods, but hacking our way through the black, forbidding forest was going to be a feat in itself.

"Oh ... man ..." I gasped, my chest heaving with each breath, "I'm beat. I never thought we'd make it, especially when those wolves started chasing us ..."

"Those weren't wolves," Hank smirked, still jogging in place, "just a few friendly German shepherds. You should really keep moving, Mike.

Helps keep the muscles from stiffening up."

"I don't have any muscles left," I puffed, "they collapsed fifteen minutes after we began this marathon. In fact, I lost them altogether while we were running through that last village ... fell right out of my legs, onto the street ... looked like strips of beef jerky ... that's what made the wolves stop chasing us."

Hank wasn't paying any attention. He was too busy surveying the wall of foliage that stood between where we were, and where we wanted to be, in an effort to find a path that would lead us through the woods. "Okay," he said authoritatively, "here's the plan. I don't see a path, but if we keep sight of the North Star and head in that direction, we'll eventually run into the base."

I frowned. "Who are you, Columbus? Why don't we just stay on the outskirts, and follow the rim of the woods until we find the main gate?"

"That could take hours," Hank responded, without even looking at me. "If we cut straight through the woods, we'll save a lot of time. I guarantee it."

Needless to say, by this point I didn't have a whole lot of faith in Hank or his guarantees, but I was too worn out to debate the issue. So with great trepidation, I surrendered. "Okay, okay, whatever you say, Hank. My life is in your hands."

Hank lived for moments like these. He was at the helm, firmly in charge, General Custer about to lead his troop, me, into the wilderness, dedicated to his cause, determined to succeed, accepting nothing less than total victory!

And willing to die trying.

As we plunged into the thick tangle of trees, I felt like Dorothy, boldly tiptoeing through the haunted forest towards Oz—lions and tigers and bears, oh, my—and I hoped that Hank, like the Scarecrow, did indeed have a brain.

We trekked through the woods, our eyes glued to the North Star, two not-so-wise men on a quest for the holy military base. Just as I actually started to believe we might get out of this alive, the woods became so dense that even the moonlight couldn't penetrate the menacing branches that towered overhead, and I lost sight of Hank in the profusion of underbrush.

Following Hank's instructions—Hank had decided that we should stay as quiet as possible; after all, who knows what kind of crazies are running around in the middle of the woods at four o'clock in the morning—I hissed, "Hank, where are you, Hank?"

Nothing.

"Hank," I repeated, a little louder, "ohhh, Ha-ank ... listen, man, if you're just jerking with me, cut it out. I'm not kidding around, now ..."

Silence.

"Hank!" I screamed, "where the hell are you?!"

Suddenly, a hand reached out from the darkness and touched my shoulder, sending my heart leaping into my throat.

"I'm right here, man," Hank angrily uttered, annoyed by my breach of security. "What's your problem?"

"What's my problem?" I shot back, spitting out the words through gritted teeth. "It's like goddamn Vietnam out here! I can't see shit, my legs hurt, I'm over three hours late getting home, and you want to know what my problem is. Do you have any idea what you're doing?"

"You questioning my leadership ability?" Hank screamed.

"No, Hank," I grumbled, "I'm questioning my sanity. We're in Hell, Hank. Somewhere along the way, we entered the on-ramp to Hell and, no matter what we do, we can't get off. We're never ..."

"You're freaking out, man," Hank interrupted.

"Oh, I'm beyond freaking out, Hank," I lamented, walking around in circles and flailing my arms in the air, "way past freaking out. I swear, if I had a gun right now I'd send my head ..."

"Quiet," Hank broke in, "I hear someone."

I froze in my tracks, and crouched down beside Hank. "You heard someone?"

"Someone or something," Hank whispered.

Some ... thing?! Perfect. We couldn't find an entire Air Force base, but managed to run right into the only Bigfoot in all of Europe.

"What is it?" I questioned.

"Listen," Hank said softly, "it's like a low hum. Hear it?"

I couldn't hear anything except the sound of my own heart, thumping wildly in my chest.

"It's coming from over there," Hank pointed, "I'll be right back." And before I could say a word, he shot off into the woods, leaving me and the North Star to fend for ourselves.

Alone in the woods, (at least I hoped I was alone), the thought of being mangled by Bigfoot still loomed large in my mind, and I looked around for a tree to climb ... just in case.

I found a tree with low-hanging branches, and was about fifteen feet off the ground before deciding that, in the event an actual Bigfoot did make an appearance, it would be better to be mobile than to be trapped up a tree, with no escape. However, climbing up had proved to be a lot easier than climbing down and, as I dangled my leg in an attempt to get a foothold on the branch beneath me, something suddenly grabbed my ankle and I screamed like a scared little girl. I couldn't look down ... didn't want to. Better to be torn to pieces with my eyes closed—maybe it wouldn't hurt as badly.

"Gotcha," Hank laughed, still holding onto my trembling leg. "What are you doing up there?"

I let out a heavy sigh of relief. "I thought maybe I'd be able to see the base from the top of this tree," I lied, my voice quivering. "Hope I didn't scare you."

"I found it," Hank smiled proudly.

"What?" I credulously responded, jumping to the ground. "The base? You found the base? Don't bullshit me now, Hank."

"No bullshit," Hank chortled, "it's right through there, about 250 meters from here."

"Are you sure, Hank? Really sure?" I questioned.

"Sure, I'm sure," Hank beamed, "of course, we're still gonna have to find a way in. That sound I heard was the generator that powers the electric fence around the flight line."

Electric fence? Did he say electric fence? Oh well, it didn't matter; when compared with my vision of Bigfoot, even the possibility of being charbroiled alive was a welcome thought.

I stumbled through the woods, never letting Hank out of my sight, and before long we came to a tall fence. Barbed wire stretched formidably across the top of the metal obstacle, and bright yellow signs loudly declared "WARNING! U.S. GOVERNMENT PROPERTY. DANGER. HIGH VOLTAGE!" At that moment, those were the sweetest words I'd ever read in my life.

"Well," Hank mused, scratching the top of his head, "we can't go over it, so I guess we'll just have to dig under it."

Dig under it? Hank was taking this commando thing a little too far. "Why don't we just start yelling until somebody hears us?" I suggested, but he was already on his hands and knees, loosening dirt that was packed around the bottom of the fence.

After about thirty minutes of digging, we managed to open a crawl space large enough to shimmy through (a true tribute to base security), and finally we found ourselves walking down the flight line and past the jets, toward a dimly lit hangar. It was 4:40 in the morning.

As we continued weaving our way down the tarmac, two headlights split the early morning haze and, within minutes, we were confronted by the military police. "One of you guys named Mike?" the officer asked. "Your mother's been calling all over the base, looking for you."

I imagined my mom, pacing the floor, wondering if I was alright and, if not, how much it was going to cost her. It had been quite a night, and as I focused on Hank's dirty, weary, smiling face, I couldn't resist the temptation. "You've got the wrong guy, sir," I smiled. "My name's John."

Chapter Nine
THERE'S NO PLACE LIKE HOME
FOR THE HOLIDAYS

Everyone has their favorite holiday. Mine happens to be Halloween. There's just something about the dark side that has always fascinated me. When other kids were putting model airplanes and race cars together, I was covering my room with little plastic likenesses of Frankenstein's monster, the Wolfman, the Mummy, and Dracula. To me, these guys were cool. Dracula was the coolest. Maybe it's because he always got the girl, or the fact that no matter how many times he was killed, he always came back for more. Just a "never-say-die" kind of guy. I admire that.

I think my appreciation for horror started with my dad. Excuse me while I lapse into a little uneducated child psychology here, but it's the wish of every little boy to please his dad. This generally takes the form of sharing something in common ... a love of sports, or tinkering with cars, or wrestling, or hunting, stuff like that. But considering I had no interest in any of those things, I bonded with the old man's love for the horror movies he had seen as a kid ... old Lon Chaney, Boris Karloff and Bela Lugosi flicks. Dark, shadowy figures that crept through the night, abiding by nobody's rules but their own ... I could get into that!

Dad used to tell this great story about coming home late one night after seeing *The Wolfman* with his brother, Jerry. Seems they were each given a quarter to go to the movies: a dime for bus fare to and from the theatre, a dime for the movie ticket, and a nickel for popcorn. Of course, halfway through the picture they had both finished their popcorn and, with the return bus fare burning a hole in their pockets, decided to use the money for more popcorn and walk the several miles back home. As Dad tells the story, it was one of those cold, wet, moonless October nights, when the wind cuts your face and dogs howl their sorrow to the sky. As my dad and his brother walked along the damp, empty street, they could hear the sound of footsteps following them. When they stopped, the sound would stop...when they started walking, the footsteps would pick up again, shadowing them step for step. Fearing for their lives, they began to run, and so did the footsteps that now seemed to chase them down the dark, lonely road. They ran faster and faster, but their stalker kept pace. Finally, they spotted the porch light of the house. It was just beyond the end of the fence. If they could only run fast enough, they had to try, they had to ...

As they rounded the corner, without warning, the Wolfman sprang out from behind the fence. Jerry fainted dead away, head bouncing off the concrete. My dad bolted for the front porch. This was no time for heroics—it was the Wolfman, for God's sake!

Of course, the footsteps they'd heard were just echoes of their own, and since no kid has ever been killed by a Wolfman in East Peoria, Illinois, they figured the monster must have been some jerk in a rubber mask. But, then again, maybe it wasn't.

Anyway, I couldn't wait for Halloween! Running around in the cold, pitch-black night, the leaves blowing around your feet, just a hint of danger in the air … ah, yes, the best night of the year. I didn't even care all that much about the candy premium—it was the excitement of putting on a costume and, for just a brief time, pretending to be somebody else—somebody who didn't have a math test the next day, or the class bully breathing down his neck, or new, torn dress slacks hidden under their bed. On Halloween, kids became invincible … fearless … free!

As I said, the old man had a soft spot for Halloween, too. Every year, he'd let his creative juices flow and "make us all up" using old, discarded items that were hanging around, stuffed in the back of a closet. One year he dressed me up as a hobo and I won first prize at a costume contest—the record album *Gloria, G-L-O-R-I-A, Gloria* by the Shadows of Night. That was the first record I ever owned, and I still have it someplace. Another time he made a robot outfit out of some cardboard boxes, tinfoil, a few kitchen appliances, and some laminating plastic which he used as a window so I could see where I was going. Only trouble was, the sticky side of the plastic was up against my face. I kept sticking to it, and I had a cold that night, so you can imagine what it looked like by the end of the evening. When I pulled it off, it pulled out the three chin hairs I'd been so proud of. Pissed me right off. I hated that costume. I couldn't run in it, so all night my friends were leaving me behind, and going to the bathroom was totally out of the question. By the end of the evening, I'd taken everything off but the tinfoil body section, and told anyone who asked that I was supposed to be a toaster.

The old man didn't limit his artistic endeavors to his kids. He'd put this blue, fuzzy, stool cover on his head, paint his face white, throw on a sheet, and take my little sisters trick-or-treating, scaring the hell out of the neighborhood kids.

When we all got home with our bounty of goodies, the trade wars would begin. First on the auction block were the root beer barrels. Nobody liked them but my sister Connie, so she'd trade for them on a one-to-three ratio—one piece of candy for three root beer barrels. Connie's an accountant now ... figures. Mini candy bars were like gold, and every once in a while, if you were real lucky, somebody would give you a full-size candy bar. Man, that was Heaven! We'd always try to save them for last (Connie still had hers the following Easter) but they rarely made it to breakfast.

Holidays are magnets for memories, moments that will be remembered long after the Halloween costume comes off, or the last piece of Thanksgiving turkey is eaten, or the Christmas lights come down. Most people collect their best, and worst, memories during the holidays—the Christmas you were surprised with a new bike, or the New Year's Eve you spent alone. I remember little things, like looking for Easter eggs with my sister, Cyndy, when I was about five. Mom was big on crinoline in the early 1960s, and had dressed Cyndy in so many layers of the stuff that every time she'd bend down to pick up a brightly colored egg, the sheer weight of her dress would send her tumbling over. The dress stuck out so far that she couldn't put her arms down and, after a while, she just kind of waddled around in a circle with her arms sticking out in the air, saying she couldn't find any Easter eggs. Hell, in that outfit she couldn't find her own feet!

The Ritter kids always had new "church clothes" for Easter Sunday. We were polished to such a shine that the sunlight beaming through the stained glass windows and reflecting off us could cause temporary blindness for those unfortunate enough to look directly into it. I'm not certain where the tradition of new Easter clothes came from but perhaps it has something to do with the rebirth of Jesus. In any picture I've ever seen of the Resurrection, His shroud is always clean and pressed. Easter eggs represent birth ... new life, but what's with the Easter Bunny? I've yet to see a rabbit lay an egg ... so Easter traditions were rather confusing for me.

Without a doubt, the King of Holidays is Christmas. It means different things to different people ... peace on Earth, loving your fellow man, carolers strolling through moonlit, snow-covered streets, singing the praises of the season. But to kids, it means presents ... a chance to have all those things that parents say "no" to the rest of the year.

Every kid learns the truth about Santa Claus at some point in their lives. Some kids find out early on, while others still believe at eleven or twelve that a fat man in a red suit brings them gifts every December 25th.

But regardless of age, when a kid finds out that it's really been his folks laying out the Christmas booty all those years, it can be quite traumatic. It's like losing your virginity … nice to know the facts, but a little disconcerting just the same.

I was just six years old when a friend broke the news to me. Actually, he asked my mom "if I knew the truth about Santa Claus," which was all the prompting I needed to bug her until I got the straight skinny on the whole deal. "What truth, Mom? He doesn't really live at the North Pole? He hates milk and cookies? There is no such thing as an elf?" Finally, she couldn't stand the third degree any longer, and admitted that she and my dad were really Santa Claus. So, the truth was known, and I remember the feeling of loss, as though a miracle had become a lie. I felt I would never again experience the magical wonder of presents that appeared out of nowhere, and covered the floor beneath the Christmas tree. Besides, with the fall of Santa Claus, could the Easter Bunny and the Tooth Fairy be far behind?

In California, the temperature was usually about seventy-five degrees on Christmas morning. Some kids liked it because it meant that they didn't have to wait until spring to ride their new bikes and skateboards, but I always thought it was kind of sad. Maybe I'm too much of a traditionalist, but there's something rather pathetic about the specter of plastic Santas and reindeers sitting on green lawns, dressed in sunglasses and Bermuda shorts.

At Christmas, our house always looked like a department store. Mom took great pride in making it look "just so" for the holidays, and I have to admit, she always did a super job. Every year, Dad would paint the front window with Christmas scenes of snow and other holiday icons, and we kids would carefully decorate the tree, mesmerized by the glow of lights reflecting off the colorful ornaments, anxious for the big day to arrive. There were trays of Christmas cookies and candy placed all around the living room, as well as big bowls of mixed nuts that, more often than not, became small mounds of crushed shells scattered across the table. My dad usually ate the mixed nuts, as he was the only one who had mastered the use of a nutcracker. Every time I tried to crack open a nut, I'd end up shooting it across the room; and besides, it was too much trouble just to get at the small, crunchy treat waiting inside. I'm more of a Planters kind of guy—let somebody else do all the work.

Since my parents had five kids to please, our Christmas tree had so many presents crammed under it that they spilled about halfway into the living room. Every day we'd check to see if any new arrivals had appeared while we were at school, and would count how many gifts we each had, just to make sure that nobody was playing favorites. Some families open all the gifts on Christmas Eve, some wait until morning. We each got to open one gift on the night before Christmas, so it was very important to choose just the right package. This became very scientific, as each box was carefully examined in an effort to determine the value of the gift inside. For weeks before Christmas Day, we kids would sit around the living room holding our pick for the Christmas Eve opening (which would often change as new gifts arrived). We'd turn off all the lights in the house except those on the Christmas tree and, basking in the glow of excitement and a few well-placed candles, we'd sing along with Christmas albums recorded by everyone from Eddie Arnold to Joanie James. My favorite was a record by Paul Anka (it was the hippest one we had), singing his rendition of "I Saw Mommy Kissing Santa Claus."

Of course, the big present came from Santa, so no matter what we opened on Christmas Eve, we knew that the bonanza was still in Santa's pack, being loaded onto his sleigh. This knowledge was truly comforting if we were unfortunate enough to discover that the package we had been coveting for weeks contained socks and underwear. We were never disappointed by Santa's gift—it was always something cool, something out of the ordinary, something too big to be wrapped in a box.

Sometime around nine o'clock on Christmas Eve, the old man would swear he heard reindeer hooves on the roof, and we'd all scamper off to bed to start the countdown to daybreak. Sometimes, most of the time, we just couldn't wait, and would bound out of bed at some ungodly hour like four in the morning to see what our reward was for a year of trying to be good. My folks would leave the tree lights on all night so, when we got up, the sight of new toys sparkling under the twinkling lights would add to the feeling that this was no ordinary day … this was Christmas Day! We'd wade through a sea of presents, and by 4:20 a.m., all the gifts would be open and we'd be sitting in three feet of wrapping paper, playing with our new toys and munching on candy canes for breakfast.

Everybody has a favorite Christmas story. I don't mean A *Christmas Carol* or *Charlie Brown's Christmas*; I mean their own, private story about a Christmas they'll never forget, the one that, more than any other, gave them hope that the magic of the season still exists. I have several fond memories, but there are two that stand out, and still bring a smile to my heart.

I was eleven in 1966, and had already known the truth about Santa Claus for several years. Still, I got a real kick out of my younger brother and sisters speculating about what the jolly man would bring them. They all still believed at that point, and their joy and anticipation added to the excitement of the holiday.

That Christmas, Dad took me with him to pick out the "perfect" gift for Mom. Spending any time alone with the old man was a real treat, and I felt particularly honored that he wanted my opinion on something as important as his gift to Mom. So we left the rest of the family watching *Rowan and Martin's Laugh-In Christmas Show* and drove to Sears (it was the only credit card the old man owned).

He wanted to get her something special that she would remember for years to come, so as he was looking through the jewelry case, I strolled over to the ladies clothes department. After several minutes of picking through the racks, under the mistrusting gaze of the sales clerk, I spotted the definitive gift, a one-in-a-million item that would show Mom exactly how much the old man loved her, and would also play to her taste for expensive clothes.

"Quit looking, Dad," I yelled out confidently. "I've found it! The perfect thing!"

There I stood, among the throngs of determined women fighting one another for discounted items, waving the perfect gift over my head as if I was signaling for rescue … a gold lame pantsuit, complete with "Laura Petrie" calypso slacks that zipped up the back. One of a kind. Mom would love it!

"Wow," the old man exclaimed, taking the outfit from me and holding it up to the light, "it's … it's...beautiful, son!"

"I know! Look how the light reflects off it—people will really see her coming in this outfit!"

"Oh," the old man moaned as he gazed at the pantsuit, "this must cost a fortune! Way out of my price range."

"No, Dad, it's only $16.98. Can you believe it!?" I exclaimed.

"Sold!" The old man shouted, handing the golden garb to me. "Go find a sales girl, Michael. Your mom's gonna love this!"

I trotted over to the cash register and placed the outfit on the counter. "Well, I wondered if anyone was ever going to be …" The sales clerk remarked, pausing in mid-sentence and looking at the broad smiles that Dad and I had plastered across our faces, "brave enough to buy this charming outfit. Not everyone can pull this off you know. You must have a very courageous wife, sir."

"Yeah," the old man beamed, "she's one in a million. I can't wait to see her face when she opens this baby up on Christmas morning."

"Oh, I'd pay to see that myself," the sales clerk smiled.

Dad felt so pleased to get such a great deal on Mom's present, that he actually paid to have it gift-wrapped, and soon the two of us were headed home with our treasure, so thrilled with our purchase that we stopped to treat ourselves to a couple of chili dogs. Funny how spending a few hours alone with Dad meant so much to me; they were rare moments in my childhood, and I really cherished them.

Christmas Eve finally arrived and, as usual, the Ritter kids were involved in the church Christmas Pageant. My folks were Sunday School teachers, and every year each class put on a skit for Christmas services. The old man loved it because it gave him an outlet for all his creativity that was, for the most part, ignored in a life full of military and family responsibilities. That year, he had the kids spell out the word "Christmas", with each kid holding a different letter of the word and explaining what it meant... "C is for the Christ child, born on Christmas day ..." and so forth. He'd borrowed the idea from an Eddie Arnold album that we had sung to for years, so we all knew the words, and sang it all the way to church that night.

"You know," the old man said as he drove toward the church, "Santa just might surprise you kids this year and come while we're away tonight."

"Mike says there is no Santa Claus," my younger brother, Mark, muttered from the backseat.

"I did not!" I protested.

"You 'did not' what?" The old man asked.

"Oh, nothing," I chirped. Good! He hadn't heard Mark. Maybe nobody else did either and I won't get blamed for blowing Christmas for my little sisters.

"Mark said that Mike said there is no such thing as Santa," my sister, Ruth Ann, whined. "Is that true, Daddy?"

"Mike's not as smart as he thinks he is," the old man growled, looking at me in the rearview mirror.

"I didn't say..."

"You may just be in for a little surprise tonight," the old man interrupted, "because I heard on the news that there are so many kids in the world asking for toys this Christmas, that old Santa Claus might be forced to make a few deliveries early this year."

Church service was the usual Christmas fare, and the "spelling bee" went off alright, even though the two "S's" tried to take the stage at the same time. We sang hymns in praise of Jesus Christ as we held our Christmas candles, but it was obvious that all the kids in the place had their minds on something other than the Savior's birth. You could see it in their eyes.

We sang everything from "The Little Drummer Boy" to "Jingle Bell Rock" on the drive home from church and, as we pulled into the carport, I was feeling pretty good about the whole evening. Not only had Dad snatched Santa Claus from the jaws of disbelief, but Mom seemed very happy, and would only get happier when she opened her new, glimmering, golden apparel.

"Think he's been here?" inquired Ruth Ann.

"Maybe," the old man slyly replied, as he turned the key in the front door lock. "Wish for it very hard, kids. Sometimes wishes come true, you know."

As Dad entered the room and flicked on the light, the Christmas tree suddenly lit up, sending the soft glow from the colored bulbs dancing across the shiny chrome handlebars of new bicycles, Barbie dolls, Suzy Homemaker ovens, GI Joes and, in the corner, leaning against the wall, a unicycle like the one The Monkees rode on TV! I couldn't believe my eyes! Toys littered the living room, the stockings were full, and the milk and cookies, the milk and cookies, were gone! He'd been here! Santa had been here!

My brother and sisters tore into the plethora of presents with a vengeance. I just stood there, unable to move. Something was wrong. There was no Santa Claus. I knew there was no Santa Claus. And yet...

"Oh ... Ray...it's so ... unique, isn't it?" Mom had opened the gilded gift and was holding the top against herself, as small flecks of gold lame floated to the floor.

The old man sidled up next to me and put his hand on my shoulder. "What's that phrase that you kids are always saying?" he said softly, as he watched his wife and children rummage through the brightly wrapped packages. "Keep the faith? Isn't that it, Michael? Nice words ... keep the faith."

I later learned that my folks had asked the next door neighbors to come over while we were at church and "play Santa Claus." But I'll never forget that Christmas because, for the first time, I realized that Santa Claus, like most wonderfully unexplainable beliefs, lives not in the mind, but in the heart. You see, I knew no jolly man sporting a white beard and wearing a red suit had been in the house that night—but I believed he had.

The unicycle was one of my favorite Christmas presents of all time. The mere status of owning one removed the necessity of ever having to actually ride the silly thing. It came with two poles, like ski poles, that were supposed to be used to help maintain balance but, after several hundred attempts and as many bounces off the pavement, I reached the conclusion that the best I could ever hope for was to look good standing next to it.

Mine was the first real television generation, and most of my "want list" reflected that. Over the years I'd requested, and received, a Have Gun Will Travel western set, a Lost in Space robot that yelled "warning, warning" and "look out, Will Robinson," and a Voyage to the Bottom of the Sea diving mask and snorkel, to name a few. But my all-time favorite was the James Bond Secret Agent 007 attaché case with hidden knife, exploding locks, and a handgun with attachable barrel and stock extensions. I'd put on my old, Sunday sport coat, wrap a tie around my neck, slip on some sunglasses, stick a candy cigarette in my mouth, and enter the suave, sophisticated world of England's greatest secret agent. Aside from Dracula, no one was cooler than Bond, James Bond.

No matter how poor Mom insisted we were, at Christmas we had more than our fair share of decorations and gifts. Every Christmas, that is, except one … my favorite Christmas. It was 1970. Dad had been transferred to Germany for the second time, and after living with my grandparents for several months while he found us a place to live, we followed him to the "fatherland" and moved into an old, drafty, stone house in the village of Kindsbach.

We had waited for months for an apartment in base housing to open up, but as December rolled around we were still in the stone house, without any of our personal belongings from the States. We were operating with borrowed everything, from forks to furniture, so as Christmas neared, a kind of depression set in with the realization that we'd be spending it without any of our decorations, Christmas records, or toys.

A few weeks before Christmas, Germans celebrate St. Nicholas Day. They place one of their shoes by the front door and, during the night, St. Nicholas comes calling. If a kid has been good all year, St. Nicholas fills the shoe with candy, but if the kid has been bad, he or she just receives a lump of coal and some sticks in the shoe. Mom insisted that we participate in this cultural event, so we all placed one shoe right outside the front door

(I guess she figured we could use the coal to heat the mausoleum we were living in), and went to bed wondering why any self-respecting German Saint would bother with a bunch of displaced American kids.

I was the first one awake the next morning (I always enjoyed getting up early enough to revel in a few minutes of solitude before the masses made their way down the stairs), and opened the front door. The ground was covered with a blanket of fresh snow, and icicles hung from the rooftops, glistening in the early morning light. And there, frozen to the cement, were our shoes, brimming with foil-wrapped chocolates and small plastic toys. As I pried the shoes from the cold concrete, my siblings came bounding down the stairs. "Check it out," I said, handing my brother and sisters their respective shoes, "St. Nicholas came last night."

We all emptied our shoes on the floor (Mark and I each got a small lump of coal along with our chocolates—St. Nicholas' sense of humor, I suppose), and just as the tinfoil was coming off the first piece of candy, we heard my parents' bedroom door open.

"Don't eat anything before breakfast," Mom yawned from the top of the stairs, rubbing the sleep from her eyes, "and close the front door, it's freezing in here!"

"Look, Mom," my sister yelled, holding out her shoe, "the German Santa Claus came last night."

"So I see," Mom smiled, as she bundled herself in her terrycloth housecoat. "I guess he didn't realize that a bunch of bad American kids live here."

By the next morning, the sun was again high in the sky, and the wonderful memory of the previous day melted with the snow. That night, Dad came home with a huge Christmas tree that he'd acquired from a German guy who worked with him at the base. It was a beautiful tree, but the thrill of getting it was tempered by the fact that our ornaments were still in transit. Being kids, we made the worst of the situation, and spent the days leading up to Christmas moping around the house, avoiding the naked fir tree that stood alone in a corner of the room.

On Christmas Eve, we came home from school to find Mom at the dining room table, surrounded by a big bowl of popcorn, some fresh cranberries, construction paper, tape, scissors, glue, glitter, and needles and thread. "C'mon, kids," she said, as we stood there looking at her with confused expressions on our faces. "We'll make our own decorations this year."

My three sisters immediately got into stringing popcorn and cranberries on thread, but Mark and I just shrugged and went into the living room to watch cartoons. We weren't going to have anything to do with it. Homemade decorations ... yeah, right ... we were going to have the worst looking Christmas tree ever. As we sat there watching Popeye, we could hear laughter coming from the kitchen. Mark stood up several times, but each time I would glare at him as if to say that we boys needed to stick together in our protest of this ill-fated attempt to revive our Christmas. But I guess their laughter was more powerful than his resentment, and within a few minutes he, too, had joined the rest of the family in making Christmas decorations, leaving me in front of the television to feed my depression alone.

As the sounds of joy coming from the kitchen increased, Sergeant McMullen appeared on the TV to read the news. I nonchalantly strolled into the other room to find my entire family drinking eggnog, a small mountain of popcorn and cranberry strands piled at their feet.

Even though I have a habit of biting off my nose to spite my face, I know a good time when I see it, and these people were having a good time. I really wanted to join in the festivities, but pride prevented my joyful participation, so I took the only route available to me.

"You know," I said, yanking a string of popcorn from my brother, "this would look better if you alternated popcorn and cranberries so you get a red and white effect. And Cyndy, make those strips of construction paper smaller so that you can make them into little rings, and they won't take up so much room on the tree. Can't you guys do anything right?"

Mom looked up from her handiwork and smiled at me. "You see, we need you, Michael. You're so creative, I'll bet you could make some really beautiful decorations without even trying."

I smiled back ... my way of thanking her for allowing me to take part, and for pardoning my bad attitude. We spent the next few hours stringing garlands out of construction paper and food products. Then, as we carefully wrapped them around the tree, it slowly started to take shape, the bare branches springing to life with each new strand of handcrafted decoration. We had just placed the last strand on the tree and stepped back to admire our creation when the front door swung open and in walked Dad, carrying what looked like a small suitcase under his arm.

"Look, Daddy," my youngest sister said, pulling on his pants leg, "we fixed the Christmas tree."

"You sure did, baby," the old man smiled. "It looks just beautiful. Reminds me of my Christmas tree back when I was a boy. When I was your age, we never bought any decorations for our tree, and I thought we always had the most beautiful tree in the neighborhood."

"What's that?" Mark asked, pointing at the small suitcase under Dad's arm.

"It's a record player I borrowed from the office. They won't need it tonight, and I thought we could use a little Christmas music around here."

"Too bad we don't have any of our Christmas records," I mumbled.

"There you go again, Michael, no faith in the spirit of Christmas," the old man said, as he hung his coat in the closet and slowly pulled out a large sack from way in the back. "Now who put these here?"

As Dad emptied the mysterious sack, we suddenly realized they were all there—every Christmas record we'd ever owned: Bing Crosby, Johnny Mathis, Brenda Lee, Paul Anka, Eddie Arnold, Joannie James ... all of them! It was a miracle!

"Your Mom kept these out when we left California," the old man smiled. "I guess she knew we'd be needing them."

That night, in the soft glow of small, white candles Mom had placed all around the living room, we sang to all our old Christmas favorites. As we went off to bed, I turned to look at the darkened living room and my parents holding one another, gazing at our Christmas tree. In that moment I finally realized what Christmas was all about. We had the most beautiful Christmas tree I'd ever seen, because our tree was decorated with love and, after all, that's the greatest gift anyone could ever receive on Christmas.

Chapter Ten
GI JIM

"Okay ... OUT OF THOSE RACKS YOU BUNCH OF PANSIES! THIS AIN'T YOUR KIND, OLD, GREY-HAIRED MOMMA TALKING ... YOU'VE GOT JUST SEVEN MINUTES ... THAT'S SEVEN MINUTES EXACTLY, GENTLEMEN ... TO MAKE UP THOSE BUNKS, GET TO THE LATRINE, AND LINE UP OUTSIDE FOR A TEN MILE HIKE. C'MON SWEETPANTS ... THIS MEANS YOU ... LET'S GO ... LET'S GO ... LET'S GO!"

I awoke in a cold sweat, my hands clenching the mattress, as I listened in the darkness to the pounding in my chest. Thank God! ... I was still in my Maid's Room, safe in Ramstein, Germany, nowhere near a boot camp. But just to make sure, I grabbed my chest ... felt my face ... yep, still here, it was merely a nightmare. Gripping the side of the bed with one hand, I slid my legs around until my feet touched the cold floor, intensifying the chills that were already running rampant through my body, the memory of the phantom image still fresh in my mind.

Although I grew up in an olive-drab world, my biggest fear, the terror that sent shudders crawling up my spine, was the thought of spending compulsory time as a soldier in the military. Even though Nixon had ended the draft, I'd known old Tricky Dick to change his mind before, so the thought of receiving that dreaded RSVP invitation from Uncle Sam continued to loom large in my seventeen-year-old consciousness. I simply dreaded the thought of ever having to serve my country in any way that had anything to do with the wearing of a uniform.

Now, before anyone gets their patriotic panties in a wad, let me say that I have the utmost respect for those individuals who choose to make a career in the armed forces. Granted, I only resided in the suburbs of military life but, even from my sheltered vantage point on the front porch, I can attest to the fact that it's not an easy existence. And believe me, I'd be doing the military a favor by turning down any request for a dance. It wouldn't work out ... no way. It'd be like mixing catsup and peanut butter ... you can do it, but don't expect anyone to smack his lips and come running. Basically, I just don't have it in me: I don't follow orders well, particularly those that don't make any sense; I'm not a team player; I don't have any John Wayne, apple pie, guns-for-God sentimentalities; I'm a picky eater; I don't look attractive in short hair; and my opinion of service to country runs more along the lines of liberating people from poverty and ignorance. I couldn't see myself worrying about whether some drill sergeant could see his ugly puss in the spit-shine of my nifty, black boots.

But all other reasoning pales in light of the real issue that kept me from ever wanting to turn in my blue jeans for a new, green wardrobe … the bathrooms. I'm an intensely private kind of guy—hell, I lock the bathroom door even when I'm alone in the house. I know, I know, it sounds silly, but it's true and, as we all know, a good soldier isn't a constipated soldier. There is no way I would ever be able to relieve myself while sitting right next to some guy, with nothing separating us but noxious fumes, as he reads me a letter from his girl back home. Nope, not me, wasn't going to happen. I'd rather explode. Needless to say, I have nothing against those guys who join the military; if not for them, there'd be no Ramstein and I'd be growing up in some Last Picture Show town, someplace in Iowa. I just have no desire to walk a mile (or ten) in their boots.

On any base, there's an unspoken rule that governs the interaction between government-issue personnel and we civilians, who are just along for the ride. The GIs try their damnedest to fit into our makeshift America, and we show the same resolve in keeping them at bay, away from our girlfriends and those areas of the base that we've claimed for our own. It's like oil and water … separately, they both have useful functions, but put them together and you've got the makings of an environmental catastrophe. The uneasy peace that presided over the base was under constant threat from these feelings of mistrust and prejudice and, much like a Southern town in the 1960s, the time was right for some brave soul to break out and challenge the status quo.

Unlike water, friendships can be drawn from dry wells … I realize that sounds like fortune cookie philosophy but, in this case, it is worthy of contemplation. For some reason, it's often those fortuitous meetings, the ones that start out with little more than a passing glance, that blossom into enduring kinships. Funny how that works. At any given moment, we may stumble across someone who will affect our lives in ways we couldn't have imagined. These are our mystical encounters which lie beyond the grasp of our reasoning, entities unto themselves which, given a chance to develop, can create circumstances that strike at the core of long-held beliefs and usher in fresh attitudes. Such was my encounter with Airman Second Class James T. Bronson.

Every Saturday night, our gang converged at the Rome Inn, an on-base pizza and beer joint that was clearly designed for the amusement of military personnel. While we were the first to gripe about any intrusions by the GIs into our domain, we rarely afforded them the same consideration as we invaded their territory with reckless abandon. The GIs clearly resented our incursion, but the military dishes discipline with a heavy hand, and we knew that the pleasure they'd get from hassling us wasn't worth the price they'd have to pay. So, even though we made full use of our advantage, our weekly raids onto their home turf usually went unchallenged.

It was a windy Saturday night in late autumn, and the group was congregated on the patio of the Rome Inn, busily slamming down Heinekens, under the sour stare of several GIs. Since I've always made it a rule to know my surroundings (a safety precaution, should I ever need to beat a hasty retreat), I scrutinized the area around us for potential peril. A few tables away, I noticed three dark, somber individuals who were staring in our direction. Rising from their table and traveling on the cool breezes that whisked around the patio umbrellas was the faint sound of Italian being spoken. The military often hired foreign nationals for the less desirable jobs on the base, primarily building maintenance and lawn care, and I figured these guys were fresh off the truck, lonely and full of resentment. Sitting alone at a corner table next to the Italians was the semblance of a man, his features difficult to discern under the dim party lights that were draped haphazardly around the patio.

"So then what happened?" Jessie asked, as she sat down with a fresh beer in her hand. "Did I miss anything?"

"Huh?" I responded, my room surveillance broken by the question.

"You were telling us how you and Rob are house-sitting for that friend of his father," Jessie recapped. "I told you to wait 'til I got back."

"Oh, yeah," I smiled, my train of thought restored, "the 'Playboy House'."

Rob's old man had a friend who was a professional bowler—why he was living in Germany, I have no idea—and he often toured Europe on the bowling circuit. This particular tour, he'd arranged for Rob and me to watch his place while he was away ... feed his cats, water his plants, stuff like that. The bowler was a single guy in his early thirties, who lived in a fairly large, two-story house that was decked out with all the "early-seventies hip" accoutrements: inflatable furniture; waterbeds; large, furry, overstuffed pillows; a bodacious stereo system; mirrored walls; stag films; even a slot machine that actually paid off now and then. It was a great place, a high school boy's vision of the life that awaited him just around the corner in the exciting world of bachelorhood. The house was located in a small village about thirty kilometers from the base, and Rob and I went over there every other day or so to fulfill our obligations and to take full advantage of the benefit package. Since we had promised to take a few of the gang out to the place after we left the Rome Inn, Jessie had been grilling us about the house.

"Well," I continued between swallows of brew, "then we went downstairs where we found a pool table, a bar, and these great posters showing couples in various sexual positions."

"Look," Jessie curtly interrupted as she touched up her lipstick, "don't get the idea that just because we agreed to go there with you guys we're gonna screw around with you. We just want to see the place because, personally," she grinned, smacking her lips together, "I think it's all bullshit."

"Bullshit, huh," Rob growled. "What's the bet?"

"I'm not betting you anything," Jessie grimaced.

"Not too sure of yourself are you, babe?" Rob chided. "C'mon ... I'll bet you thirty minutes alone with me that everything Mike's telling you is true," he continued, raising his eyebrows up and down like Groucho Marx.

"And what do I get if I win," Jessie smirked.

"That is what you get," Rob laughed while lighting a cigarette, "thirty minutes alone with me. If I win I get thirty minutes alone with you. What a deal, huh? Either way, you win."

"I'd rather kiss a horse's ass," Jessie retorted.

"Well, Rob's the closest thing we have to one," Tim grinned. "Sure he won't do?"

With the exception of Rob, of course, everyone got a good laugh from Tim's remark, but I was too busy eyeballing the table of Italians to take full advantage of the fun. Clearly, their resentment toward our merry little band was growing in direct proportion to our escalating cheer and, although there was every possibility I was being overly paranoid, I couldn't shake the uneasy feeling that we were headed for an international incident.

After another hour or so of carousing, the beer was starting to float my back teeth and I felt the need to make a pit stop. As I made my way to the opening in the patio fence that led to the restroom, I noticed one of the Italians coming toward me, a defiant look on his face. When our paths crossed, he purposely bumped into me, sending my bottle of Heineken crashing to the floor. While I've never run from a fight, I have been known to avoid them at any cost, so I apologized to my potential nemesis. But he seemed ready to rumble and, as I turned to continue my quest for necessary relief, he suddenly grabbed me by the shoulders and recklessly propelled me into a table of GIs, causing beer to splash all over them.

The situation grew ugly as the Italian held me against the table and assaulted me with a verbal barrage that sure sounded threatening, despite the fact that I couldn't understand a single syllable. The freshly beer-drenched GIs crowded around, egging on their new ally in their war against civilian slackers. My friends were oblivious to my plight, too busy having fun to trouble themselves with the near-death experience that I was having just a few tables away. As I struggled to break free from my attacker, he suddenly let go with a punch and, in an effort to protect myself, I thrust my hand in front of my face, catching his knuckle missile in mid-flight. My startled aggressor paused, his face contorted in amazement, obviously contemplating his next move. I was in shock, dumbfounded by my good fortune. Finally, a payback for all those hours spent watching bad Kung Fu movies. What talent … what ability … what dumb luck.

Out of the corner of my eye, I could see my assailant's buddies heading our way, apparently acting on the delusion that their friend needed help, and I readied myself for a beating with an international flavor. And then suddenly, from out of the blue, someone grabbed the Italian from behind, wrenched him upright, and cast him aside. I expected to see Rob, or Sean, or one of my other wayward friends, but when I stood up to thank my protector, I was struck speechless. Not only had my rescue been pulled off by the guy who had been sitting alone but, even more confounding, he was a GI.

Although he was a little guy, at least five inches shorter than me, his mettle caused the Mafia cavalry to stop dead in its tracks. The GIs who had been cheering my demise, were now jeering their fellow comrade for his fearless intervention, and the better-late-than-never platoon, my half-wasted friends, were at last amassing on the border, readying themselves for what was shaping up to be a world-class brawl.

Instead, something strange and downright miraculous happened … or didn't happen. Perhaps everyone in the room came to the realization, at exactly the same moment, that I wasn't worth an escalation to WWIII. Whatever the reason, and much to my astonishment, the incident ended as quickly as it had begun and, without uttering a word, the feuding factions slowly retreated to their respective corners.

"Thanks, man," I wheezed, turning to shake the hand of my new bodyguard, "thanks a lot. Don't know what I would have done if you hadn't come along. My name's Mike."

"Jim ... Jim Bronson," he replied, returning my greeting. "You looked like you could use a hand."

"Really?" I laughed. "Actually, I was just biding my time, waiting for the right opportunity."

"Which, I assume, would have been sometime before your face hit the floor?" Jim grinned.

"So, how long you been in the Air Force?" I queried.

"You can tell?" Jim anguished. "Oh, man ... you can tell? Damn."

"It's the hair." I smiled. "Only GIs and geeks wear their hair that short, and you handle yourself too well to be a geek, so ..."

"Two years," Jim solemnly replied.

"Huh?"

"Two years. I've been in two years. Two years of kissing ass, playing Johnny Soldier Boy. I fuckin' hate it."

Alright, a rebellious GI with an attitude. Could be the beginning of a beautiful friendship.

"C'mon," I coaxed, "I'll buy you a beer ... least I can do to show my appreciation. So, why'd you enlist if you hate it so much?"

We sat at the end of the bar, and I listened while Jim gave me the Readers Digest version of his life story. He was twenty years old, he'd grown up in Orlando, Florida, and his parents couldn't afford to send him to college. So, like countless other guys his age, he'd agreed to barter four years of his life for a college education through the GI Bill. He'd served two years, absolutely hated the military, and had started counting down the days to freedom from the moment he'd faced the flag, with other freshly sheared recruits, to swear allegiance to God, country, and his new, albeit desperate, career move. A certain sadness colored his words, and I could tell that he regretted the daily hypocrisy imposed upon him by economic circumstance.

I slurped down the last of my beer. "C'mon," I said, "I'll introduce you to the rest of the gang."

Jim slowly returned his glass to the table. "Oh, I don't know," he stammered, "maybe some other time."

"You've got something better to do?" I sarcastically replied. "Boots that need shined or something? C'mon ..."

"No, it's not that," Jim interrupted, "it's the GI thing. I'd feel like such a ... meat."

"Meat?" I repeated. "What's a meat?"

"You know," Jim grinned, "a dick, a meat ..."

"Tell you what," I smirked, throwing a dollar on the bar, "you just come over to our table. There are so many 'meats' over there now, one more won't make any difference."

As I herded Jim in the direction of my partying friends, I felt strangely like Little Bo Peep, gently returning a stray to the fold; but, judging from the raucous behavior of my companions, I hoped I wasn't also leading a lamb to slaughter.

When Jim and I arrived at the table, Jessie and Rob were at each other's throats about something pointless, as usual. "Who's the skinhead?" Rob demanded, interrupting his taunting long enough to glance up at my new, hair-challenged friend. "What's the deal, Mike? Is this national Adopt a GI Week, or somethin'?"

"Listen up, guys," I smiled, placing my hand on Jim's shoulder. "This is Jim, the guy who came to my rescue while the rest of you were busy playing with yourselves."

"I resent that," Rob laughed. "I was playing with Tim."

"Bite me, Mathison," Tim responded as he stood up and leaned across the table to shake Jim's hand. "Pay no attention to him, Jim," he continued, "Rob was born with a handicap ... his brain's in his butt."

"Yeah," Jessie snickered, hungrily eyeballing Jim like he was a piece of prime rib, "don't mind Rob ... or, as we affectionately call him, Mr. Shit-for-Brains. By the way, my name's Jessie," she cooed, as she began to massage Jim's hand in hers, "but you can call me ... as often as you like."

"Down, Fido," Rob huffed, seemingly annoyed by Jessie's flirtations. "Give the guy a chance to sit down before you try to jump into his lap."

"Woof, woof," Jessie coyly replied, still clutching Jim's hand. "Why don't you have a seat right here next to me?"

Jim had this weird, glazed-over expression on his face, a perfect combination of sheer horror and machismo pride, as if his mother had just found a condom in his wallet. "Uh, sure," he stuttered, "nice to meet you."

"Would that be m-e-e-t or m-e-a-t?" I chuckled, nudging Jim in the side with my elbow.

"What'd you say?" Jessie asked.

"Private joke," I chortled, as Jim slid into the seat beside Jessie. "Why don't you introduce him to everybody, Jessie ... it's critical that I take a leak."

I returned from the restroom to find my friends in a state of heightened excitement. "Jim says he can get us into the Airman's Club," Rob beamed. "This is gonna be great! Maybe I'll get lucky and pick up a nurse or something! I always wanted to make it with an older woman."

"Or any woman, for that matter," was Jessie's retort, as she cozied up even closer to Jim.

Now, unbeknownst to the gang, my old man had just started his latest in a series of second jobs ... this time, as a bouncer at the Airman's Club. The father of one of my school chums was the manager of the club, so when the old man was in need of some additional income to get our family through the upcoming Christmas rush, I hooked the two of them up, and Dad began his temporary career as a strong arm for the USO. Three nights a week, the old man would slip into his official "tough guy" uniform—a white shirt, black bow tie, and black slacks. Truth be told, Dad was not cut out for the job ... the man doesn't have a violent bone in his body, and the get-up made him look about as threatening as a waiter in a cheap restaurant. But his peaceful nature took a back seat to whatever would ensure a good Christmas for his family, so Mom began an eight-week vigil of pacing the living room floor, wondering if her pacifist husband would arrive home in one piece. Even though I shared most everything with my friends, I had purposely left them in the dark about Dad's new career. Quite frankly, I knew too well that they would quickly try to pressure me into using my club connection to sneak in nine or ten "underagers", while expecting my father to look the other way. Besides, I preferred that Dad think of me as a slightly twisted Wally Cleaver, rather than the party animal that I was. But Jim's invitation was about to change all that, so I reluctantly pasted a counterfeit grin on my face and joined my friends in their moment of revelry.

Fifteen minutes later, looking as out of place as Klansmen at a Black Panther meeting, we arrived at the Airman's Club. On the door, a sign with large, stenciled letters warned, "RESTRICTED TO UNAUTHORIZED PERSONNEL." "Well, that's it," I bogusly bemoaned. "We can't go in."

"Just wait a minute," Rob scowled. "I'm not giving up that easy. It says 'unauthorized personnel' ... I think that's a loop-hole. I mean, who could be more unauthorized than us?"

"True, true," Tim grinned. "This isn't a warning ... it's an invitation."

"Hold on," Willie cautioned as he backed away from the door. "That's bullshit. It means we can't go in."

Tim walked over to the sign, and pointed to each word as he read it aloud, "Restricted to unauthorized personnel ... that means only unauthorized personnel are allowed in."

"I dunno," argued Willie. "Why would they put up a sign to tell us we can go in?"

Jim extricated himself from Jessie's vise-like grip long enough to open the door. "It's the military, man ... nothing makes sense. Don't worry about it, I'll vouch for you."

The repugnant combination of liquor and cut-rate cologne filled our senses as we each hesitantly entered the club. The front door opened into a narrow, dimly-lit hallway that emptied into an enormous room illuminated by blinking, multicolored lights. The clamor of many voices talking at once, combined with the deafening rhythms generated by the band, made it nearly impossible to hear one another, so we followed Jim as he led us toward an open area by the bar. I had gone only a few feet when a hand gripped my shoulder from behind, followed by the words, "What are you doing here, boy?"

Without even turning around, I knew it was Dad.

He had me, the fuse was lit, and there was nothing I could do except wait for the impending explosion.

"Having a good time?"

Hmmm ... not exactly what I'd expected, but it suddenly occurred to me that if I pretended to take his question seriously, I might be able to throw him off guard and buy some time. "Hey, Pop," I nonchalantly responded. "Actually, I just got here, so let the good times begin. Looks like a happening place." I glanced at Dad out of the comer of my eye, as I continued to survey the crowd. His cryptic expression was hard to read, but since he wasn't yet escorting me out, I figured I might be able to avoid a humiliating scene in front of my friends. Taking a step forward and grabbing the comers of Dad's bow tie with my fingertips, I attempted to compliment him into submission. "Man, quite the threads, huh? Got this kinda savoir faire thing goin' ... looks good on ya," I brown-nosed.

"Uh-huh," the old man nodded skeptically. "Now, how 'bout cutting the crap and getting out ..."

"Have you met Jim?" I deflected, while endeavoring to attract the attention of my new Government-Issue buddy. "He's in the Air Force too ... just met him tonight. Jim ... hey, Jim, c'mon over here and meet my old man."

Probably not a good idea. Without considering the consequences, I'd involved Jim in my parental dispute, and inadvertently implicated him as the responsible party for my presence at the club. I could literally see Jim's body slump as his eyes widened in disbelief, and I knew he was feverishly searching for a way out.

Jim dubiously dragged his weary body to the spot where we stood, never taking his eyes off my old man. Several steps before he reached us he thrust out his hand in greeting, and before my father knew what hit him, Jim grabbed Dad's hand and began pumping his limp arm, like he was priming a well. "Nice to meet you, sir," Jim beamed, "Mike speaks very highly of you."

"At ease, Airman," the old man said, a faint smile curling across his lips. "Save the bullshit lines for your date. You responsible for my son being here?"

"Just following orders, sir," Jim replied, as he took a step back.

"Orders?" the old man barked. "What orders? Somebody ordered you to bring my kid and his friends in here?"

"The sign, sir," Jim quickly explained, "on the door. It says 'restricted to unauthorized personnel,' so I thought this must be a special night, like Civilian Night or something."

"Civilian Night?" Dad pressed, tilting his head to one side. "And what exactly would Civilian Night be?"

Jim shifted from one foot to the other several times while contemplating his response. "You know, sir," he finally clarified, "doing our part for base morale by bringing a civilian to the Airman's Club. The sign said 'restricted to unauthorized personnel', so I figured …"

"Before you sink any deeper," the old man interjected, holding his hand up in front of Jim, "you should know that I'm not as stupid as the guy who painted that sign. I know what the sign says, and I know what the sign means, and I know you know. If you were that big an imbecile, you'd be in the Army. So let's just can all this unauthorized, Civilian Night horse-shit."

"Yes, sir," Jim stammered.

Then, Dad floored us both when he turned to me and said, "Here's the deal, Mike. I haven't seen you, I don't know you, and if you get into any trouble I'll throw you and your buddies out of here so fast, you'll leave skid marks on the sidewalk with your butts. Now, have a good time."

Jim and I stood motionless, jaws dropped, looking at one another in amazement. "Hey, Mike," the old man shouted back as he walked away, "you really like this outfit?"

We spent the next hour pounding down rum and cokes and fending off advances from a pack of Airmen who were circling our table, drooling over the girls like The Big Bad Wolf and five of his closest friends at a Little Red Riding Hood convention. The Airman's Club mirrored the racial unrest back in the States, and an atmosphere of "separate but equal ... but, definitely separate" prevailed that was fascinating to watch—in a carnival freak show sort of way. The African-American GIs, dressed in their finest "Superfly" ensembles, took ten minutes to greet one another with a flurry of hand gyrations that would stupefy even the most experienced of major league baseball coaches, but barely acknowledged their white counterparts, who sported love beads and short hair, parted down the middle and stretched over their ears, in order to make it appear longer. Any interaction between the two factions was usually initiated by some pointless disagreement, more befitting eight-year-olds in a playground brawl. It was definitely a testy situation, a melting pot about to boil over, and every once in a while I'd cast a concerned eye at my old man, in the knowledge that in case of a fire, he was the guy who'd be left holding the hose.

The evening rocked along in typical fashion for a while: Jim was happily playing grab-ass with a very affectionate Jessie; Rob and Tim were hustling the waitresses; the other girls in our group were relishing the flirtatious attentions of a plethora of horny Airmen; and Willie, leaning nervously back in his chair with his arms folded, was waiting for something terrible to happen. He didn't have to wait long.

Just as the evening's entertainment, a band called The Funky Chickens, was breaking into a rendition of the theme song from Shaft, the clamor of people screaming at one another on the dance floor split the air. As I strained to discern what was happening, I could see Dad wading into the fray. I sprang from my chair, grabbed Jim, Rob, and Tim, and the four of us headed for the dance floor.

Suddenly, the houselights came up and, from my vantage point at the back of the amassing horde, I could see Dad engaged in a verbal confrontation with a very large black man. We inched our way through the swarm of angry spectators, and just as we were closing in on the old man, he was being threatened with the words, "How'd you like me to punch you in that straight nose of yours?"

Dad made no response. He simply turned around and strode back through the thick throng of jeering Airmen assembled near the dance floor, and into a small office located at the back of the club. Several tense minutes passed before he reappeared, a baseball bat gripped in his hands. I was sweating bullets, but the old man appeared unflappable as he wound his way through the crowd, returning to confront the large, menacing Airman who, only moments before, had volunteered to give him a free nose job.

Dad stood before his antagonist, gently tapping the bat against his open hand. "What do you think you're gonna do with that?" his foe challenged. "Oh, nothing," the old man said softly, "unless I have to."

The large, young Airman laughed, "Yeah ... you and what Army?"

It was one of those nightmarish moments, the kind every kid imagines but never expects to happen. My old man was right next door to getting his ass kicked, and all I could think about was how mad Mom would be when she learned I was here when it happened. As I searched my soul for some sliver of courage, a voice from behind me responded to the barbarous Airman's gauntlet, "What Army? Well, me for starters." The voice belonged to Jim, and without a moment's hesitation, he slithered through the throng of sweaty bodies and took his place at my old man's side.

Dad gave Jim an appreciative smile; then, returning his attention to his potential assailant, scowled, "I don't need an Army, chief. I've got the Mangler on my side."

The angry Airman took a step forward, pointed at Jim, and through clenched teeth defiantly thundered, "You're gonna need more than this scrawny puke and a bat with a cute name to keep me from bouncing you off the floor."

"Oh, this ain't the Mangler," Dad placidly replied, as he handed the bat to Jim and motioned to the club manager, who was standing in the back of the room. "This is."

With that, an enormous black and grey German shepherd bounded through the crowd, and stopped right at the feet of my old man. Growling through slobber-dripping jaws, the dog shook with intensity as Dad gently stroked the head of his fur-covered protector. "Meet the Mangler," Dad grinned, as the young Airman backed away. "He's kind of the bouncer's bouncer."

Dad continued to massage the dog's head, then abruptly said, "Mangler, stage." With those two words, the huge dog darted through the crowd and jumped on the stage, causing the band to dive for cover. "Here's how this is going to work," the old man said, his voice calm and devoid of emotion. "Mangler's going to sit on the stage, and the band's not going to play again until you make tracks out of here."

"And what if I don't," the now jittery Airman asked.

"Well, then," Dad grinned, "I guess Mangler's in for one hell of a dinner tonight."

At that point, several of the black Airman's friends joined in the argument. "You're just doing this because my man's a brother," one of them yelled. "If he was a white guy, you'd never call in the dogs."

"Not true," Dad responded, "white meat, dark meat, it doesn't matter to the dog ... or to me. Now, what's it going to be, chief?"

Several laborious minutes ticked by while the Airman contemplated his situation. At last, he brusquely hollered, "Okay, straight nose, you win ... this time."

The crisis abated, my limp backbone miraculously stiffened and I joined Jim and my old man at the center of the dance floor. As the Airman and his buddies headed toward the front door, I couldn't resist the temptation to redeem myself by adding my own little insult to their injury. "You got away lucky this time, boy," I retorted.

Stupid, stupid, stupid thing to say. I hadn't meant it as an inflammatory racist remark. I used the word 'boy' all the time, but it was enough to send the fuming Airman rushing back through the crowd while bellowing, "Who you calling 'boy'?"

"Damn, Mike," the old man muttered under his breath. "Thanks ... thanks a lot."

At once, the whole club erupted into threats, as white and black Airmen formed two separate groups on either side of the dance floor. Mangler was barking his head off and the air was thick with hostility, when Jim bravely stepped forward, his arms raised in the air. "Hold it you guys," he shouted, "just hold it a minute."

There we were ... the three of us, with no place to run, surrounded by angry Airmen. Jim persisted in his struggle to quiet the mob. "It ain't worth it," he pleaded, "you guys really want to give the man a reason to close this place down, just because of some brainless remark made by this retarded freak?"

The incensed mob continued to close in on the three of us, our circle of safety shrinking with each advance.

"He's just a jerk-off kid," Jim admonished, "let it go. Listen, I'm one of you guys, so I know what a pain in the ass these little civilian bastards can be, but I'm telling you, it ain't worth it. Kick his ass now, and spend the night as guests of the Military Police. I don't know about you," he grinned leeringly at Jessie, "but I've got better plans for the rest of the evening."

I could actually feel my asshole tense up as I waited for the response to Jim's entreaty, but remarkably, at long last, the mob slowly dissipated. With a cue from Dad, the band again began to play while keeping a watchful eye on their new, four-legged band member, who still sat motionless on the stage.

"On behalf of retarded freaks everywhere," I laughed as I patted Jim on the back, "let me just say thanks for keeping me from getting killed ... for the second time tonight."

"No problem," Jim panted, his composure regained. "No problem at all."

Dad approached Jim, his hand extended in gratitude, and said, "Thanks, Jim. Quick thinking. Nice to know my son has at least one friend with a few brains."

"I take them out for a walk now and then," Jim quipped as he shook Dad's hand. I felt like crawling into a hole, embarrassed by my hesitation to come to Dad's aid, and ashamed of the feelings of resentment that bubbled through my chest as I watched Jim and the old man become instant friends, comrades in arms.

Through splits in the shadows, I could see my father plodding toward the office and, as he slipped into the crack of light that flickered beyond the door, I knew there was more on his mind than a few drunk Airmen.

My focus on Dad's plight was cut short when Jim sidled up beside me and declared, "Your Dad's pretty cool, Mike. Brave too ... I don't think my old man ..."

"He hates it," I angrily lamented, my eyes still fixed on the office door. "Hates everything about it ... the fights, the drunks, the late hours. He doesn't belong here."

"Then why...?" Jim asked.

"Commitments, man ... he's got a wife and five fuckin' kids," I spit the words through gritted teeth. "And the goddamn Air Force doesn't pay for shit, that's why. He's always had to work some crummy second job to make ends meet ... and, with Christmas coming next month ..."

"He can't quit," Jim quietly finished my thought, as if speaking from personal experience. "I understand."

"How could you understand?" I snapped at Jim. "Just go back and play grab ass with Jessie, I'm gonna go talk to my father."

As I turned to walk away, Jim grabbed my shoulder and whispered, "He'll be okay, man. Leave him alone right now ... it's not your burden."

I swung sharply around and glared at Jim. "He's my old man," I shouted, "not yours! What do you know about it?"

Jim smiled and pulled his wallet from his back pocket. With all the finesse of Sergeant Friday on Dragnet, he flipped open the leather case. "See this?" he demanded, pointing at his green military I.D. card.

"No, I'm fuckin' blind," I sarcastically roared. "Of course I see it. So what?"

"This defines me now," Jim sighed, as he rubbed the small, laminated card between his thumb and forefinger, "and that's my burden. I mean, it's great that I get to see Germany and all, and there are times, like tonight, when I'm even glad I joined the Air Force. But, there's always the bullshit that goes with it ... the Yin and Yang, the good and bad, the trade-off."

"Yeah, well, that's your problem," I scowled unsympathetically. "Everything costs. What's it got to do with my old man?"

"This little piece of plastic certifies my membership in the armed forces of these United States," Jim grinned, and threw me a mock salute, "with all the responsibilities and privileges contained therein. Yes, sir," he continued, flicking the laminated card with his finger, "this is my ticket to a world of new experiences: scrubbing down a latrine with a toothbrush; wearing my hair like Curley from The Three Stooges; living in a barracks with two hundred other guys; pulling guard duty at two-thirty in the morning ... in the cold ... in the rain. But, there's money for college at the end of the tunnel."

"Okay, Gomer Pyle," I impatiently cut in, "so, what's your point?"

"It's all payback for the good things in life," Jim replied, and slid his wallet back into his pocket. "As you said, everything costs. Your old man's working here to pay the tab for the life he chose ... a wife, kids, nice stuff, a career in the military ... it's a burden, man, but it's his burden. So, why don't you let him decide the best way to carry it." And with that, Jim melted into the crowd.

"Hey chief," my dad's voice boomed from behind me, "I thought you'd have had enough of this place by now." I turned to see the weary face of my father, who was rubbing his eyes. "Damn smoke really gets to me."

"Rough night, huh Pop?" I quietly commented.

"Oh, yeah, but you do what you've gotta do. Listen, bud," the old man winked, "if you get home before I do, tell your mom to wait up for me, and that I said I'm not 'too tired' ... she'll know what I mean."

I couldn't believe it. Here I was feeling sorry for my father, and he had already put the evening behind him, choosing instead to appreciate what awaited him at home. It was a poignant moment—the vision of my parents having sex notwithstanding—one that made me reappraise Jim's words of wisdom. If he was right about having to pay the tab for the life we choose, Dad didn't appear to have any problem with the bill. Maybe that's what life is all about ... tradeoffs, compromises, a view of the big picture, and a willingness to pay for fulfilled dreams. Maybe we're all sent into this world on individual quests for happiness, and the real challenge isn't to rid your life of burdens, but to respect them as blessings, paths to ultimate fulfillment, and worthy of momentary sacrifice.

My revelation was put on hold by Rob's shouting in my ear, "C'mon, Ritter, I'm taking everybody to the 'Playboy House'."

"If we get caught," I muttered, "your old man will kill us."

"Yeah, I know," Rob smirked, "but hey ... everything costs."

Rather than convoy the thirty kilometers to the 'Playboy House', we all piled into Jim's 1966 Volkswagen van, and it took the better part of an hour to reach our destination. We spent the rest of the evening in teen heaven, bouncing on the inflatable furniture, playing the slot machine, drinking beer, watching bad, 8mm skin flicks, and generally being rowdy. Until that night, there had been no romantic involvement within our circle, but Jim and Jessie couldn't avoid taking a dip in the waterbed, which served to solidify Jim's groundbreaking membership in the club.

Over the next few weeks, Jim became a fixture at my house. My sisters, especially Cyndy, thought he was adorable; Dad considered him a stable, mature addition to my usual gang of misfits; and Mom, well, Mom saw Jim as a little, misplaced duckling and lost no time in taking him under her wing. While I often felt as though Mom didn't have the time or patience for me, the same couldn't be said of her manner towards my friends. She was the back-up Mom, a pinch hitter who would do things for my buddies that their own mothers were either too busy or unwilling to do. The woman spent hours "pegging" my friends' pants, an arduous process of turning the garment inside out and stitching another seam up the inside of the legs, so that, when worn, the pants fit so tightly that the wearer strode around with all the agility of a person in a full-body cast. But that was the style, and although Mom thought it quite stupid, it did, after all, appeal to her fashion consciousness.

Dad must have made enough during his temporary career as a bouncer, because Christmas arrived with the usual fanfare, and Jim spent the holiday as an adopted member of the Ritter family. To show his appreciation, Jim generously bought gifts for each member of my family, and joined in our family tradition of singing Christmas songs, with the room lit only by the dim glow of the tree lights. On Christmas Eve, Jim even danced with Mom, much to the glee of my starry-eyed little sisters. He was patient and kind, the big brother that my brother Mark and I never had. But the biggest plus to hanging out with Jim was that my folks trusted him ... knowledge that I used to my advantage later that night, when I asked if I could join Jim on a weekend ski trip to Austria.

In truth, I'd never been skiing in my life, but that wasn't my true motivation for wanting to go anyway. While Jim spoke excitedly about swooshing down snow-covered slopes, I envisioned cozy nights in front of a fireplace at a ski lodge, the aroma of warm brandy wafting through the air. I'd be feigning a twisted ankle and regaling blonde ski-bunnies with tales of winter sports feats that I'd never have to prove.

Our transportation for the nine-hour trip to Austria was Jim's VW van, a blue and primer-colored bucket of bolts that he managed to assure my folks was more reliable than it looked, even though it was held together by rust. There was actually a hole in the floor on the passenger's side, enabling the co-pilot not only to direct the route, but also to give a colorful description of everything that the van ran over along the way.

On December 28, a clear, bitterly cold day, we left with high hopes, a little money, too many clothes, and no tire chains. As we skidded away on the ice-covered street, I waved goodbye to my folks while shouting through near-frozen lips, "Don't worry about me ... Jim knows what he's doing."

We'd been on the road about forty-five minutes when we heard the van's first aberrant sound, a sort of high-pitched whining that seemed to originate from the back of the vehicle, and followed shortly by a loud, clunking clatter. Jim slid the van to a stop and hopped out to study the problem, returning after several minutes to say that he didn't see anything wrong. The engine turned over and, with a shrug of his well-insulated shoulders, Jim slowly maneuvered the van back onto the Autobahn and we merrily continued down the road, opting not to worry.

Outside, the air was freezing, and the van's small heater worked overtime to combat the gusts of frosty wind that whipped through the hole in the floorboard. To take our minds off the fact that our legs were going numb, we sang along with a tape of the soundtrack from *American Graffiti*, and played "guess the pavement stain," but with each mile the air seemed more frigid, until all we could muster up for entertainment was an occasional chatter of teeth, followed by outbursts of shuddering laughter.

I'd just about adjusted my internal temperature dipping below the freezing mark when we came upon a series of narrow, two-lane mountain passes that would lead us up the snow-encased peaks to the warmth of our ski resort. A stream of cars meandering up the mountainside, following each other so closely that it appeared one vehicle was actually pushing the one in front of it. The only thing between us and a plunge down the sheer cliff was a bank of hardened snow. This was definitely an "enter at your own risk" situation, and even though I was on the verge of turning blue, I drew comfort from the fact that we were on the last leg of our journey and the engine was still chugging along so at least...

KABLAM! Kerchunk ... kerchunk ... kerchunk ... I looked at Jim, he looked at me ... wheeeezzzz ... palump! Abruptly, the engine turned up its toes and died. By that point, I wished I could do the same, but I had lost all hope of ever regaining the feeling in my toes. Jim sat motionless, his arms resting on the steering wheel, staring at the Mercedes in front of us as it continued up the steep road, its white, crystallized exhaust smoke engulfing our van.

When faced with a crisis, people often show true compassion. In this case, however, it took about thirty seconds before they registered their concern with a chorus of squealing car horns and multilingual curses. There was nothing we could do. The van wouldn't budge, and there was no way to turn it around. Besides, we had been lucky to make it this far on semi-bald tires, and moving the bus from a dead stop would be nearly impossible. "Well," Jim sighed, "looks like we have two options ... leave the van here and hitchhike back home, or ..."

It was the "or" that worried me.

"... you push the van and get it rolling, while I pop the clutch and try to start the engine."

These were dubious plans, at best, and reminded me of the adolescent game "Would You Rather" ... "Would you rather slide down a giant razor blade, naked, into a pot of boiling oil, or drink a bucket of spit?" Both options were painful and nonsensical, and we kids rolled with laughter at the absurdity of having to choose between horrible and unthinkable. But I wasn't laughing now, as I envisioned myself and the van rolling right off the cliff. And besides, the latter plan involved my running alongside the van, and the only part of my body that was apt to be running in a temperature this low was my nose. Maybe I was being overly pessimistic, but the possibility that I could muster the Herculean strength to push the van up a mountainside, with enough speed for Jim to jumpstart the engine, was about as remote as ... well, as my being able to push a van up a mountainside! It just wasn't going to happen. "You're kidding, right?" was all I could offer.

"Okay," Jim said, while engaging the emergency brake, "you stay in here, and I'll push."

My mind was immediately filled with terrifying visions of the van, tobogganing wildly over the edge with me in it, hurling down several hundred feet, and slamming onto the jagged rocks below. I made a quick decision that, as cold as it was outside, I'd rather take my chances with the snow than risk being forever entombed in a frozen hunk of twisted metal. "No, no," I said with false bravado, "I'll do it. Just be careful, huh?"

I climbed out of the van, opened the sliding panel door and, gripping the glacial frame with my gloved hands, pushed hard against the vehicle. It didn't even budge, which is more than I can say about my foothold, since I promptly slipped on the frozen ground and slid under the van.

I lay on the ice-covered road, staring up at the bottom of the bus for several seconds before I heard Jim yelling, "Mike, Mike … you okay? Where are you?" Like a reluctant groundhog, I peered up at Jim through the hole in the van's floorboard. "Oh, just peachy," I snarled sarcastically. "Want me to change the oil while I'm down here?"

Jim stared down at me through frosty glasses, and shook his head. His face was bundled up like an Egyptian mummy, but I managed to hear the muffled words, "Hmmm, that didn't work too well, did it? Wanna try it again?"

As I climbed out from under our stalled van, the burgeoning parade of cars behind us was on the second verse of its bleating-horn serenade. I resumed my post beside the open door, Jim assumed a position on the other side of the van, and the two of us pushed against the frozen metal, carefully inching the dilapidated vehicle forward with each shove.

Now, I've tilted at a few windmills in life, and I don't mind losing the good fight, but it didn't take long to realize that all the intestinal fortitude in the world wasn't going to be enough to shove this metal iceberg up the mountain. "This is bullshit, Jim," I wheezed, my breath freezing into puffs of smoke. "Why don't you try the engine again?"

Jim obliged, happy to have an excuse to return to his meat locker on wheels. He gazed toward the heavens and mumbled a silent prayer, while slowly turning the ignition key. The engine made a valiant effort, and managed to choke out a few half-hearted, grinding spurts before it went silent, taking my evaporating hopes with it.

Through the frost-laden windows, I could see Jim slumped in his seat, his forehead pressed against the steering wheel. Trudging up to the door, I swung it open and offered the only words of consolation I could call up. "Maybe it's just out of gas."

Jim hesitantly raised his head and pried his nearly frozen hand from the steering wheel. He wiped a thin layer of ice from the small gas gauge on the metal dashboard, thereby revealing the tiny bent arrow that pointed to "E".

"That's it," Jim cheered, "we're out of gas!" He leapt from the van and the two of us hugged each other and jumped up and down, spinning in a small circle while singing, "We're only out of gas, we're only out of gas!"

I guess, as with most things in life, disasters are also measured on a sliding scale, because suddenly our desperate journey had taken a turn for the better. Although we were still stuck on a mountain, in a snowstorm, with an empty gas tank, a ray of sunshine had given us cause for momentary jubilation. "Okay, okay," Jim grinned, "let's get a grip. Look in the back of the van for something to hold gas, and we can panhandle for fuel."

We rifled through our belongings, searching frantically for anything that could be used to transport gas, and finally settled on a thermos and a pair of rubber boots. That took care of the containers, but we still needed a way to siphon fuel from the gas tank to the receptacles, so we detached the hose from a small air pump, and cut off the ends to create an 18-inch tube. Giddy with renewed hope, we gathered our makeshift supplies and set off on our quest for self serve gasoline.

With heads bowed against the bone-chilling wind and driving snow, we stopped at the first car of irritated travelers and tapped sheepishly on the window. The driver rolled his window down, but before we could spit out even a few plaintive words, he started yelling at us in broken English, "*Nein, nein,* I no want to buy your boots. Your auto, go, go ... *schnell,* hurry ... go mit your auto." We smiled politely and, through chattering teeth, tried to explain that we weren't selling rubber boots, but he dismissed us with a wave of his hand and rolled up the window, taking the short blast of warmth from his car heater with him. We knocked on several more windows without success, before finally approaching an elderly couple from England.

"Bit of a sticky situation, say what," the driver grinned, "but I suppose I can spare a few drops of petrol to help out you young Yanks."

Jim stuck the small hose into the gas tank and sucked until the life-saving fluid appeared, while I held a rubber boot under the fuel door, in anticipation of victory. We filled the two rubber boots and the thermos, thanked our host, and trudged back to the van, leaving a trail of dripping gasoline behind us.

"God," I silently prayed, "please, please let this work. If you let this work, I swear I'll never … I'll never … uh, just let it work, okay?" It was the best I could do … I saw no point in compounding my difficulty with a promise I couldn't keep.

By now, the snow was coming down in sheets. As I carefully poured the gas into the dry tank, Jim yanked open the frozen car door, crunched down on the frigid front seat, and cautiously turned the ignition key. The engine whined, sputtered, and then wondrously filled the air with a loud varoom. Success! We were moving! We had achieved movement and, at that moment, everything was right with the world. Like the astronauts on Apollo 13, we had repaired our marooned vehicle with only the materials we had on board —along with a little help from our friends. As the feelings of relief and joy warmed our nearly frozen bodies, an audible cheer echoed through the hills from the freed wayfarers trapped behind us.

"Oh, man," Jim grinned, "are we lucky, or what?"

"Oh, yeah," I shuddered, "luckiest guys on earth. Let those other people enjoy their heated cars, dry clothes, and hot chocolate; we've got a pair of rubber boots!"

"Yeah," Jim chuckled, "never leave home without them."

Thirty minutes later, we arrived at a rest area and service station. While we filled the van's tank with gas, the cars that had been stuck behind us sped past. One by one, they honked their horns in a salute to our stamina. We'd had a "grasping victory from the jaws of defeat" moment, and neither of us would soon forget it. Buoyed by our triumph, we gleefully proceeded up the winding road for another two hours. Just as the darkness of night overtook the twilight shadows, we coasted into the parking lot of our ski lodge. Sanctuary! We'd made it!

Lights from the building illuminated the chair lift and the few adventurous souls still gliding down the mountainside toward the warmth and comfort of the ski lodge. Smoke billowed from the lodge's chimney, creating a sheer, white blanket against the star-suffused sky. We checked into our room, and as I collapsed on one of the beds I heaved a sigh of relief, knowing that the worst was behind me.

I should have known better.

The next morning, we found the dining room and hungrily gulped down a continental breakfast of hot tea, cheese, and hard rolls slathered with fresh, homemade jam and real, calories-off-the-chart butter. We were in a hurry because we still had to go into the village to rent skis, boots, and all the other necessary accoutrements, so at least we could appear to know what we were doing out on the slopes.

"I'm gonna get some black skis with red stripes to match my ski jacket," I grinned at Jim, as small crumbs of buttered bread fell from my lips and bounced across the white linen tablecloth. "Gotta look good out there."

Jim smiled and took another sip of the warm herbal tea. "Maybe you oughta concentrate on getting the best beginner skis you can, no matter what color they are," he advised.

"Oh," I smirked, leaning back in my chair, "skis, shmeeze—who cares? I mean, how hard can it be? All you gotta do is keep your legs together and slide down the hill ... what's the big deal? It's much more important to look the part than it is to play it. Just take me to the top of the mountain, point me in the right direction and, in no time, I'll be skiing like James Bond in *Her Majesty's Secret Service*."

"As I recall," Jim laughed and pushed away from the table, "007 got buried by an avalanche in that movie."

"Details," I grinned, waving the air with my hand, "mere details."

"Uh-huh," Jim sarcastically replied, "I'll tell your folks that your last thoughts were of them."

The ski rental shop was hopping with activity when we arrived, and I was forced to settle for a pair of extremely long blue skis and yellow boots, which threw my whole ensemble into disarray. "This sucks," I complained to Jim, who was busily selecting a set of ski poles. "I'm gonna look like such a jerk."

"Probably," Jim retorted, "but it's got nothing to do with what you're wearing."

I've always labored under the apparent misconception that all one has to do to accomplish something is set his mind to making it happen. While this may work in meeting personal challenges, I was soon to learn that it doesn't have the same effect on physical prowess. As we made our way to the chair lift, an internal battle of biblical proportions was being waged between my brain, which envisioned me skiing with all the finesse of an Olympic athlete, and my instincts. In yet another in a series of bad decisions, I opted not to listen to my intuition which was screaming, "Hey, fool, start out on the bunny slope," and joined Jim on the lift that took us to the top of the mountain. As we rode the shaky ride to destiny, I watched with wonder the multitude of happy skiers, whooshing down the frosted hillside, and for a moment actually thought I'd be able to pull it off. After several minutes, we reached the summit, the point where the ride ended. "This is gonna be great," I stammered to Jim, a vain attempt to bring my shaking legs under control. "As soon as they stop and let us off, I'm gonna show you some real skiing."

"It doesn't stop," Jim scoffed, "you've got to jump off."

"Jump off," I yelled, turning toward Jim and gripping the chair. "What do you mean, 'jump off?'"

"Jump off," Jim restated, as he tightened the straps on his gloves, "they don't stop the lift, you have to jump off and get out of the way of the next chair."

I shuddered at the thought—I had to get off the lift without looking like Jerry Lewis, and get out of the way before getting smacked in the back of the head by oncoming traffic. Finally, my brain abdicated control and self-preservation kicked in. I nonchalantly turned to Jim and said, "Maybe I'll just ride it back down and practice for a few minutes ... I don't want to hold you up."

"You can't ride it back down," Jim informed me, while adjusting his sunglasses. "It's a one-way ticket."

"Wait a minute," I yelled, my voice trembling with panic, "a one-way ticket? Nobody said anything about a one-way ticket. How the hell do they expect you to get back down?"

"By skiing ... remember, skiing ... the reason we're here?" Jim smirked. "What do you think this is, a carnival ride?"

"Well ... no ..." I stammered, "but they could at least warn you, or give you a way out, like a parachute or something."

All fantasies of matching James Bond's skiing finesse had vanished, and I looked down in terror at the unyielding ground as it inched ever closer to my dangling skis. Am I crazy? I have no business being here. How can I expect to ski down a mountain, when I don't even know how to get off the damn ski lift? "C'mon," Jim smiled and patted me on the back, "you'll be fine. Just hop off the chair, and when you hit the ground, glide to your left."

Oh sure, I thought, easy for you to say. But with the moment of truth at hand, and no other way out, I held my breath, closed my eyes, and leapt from the chair, the faint sound of Jim's cry, "No, not yet!" still ringing in my ears.

I crashed into the frozen earth like a meteor, forming a large crater in the snow and providing unsuspecting skiers the chance to hone their diversionary moves. I rolled over on my back just in time to see Jim gracefully exit the chair, as it floated over me. I lay there in the snow, a testament to stupidity, feeling like the Scarecrow in the Wizard of Oz after the flying monkeys tear him apart, and wondering how long it would take that Saint Bernard with the keg of rum around his neck to reach me. A few seconds later, Jim's smiling face came into view, "Nice form, Ritter," he laughed. "Reminded me of that guy in the opening credits of Wide World of Sports."

"That's right, laugh," I sulked, "I could be seriously hurt here, you know?"

"Are you?" Jim queried.

"No," I dubiously responded, "but I could be."

"But you're not, so quit being such a wuss and get up from there. C'mon, man," Jim cupped his hand at the side of his mouth and quietly urged, "everybody's staring at us."

And they were, too. Maybe it was because I hadn't moved in so long that they thought I might actually have suffered a broken leg, or a concussion, or death from embarrassment. That was probably it ... they were concerned about me. I smiled and waved one of those Queen of England waves, polite but noncommittal, at the small crowd that had gathered at the end of the ski lift—just enough to let everyone know I was okay. A few of them waved back, their smiling faces acknowledging my signal of well-being. Soon, several more well-wishers had joined the others, and the "concerned" crowd quickly grew to fifteen or twenty skiers, flashing toothy, pearly-white grins in my direction. I sat there in the snow, waving and smiling, and waving, and ... smiling ... and ...

"Having a good time?" Jim sneered, as he squatted down beside me.

"Huh? ... oh, yeah," I grinned.

Jim peered at me over the top of his sunglasses, and said, "You do know they're laughing at you, don't you, Ritter?"

"No they're not," I snapped, when Jim grabbed my elbow in an attempt to get me to my feet, "they're just being ... thoughtful. Leave me alone, I can get up on my own."

"Okay," Jim sighed, "whatever you say, man. C'mon then, get up ..."

Get up. A simple request that doesn't take much thought—an instinct, really, more like a reaction, than an action. That is, unless you're wearing skis. Then, it takes effort, concentration, a degree in engineering. I flipped around on the frozen earth like an overturned cockroach, legs flailing, trying desperately to get to my feet. The laughter from my uninvited entourage grew with every contorted squirm, until frustration and embarrassment reached a boiling point and I yanked off my skis, childishly throwing them into a nearby snow bank.

"Tell me it gets better," I snorted at Jim.

Still shaky, and more than a little perturbed, I followed Jim until we reached a clearing in the trees and a wide smooth slope that cascaded down the mountain for several thousand feet, its shroud of snow laced with ski tracks, like tattoos on delicate, white skin. The wind blew against my flushed, cold face as I stood, awestruck, on the edge of the abyss and stared down in terror, my instinct again waging a battle with my brain.

Don't be afraid, my brain chanted, you can do this.

Bullshit, my instinct rebutted. No way. Pitch the hardware and catch the next snowmobile down. You don't know anything about skiing!

You need to address your fears, my brain counter argued, show some guts.

Oh, you're gonna show some guts alright, my instinct shot back, they're gonna be splattered all over the mountainside.

Growing impatient with the debate, my brain again took control of my body. Suddenly, my knees bent, my hands gripped the ski poles and, with my instincts trying feverishly to rally a counterattack, my body lurched forward uncontrollably. Like it or not, I was going skiing.

Too late, I learned what must have been my lesson here … always go with your instincts. I'll spare you the gruesome details of my blind date with destiny, except to say, shortly after my flight down the mountain, I suspect the Austrians passed a law that makes it a capital offense for anyone named Michael to attempt skiing without a special dispensation from the government. Several minutes passed before Jim caught up to me, lying crumpled in a heap at the bottom of the hill, my skis in a chokehold around a fatally wounded, cardboard Mickey Mouse that had, only moments earlier, decorated the Kiddie Slope.

"Did I kill anything?" I wheezed to Jim from under my shroud of snow.

"Only any thoughts I had of going skiing with you again," Jim grinned. "You okay?"

I did a quick check … all my fingers were still there, my arms and legs still functioned, and I didn't see any major organs laying in the snow, so I guessed I was okay. "Yeah, fine," I grumbled. "Just glad to be alive."

"Man," Jim exclaimed as he helped me in my struggle to stand up, "you must have been going fifty miles an hour down that hill."

"Yeah, yeah," I moaned. Really? Fifty, huh?

"At the least," Jim smiled.

My mind was already working busily on the story I'd tell back home. Yeah, man, I'd say, you should have seen me flying down that mountain! At one point I was doing fifty miles an hour! That's five-oh miles an hour! People were so shocked by my ability that they scattered when they saw me coming. Afraid? Me? No way … but I knew I'd never top that, so I didn't ski the rest of the time we were there. Wanted to go out a winner.

"Now can we go back to the lodge?" I pleaded.

Jim continued to dust me off. "Listen, buddy," he said, "I think you've earned a rest. Why don't you go back to the room, and I'll meet you later. I just want to make one more run down the mountain. I won't be long."

As I watched Jim trudge back to the ski lift, a plethora of emotions churned through my body. My huge embarrassment had left me in need of a target for my acrimony. At first, I was pissed off at Jim for leaving me, then I turned the anger against myself for being such a jerk. Finally, I concluded that the real villain wasn't any one person or thing, it was this entire place—Austria, the snow, the whole stupid sport. And I wasn't going to turn the other cheek.

Tossing my skis aside, I walked over to a clearing in the snow and started heaping the flaky substance into a humongous pile. With the determination and skill of a Greek sculptor, I slowly molded the pile into the shape of a four-foot-tall fist, its middle finger raised toward the heavens in a salute to this frozen country.

I was just putting the finishing touches on my tribute when I heard Jim ski up behind me. "Nice work, Ritter," he puffed. "Hope it's not aimed at me."

"No," I grinned, "not you. It's my little homage to Austria. What do you think?"

Jim removed his skis and strolled around the finger of fate, smiling and shaking his head while he examined my work of art. "Well," he finally replied, "you've certainly made your point. You do realize, though, that Europeans don't use this gesture to tell someone to fuck off."

"Huh," I frowned, "they don't? Well, what the hell do they use? Tell me and I'll build it."

"I'm not sure," Jim continued, "but I know a way we can fix this that will really screw with their heads."

"Okay," I enthusiastically agreed. "Let's do it."

Jim pondered the sculpture as he spoke, "I know you're pissed off at the way things turned out, and you want to leave behind a symbol so everyone will know how you feel …"

"Right," I cheered. "Right! I wanna pay them back for laughing at me … show these pricks that I'm not defeated."

"Exactly," Jim assured. "So let's do a little remodeling."

I watched with trepidation while Jim tossed another mound of snow on the fist, next to the extended middle finger. With great care, he formed a full index finger, transforming my obscene commendation into the universal symbol for peace and victory.

"There," Jim smiled, "that's better."

"What do you mean 'that's better'?" I snapped.

Jim moved next to me and put his hand on my shoulder. "You want to let them know that you're better than they are, right?" he asked.

"Well … yeah," I mumbled.

"That you aren't going to let them get the best of you. That you're bigger than they are."

"Well … yeah," I smiled.

"Well," Jim grinned, "there you are. You're victorious. You made it out alive, man. This isn't a slap at them, it's a monument to yourself."

"Yeah," I smiled proudly. "Yeah! A monument to myself. The Ritter Memorial."

"Right on," Jim laughed and slapped me on the back, "Washington, Jefferson, Lincoln and Ritter. Now, how 'bout we get back to the lodge … I'm freezing my nuts off out here."

Given our recent difficulties with the van, we got an early start for home the next morning. As we chugged away from the lodge, I took a look in the rearview mirror and saw several people merrily checking out our statue. Children were playing on the fist, and as I continued to watch, I could see the new addition that Jim had added break off and tumble to the ground, restoring the image to its original intent.

"Stop, Jim," I shouted. "The sculpture broke. The hand's flipping the bird again."

Jim smiled and shifted the van into third gear. "That's okay," he grinned. "Screw 'em if they can't take a joke."

Chapter Eleven
WITH MANY A WINDING TURN

"There's an old adage, Mike … 'I may not agree with what you say, but I'll defend to the death your right to say it.'"

Mr. Dwight … Sam. My favorite teacher. Open-minded, fair, a guy I could really relate to...

"But," Mr. Dwight continued, while sitting cross-legged on his desk and stroking his chin pensively, "having said that, I gotta tell you, I think you missed the point."

We were discussing Vietnam, again. Mr. Dwight loved to discuss Vietnam. Sam Dwight was my history teacher, a guy in his late twenties with an early Beatles-style mop-top haircut who embodied everything I thought a teacher should be. He was the first instructor I knew who actually talked to me instead of at me, and I enjoyed playing devil's advocate just to watch his passionate rebuttals. He viewed history as a long story that never ends—no final chapters are ever written. Mr. Dwight contended that each new day directly impacts our perception of the previous one, and because perceptions change over time, which has no end, we can never really know all the ramifications of a moment in history. In other words, he believed the present is constantly reshaping the past. I liked that concept … it was history with a "to the best of our knowledge, at this point" disclaimer.

I was passionately arguing the standard fare in viewpoints at that time … if we withdraw U.S. troops from Vietnam before we are victorious, then all the soldiers who were killed in the war had lost their lives for nothing.

"That's where we disagree, Mike," Mr. Dwight smiled as he hopped off his desk. "I don't think they died pointlessly. Maybe they died so that America could learn the lesson of humility. To survive in a world that aches for equality, maybe we as a nation need to get our ass kicked by the little guy. Considering the planetary destruction possible in our insane nuclear age, I'd say we got off easy."

"Oh," I replied sarcastically, "you're saying that losing is a good thing?"

"No," Mr. Dwight grinned, "but sometimes it is the best way to learn."

"Okay, Mr. Dwight," I shot back.

"Sam," Mr. Dwight interrupted, "it's Sam. We're all equal here. Respect is shown through action, not titles."

"Okay, Sam, who says we're going to learn this lesson? What

guarantees do we have that there won't be another Vietnam down the road?"

"There's another saying, Mike," Mr. Dwight responded as he plopped down in the chair behind his desk. "'Those who don't learn from history are doomed to repeat it.' Did we learn anything from Korea?"

"Exactly my point," I smirked. "We didn't win in Korea, but that didn't stop us from going into Vietnam."

"So, I assume you think all those Americans who were killed during the Korean War died for nothing."

"Well ... yeah," I stammered.

"In the wake of Vietnam," Mr. Dwight replied softly while rocking slowly in his chair, "I have to agree with you ... maybe they did die for nothing ... so far."

"So far." There it was—the disclaimer.

"By a show of hands," Mr. Dwight continued, "who here still supports the war? Who thinks we should stick it out no matter how long it takes?"

I didn't believe in the war but, I have to admit, for less honorable reasons than Mr. Dwight's. I'd never really thought about the Vietnam conflict in geopolitical, good and evil, imperialism versus self-determination terms ... I just didn't want to get my ass shot off.

Sam's impromptu political poll was interrupted by the sound of the classroom door being forcefully flung open. Startled, we collectively jumped in our seats as two military police officers and the school principal stepped through the door. Mr. Dwight strolled over to meet them, and the four men spoke in hushed tones for several minutes before Sam returned to his desk. The uneasy silence that filled the room was shattered by the words, "Mr. Pickett, would you please join these officers in the hallway? They have something to discuss with you."

An audible "Oh, shit" gasp rose from the crowd of jittery students. Willie slowly rose from his seat and cautiously slinked to the door. He paused for a moment, turned to look at his classmates, shook his head, took a deep breath and walked into the hallway, closing the door gently behind him.

The click of the door latch still lingered in the air as Rob blurted, "What's this all about? What the hell's going on, Sam?"

Mr. Dwight leaned against his desk, his hands in his pockets, his head slightly bowed. "Well," he quietly began, as he brushed shaggy strands of hair from his forehead, "it seems Mr. Pickett ..."

"Willie," Rob interrupted.

"...Willie," Mr. Dwight continued, "has a problem with the police."

"That doesn't tell us anything," Rob barked. "We all have a problem with the police."

Mr. Dwight grinned. "I guess I should have said that the police have a problem with Willie."

"And, and ..." Rob exclaimed, searching for an explanation.

"And," Mr. Dwight sighed, "the best thing we can do is let the law run its course."

"That's it?" Rob screeched. "Let the law run its course?!"

"For now," Mr. Dwight murmured, "for now. So, why don't we ..."

I've never been one to directly challenge authority, preferring to go around obstacles rather than through them, but Mr. Dwight's ambivalence, particularly in light of the "up-against-the-wall" image he projected, was more than I could stand. "This is bullshit, Mr. Dwight," I shouted. "I can't believe you're coming down on the side of the law."

"It's Sam," Mr. Dwight calmly returned, "and ..."

"I don't think so," I sneered. "From now on you'll always be Mister Dwight."

Sam stared intently at me, enabling me to see the hurt in his eyes. It was the worst thing I could have said because, with those few words, I'd let him know that any admiration or affection I'd had for him had walked right out the door with Willie. Several seconds passed while Mr. Dwight continued to stare right through me. Then, in a low, even-tempered voice he said, "You know, maybe you shouldn't jump to any conclusions before you have all the facts."

Maybe so, but I figured I knew the facts: fact one, Willie had been busted; fact two, we didn't know why; fact three, Mr. Dwight was going to do nothing about facts one and two. It was that simple ... and that complicated.

The shrill sound of the bell signaling the end of class shattered the tense silence, and we hurriedly gathered up our books and made a beeline for the door, in the hope of catching up with Willie. The hallway was already flooded with students, and as I was about to join the flow of the human wave I turned to glance at Mr. Dwight, his legs propped up on his desk, the morning newspaper in his hands. Man, I thought, he really doesn't care! How could I have been so wrong about him?

I'd barely stepped out of the classroom when I recognized the deafening buzz of drama unfolding. Hushed conjecture evolves slowly, but inevitably, into roaring half-truths, and in the case of Willie Pickett, that evolution took about fifteen minutes. I spied Jessie running towards me, clutching her books tightly and struggling to maneuver through the crowd of students. "I heard about Willie," she gasped. "Where is he now?"

Rob grabbed Jessie's arm and growled softly, "Quiet! We don't want this getting all over school. Man, now that a loud-mouth like you knows, everybody's gonna know!"

"Screw you," Jessie sneered, "everybody already knows. Madeleine Heaton told me."

"Who's Madeleine Heaton?" Rob hissed.

"Exactly," Jessie responded as she shoved Rob away. "What do you think Willie did, Mike?"

"Who knows?" I replied, rubbing my eye with the palm of my hand. "Dwight wouldn't tell us anything. Jesus, I mean we're talking about Willie—Mr. Honesty, Mr. Nice Guy—Hell, the guy's so innocent he still wears Mickey Mouse Pajamas to bed."

"That's probably why they arrested him," Rob smirked.

"That's so typical," Jessie scolded. "Our friend's in trouble and you're making jokes. You never did like Willie."

"Wait a minute," Rob protested. "This isn't about me. You know, I'm getting sick of you using every opportunity to jump my ass. Have I ever let a brother Stud down before?"

"C'mon, Mike," Jessie continued, ignoring Rob's objections. "You're the vice-president of the Senior class ... you can find out what's going on with Willie."

"Yeah, right," I scoffed. "I'm just vice-president. You think Nixon tells Agnew anything?"

Rob stepped in. "Look, we need a plan, okay? We've gotta find out why they bounced Willie before the rumor mill starts churning."

"Cocaine," came a meek voice from behind Rob. We turned to see a short kid standing alone. "They found cocaine in his locker," the short kid grinned.

Rob grabbed the kid by his shirt collar and yanked him closer. "That's bullshit!" Rob bellowed. "No way, not Willie! Where'd you hear that?"

The quivering kid kept a watchful eye on Rob's shaking grip while he tried to explain. "From the Principal," he stuttered.

Rob dropped the kid like a sack of potatoes, a look of shock on his face. "Oh, man," were the only words he could muster.

Jessie freaked out. "Oh, God, oh, God ..." she stammered, nervously shifting from one leg to the other, "his parents will kill him."

"Stupid shit," Rob groaned. "I'll kill him! Look, Jessie, you get with the other girls, we'll get the word to Sean and Tim and the rest of the guys, and we'll all meet right after third period."

He didn't have to say where. In times of crisis, we always met at the same place ... in the student park, at the statue. Stud Statue. Last Fall, Rob, Tim and I had built a three-headed, ten-foot statue in art class, and had donated it to the student park as a tribute to ... well, ourselves. And in its shadow, we would put together a plan for getting Willie out of this jam.

Spring sunlight reflected off the metal statue, blinding me as I jogged up and joined the rest of my crowd who had already gathered. The girls were huddled in one area, while Rob and Tim busily searched for cracks in the cement base of our homage to ourselves. Sean was pacing back and forth in front of the statue, a deeply concerned look on his face. Cissy looked up to see me advancing, and quickly called everyone together. "C'mon, you guys," she shouted at Rob and Tim. "Mike's here."

"Stud Statue is holding up pretty well," Rob grinned as I joined the crowd. "People will know we were here long after we've left this place."

"Who gives a shit?" Sean angrily rebuked, in a rare show of emotion that only served to punctuate the severity of the situation. "What are we going to do about Pickett?"

"Yeah," Jessie interjected, seizing the moment to chide Rob, "all you care about is that stupid statue. Sometimes I can't believe the arrogance of you guys. Does your ego ever take a rest?"

"There you go again," Rob responded as he lurched toward Jessie. "If you were a guy, I'd—"

"You'd what?" Sean interrupted, stepping between Rob and Jessie.

This was getting us nowhere. "Hey, hey, hey," I shouted, "let's get back to Willie's problem. Anybody hear anything else?"

"Well, it's definite," Cissy said softly "They found cocaine in his locker. It's all over school."

"That's that," Rob despaired, raising his arms in the air and turning away.

"What do you mean 'that's that'?" Sean yelled after him. "We've got to do something."

"Like what?" Rob blared. "Just what do you propose we do, break him out of jail?" And although his words were laced with sarcasm, a strange look came over Rob's face the minute he'd offered them. We all knew what was coming next.

"Forget it, Mathison," Jessie warned as she brushed her long, blonde hair. "Don't even think about it."

"We could pull it off," Rob encouraged, his voice dripping with excitement. "He's being held in the Principal's office until they can reach his folks. All we have to do is ..."

"Forget it, Rob," Jessie repeated. "Are you crazy?"

"I thought you were concerned about your friend," Rob baited her, a gleeful look in his eyes. "Here's your chance to prove it."

"Yeah, but—"

"But nothing," Rob continued. "You're always in my face, saying how bad I treat Pickett, but now that he really needs you, you're too afraid to help. That goes for the rest of you guys, too. We can either stand here and whine about it, or we can take action. It's up to you."

Jessie mulled it over for several seconds before responding, "Okay, Mr. Tough Guy, you're on. I'm listening ... what's your plan?"

Rob, beaming with delight, glanced around at the group. "How 'bout the rest of you?"

One by one, we agreed. It was our only option. We had no idea what would happen if we got caught, but at that moment we didn't care. Besides, it was Rob's idea, and we were more than willing to let him be the hero. Slowly a plan took shape, and the great Willie Breakout caper was underway.

The plan was simple: Willie was being held in the Vice Principal's office, pending notification of his parents. The office was located at the far corner of the main building, its sole window blocked by shoulder-high shrubs, thereby obstructing the view of any passers-by. At precisely the right moment, Cissy and Jessie would start a loud argument in the hallway directly outside the office. Tim would keep watch and signal Rob and me when the Vice Principal, Mr. Jones, left his office. When we got the signal, Rob and I would creep up to the window and quietly tap on the glass, capturing Willie's attention. Assuming Willie wasn't frozen in his seat with fear, which we knew was a major assumption, he would open the window and we would whisk him to the safety of my Volkswagen where Sean waited, the engine running. With split-second timing, we'd be able to pull the whole thing off before Mr. Jones ever knew what hit him.

Rob and I huddled patiently in the thicket of greenery, biding our time until Tim gave the signal. Through the dusty office window, we could see Willie seated in a chair across the desk from Mr. Jones. The two of them were talking casually and, while we couldn't hear their conversation, neither of them looked particularly angry or concerned about the circumstances that had thrown them together. "Wow," Rob whispered, "Willie's really playing it cool. I figured he'd be a basket case by now."

"Yeah," I quietly agreed, "I've gotta hand it to him. He looks like he doesn't have a care in the world."

Several minutes passed before we saw Mr. Jones's attention focus on the door of his office. He slowly rose from his seat behind the desk and firmly strode the few steps to the door, where he paused and said something to Willie before opening the door and continuing into the hallway. At once, our eyes were riveted on the corner of the building in anticipation of Tim's signal, our fail-safe measure to ensure that Mr. Jones was fully occupied with the phony quarreling of Cissy and Jessie. A moment later, Tim gave us the all-clear sign, and a broad smile spread across my face as I realized that the Studs and Duds were operating like a well-oiled Mission Impossible machine, ready to rescue our brother in distress. Rob tenderly tapped on the window, causing Willie to notice us immediately, but he remained in his chair, waving and smiling like a homecoming queen. "Open the window, you idiot," Rob muttered through clenched teeth.

Willie's smile widened as he cupped his hand to his ear in a mock struggle to hear what Rob was saying. "Open the window," Rob huffed, his voice laced with frustration. "Will you look at this jerk, Ritter? Open the window ... open the window ... will you open the goddamn window?!"

"He can't hear you," I sighed nervously. "Maybe ..."

"What does he think we're doing," Rob grimaced, "putting on a friggin' puppet show out here?"

Willie finally sauntered over to the window and slid it open. "Hey guys," he grinned, "what're you doing in the bushes?"

"We're here to bust you out," Rob growled, between impassioned, shallow breaths. "C'mon, hurry up, we haven't got much time."

"Wait a minute, fellas," Willie whimpered as he stepped back from the window, "you don't know ..."

"And we don't care," Rob interrupted, "just climb out the window, will ya? We've got a car waiting."

"But—" Willie protested.

"There's no time to argue," I insisted. "Jones will be back anytime. We've got to act now."

"I understand," Willie stalled, "but—"

Suddenly, Rob shot up from his hunkered position and thrust his arm through the open window, grabbing Willie's shirttail. "Hold the window, Ritter," he hissed, "I'm going to save this stupid cow pie whether he wants me to or not." And with that, Rob yanked Willie toward us, literally forcing him through the window and sending the two of them crashing into me.

Without uttering a word, Rob and I each grabbed one of Willie's arms and lifted him out of the brush, pulling him behind us as we beat a speedy retreat towards Sean and the waiting Cream Machine. We'd gone about fifty yards when Willie broke free of our grips. "Hold it," he yelped, "just hold it!"

"What?" Rob panted, "will you not be a chicken shit for once in your life, and …"

"It's all bullshit," Willie gulped.

"No shit," I wheezed, "we know there's no way you had cocaine in your locker. Lousy cops probably planted it. But, don't you worry …"

"No, no, no," Willie insisted, "you don't understand. It's all a put-on … the whole thing. I was in on it. Me, the cops, Jones, Mr. Dwight … it's a civics lesson."

"It's a what?" Rob bellowed.

Willie bent over, put his hands on his knees, and took several deep breaths before he sat down on the ground and continued to fill us in. "Like I said, it's a civics lesson. Dwight worked up this scheme to have the MP's find some cocaine in my locker, on a tip from some other kid. The whole deal was to teach us a lesson about our rights, search and seizure laws, stuff like that. He's even set up a fake trial. There's gonna be an announcement about the whole thing at the end of the day."

"You mean Dwight knew about this when they were hauling you out of his classroom?" I snorted indignantly.

"Sure," Willie smiled. "Why else do you think he'd be defending the police?"

Rob and I stood in reticent astonishment, our minds reeling from Willie's revelations. After several seconds, Rob broke the silence: "Then you aren't in trouble?"

"He is now," I screeched, as I pulled Willie to his feet. "We've got to get him back to Jones's office before …"

"Oh, man," Rob lamented, hitting himself on the head with the heel of his hand. "I don't believe this."

The three of us hastily backtracked to the scene of the breakout. Slipping into the bushes, we gingerly peered through the window and, to our gleeful surprise, Mr. Jones was nowhere to be seen. Rob hoisted the window and Willie burrowed inside, landing with a thump on the hard, concrete floor. Just as we were closing the window, Mr. Jones walked into the office with Cissy and Jessie in tow. Their simulated screaming match abruptly ceased when they caught sight of Willie; Rob and I caught just a glimpse of their confused faces as we slowly slumped into the safety of the bushes.

By the end of the day, word was out that Willie's scrape with the law had been choreographed. Jessie and Cissy were given a day in detention for disruptive behavior, and Sean was pissed at us for a week because we forgot about him. He'd spent two hours sitting in my Volkswagen with the engine running. I was amazed it had that much gas!

The mock trial began the following day and, with the entire student body present, Willie was found not guilty because the police had failed to get a search warrant before "breaking" into his locker. The law had, indeed, run its course. Later that day, I passed Mr. Dwight in the hall and made a point of saying hello, addressing him by his first name.

Graduation was a mere four weeks away; at last, twelve, long years of early rising and seven hours per day of disinterest were coming to an end. The SATs were over and exciting post-high school plans were being made, but as much as we all were thrilled at the prospect of adventures that lay ahead, there was an underlying current of unspoken melancholia that tempered the joy. In four weeks we'd be saying goodbye to a lot more than high school, we'd be saying goodbye to each other. And to a military brat, that usually means forever.

As vice-president of the Senior class, I got an extra picture in the yearbook and some resume padding for college applications, but I was responsible for, well, nothing, really, which was the most appealing aspect of the job. And, other than the donation of Stud Statue to the student park, both a generous and, truth be told, self-admiring gesture, I can't think of a single initiative from any of the officers of the class of 1973. We'd have regular meetings and talk about stuff but, for the life of me, I can't recall anything meaningful that came from them. I guess we spent most of our meeting time approving minutes from the last meeting, which was really only approval of the minutes from the meeting before that; apparently, at some point, perhaps at the start of the school year, we'd actually said something worth writing down. At any rate, graduation was just around the corner and some actual decisions had to be made so, for a change, there was an agenda for our regular, Wednesday afternoon assembly.

Rob accompanied me down the hall as I hurriedly scanned the agenda for items of interest. "So, Mr. Vice President," Rob grinned, "making any important decisions today?"

"Oh, yeah," I smirked, "earth-shattering."

Rob snatched the crumpled sheet of paper from my hands. "Don't be so hard on yourself," he laughingly encouraged. "No one will ever forget how you guys got the cafeteria to approve putting gravy on French fries ..."

"And at no extra charge, I might add," I crowed.

Rob began to peruse the agenda items. "Let's see what you've got here set a date for prom king and queen nominations, decide on color scheme ..."

"Oh, man," I moaned, "do you believe ..."

Suddenly, Rob stopped dead in his tracks, his gaze fixed on the wrinkled photocopy in his hands. "Whoa, whoa, whoa," he cackled. "Look at this, Ritter. You guys have to select the class song."

"Yeah, so what," I huffed.

Rob stood directly in front of me and grabbed my arms, his eyes gleaming as he loudly whispered through clenched teeth, "Don't you get it, man? This is our chance. You can nominate the Stud anthem, 'He Ain't Heavy, He's My Brother.' It's a golden opportunity to flaunt our influence in front of the whole student body ... and their parents!"

"I dunno . . ."

"C'mon, man." Rob put one arm around my shoulder, the other one outstretched, as he gazed into the distance. "Just imagine it ... a sea of red caps and gowns awash in the loving gazes of parents, immersed in the most important moment of their lives, the entire auditorium quiet with choking emotion when suddenly, boom! ... the Stud anthem flows over them like a tidal wave."

"That sounds good," I agreed.

"Sounds good?" Rob exclaimed. "It'll be historic, man! C'mon, Mike, you can pull this off. I've seen you charm the skin off a snake."

"That's true," I grinned, my enthusiasm ignited. "You're right, I can do this. Piece of cake."

"Do it for the Studs, man," Rob beamed. "Do it for yourself."

I would champion our anthem at the meeting but, unbeknownst to Rob, not for reasons of ego or self-satisfaction. The peace signs and political statements that decorated my Maid's Room were more than just trendy hyperbole, and the sentiments expressed in the song's lyrics echoed my own beliefs. I'd do it, but not for the Studs or even myself ... I'd do it for my generation.

When I walked into the meeting of the Senior Class officers, the class sponsor, Ms. Betty Young, stopped in mid-sentence to glare at me. Ms. Young was a portly woman in her early thirties, who had lost her right arm in a traffic accident some years earlier. For the most part, I was rather indifferent to her, but her hard, plastic arm always gave me pause for concern when she was in one of her scolding, maternal moods.

"Tardy again, Mr. Ritter," Ms. Young interrupted the meeting to inform me. "Wait, don't tell me, you're late because you had to stop and brush your hair." Without waiting for what was certain to be some insipid response from me, Ms. Young turned her attention to the class Secretary, Liz. "Go ahead with what you were saying, Liz," Betty coaxed, "you were suggesting possibilities for class song."

It appeared my timing was perfect!

Liz Candler was a petite, sweet, virtuous girl ... I mean, a really good girl, the kind that put the "ice" in "nice". "Well, before Mike's big entrance," Liz began while glaring, at me, "I was saying that I think the class song should be 'I Can See Clearly Now.' The words say so much about ..."

"That song sucks," I blurted. It wasn't a terribly diplomatic way to start, but I was anxious to open the debate. "The words don't mean anything."

"They do too!" Liz shot back.

"What?" I sneered, "tell me what the words mean to you."

Liz sighed heavily and dramatically rolled her eyes. "It's fairly obvious, Ritter. Have you even heard the song? 'I can see clearly now, the rain is gone. I can see all obstacles in my way ...' It's a metaphor, Einstein! The rain is high school, and it's gone now that we're graduating, and the obstacles are all the things we're going to encounter in our new lives as adults."

"Oh, I get it, it's very ... happy, isn't it?" I responded cynically.

"What's wrong with happy?" Liz roared as she rose from her chair and leaned menacingly across the table that separated us. "Geez, Mike, we're graduating from high school, this is a time for optimism."

"No," I said smugly, "this is a time for reflection."

Liz stood with her arms crossed at her chest, looking out the window. "I, for one, prefer to look ahead," she hissed. "You can live in the past if you want to."

"I'm not living in the past just because I don't like your song," I protested. "Damn, Liz, we haven't even graduated yet and you already want to forget about your generation. What about all the friends we've made, all the friends we'll probably never see again, in a few weeks."

The class President, Ben, and Treasurer, Marcy, sat quietly in their chairs, perhaps waiting for Liz's rebuttal, but Liz just continued to stare out the window as the palpable tension mounted. Finally, Ms. Young broke the standoff. "Perhaps you have a better suggestion, Mike."

"Thank you, Ms. Young," I smiled and nodded in her direction. "I certainly do have a suggestion ... a song that reflects not only the sentimentality of fond memories, but a realistic look at just how rough a road awaits us once we leave the beloved halls of good of K-Town." I stood behind my chair, resting my hands against the wooden frame, and with all the finesse and conviction of an Atticus Finch I continued: "Perhaps you agree with Liz, that it's fine to just turn our backs, walk away, leave the past alone. But ..." I paused for effect. "But somehow, I just can't find it within me to simply ignore three years of my life, or toss out friendships like so much garbage."

Ms. Young smiled faintly as she tapped her plastic arm. She had that glimmer in her eye that said, you are so full of shit, Mike ... but keep going, I can't wait to see how this turns out.

"So, it is with this in mind," I offered in the midst of a deep sigh, "that I propose a song that stands as a testament to the values of our generation, one that will fill our hearts with pride for years to come. I submit for your consideration that soul-searching tune by the Hollies, 'He Ain't Heavy, He's My Brother'."

"Wait a minute," Liz yelped, "that's your stupid Stud song! I hear you guys playing it in the student park all the time."

"Nevertheless," I grinned, "it's still the perfect song."

"There is no way I'm going to agree to graduate under the anthem of Mike and his Stud cronies," Liz defiantly replied. "No way."

"Let's put it to a vote," I shot back confidently. "Ben, you and Marcy agree with me, don't you?"

"Point of order, point of order," Liz interrupted. "The Student Council charter specifically states that any decision we reach has to be ratified by the entire Senior class. I propose we hold a vote tomorrow and let the class decide."

"What are you talking about?" I protested. "We're the voice of the Senior class. They elected us to make these decisions. Now, the vote is three to one and I say ..."

"Point of order," Liz squawked, "point of order ..."

"Okay, okay," Ms. Young interjected, "sorry, Mike, but Liz's right.

The whole Senior class will have to decide between the two songs."

I slumped down in my chair. "Oh, man ... so much for representative government," I groused.

"Then it's decided," Liz chirped, her voice dripping with satisfaction. "We'll hold a vote tomorrow. The candidates are 'I Can See Clearly Now', or ... that stupid Stud song."

"Point of order, point of order," I blustered sarcastically.

Liz glanced up at me under furrowed eyebrows, "Or 'He Ain't Heavy, He's My Brother.' Now, if we've satisfied Mike sufficiently, let's move on to the next agenda item ... the Senior prom."

"Okay," I groaned, "I'm outta here ... you guys can decide on what color crepe paper to use ... unless the entire class has to vote on that, too."

But I wasn't going to get off that easy, and an hour later I was leaving the meeting, burdened with the chore of booking "a prom kind of band" for the dance.

I caught a glimpse of Rob as he disappeared into the bathroom and, knowing that he'd want to hear the bad news right away, decided to follow him. He was standing at the urinal, and looked up when he heard the door open. "Hey, Ritter," he grinned, "what's the word?"

"Democracy," I muttered as I faced the mirror and began to brush my hair.

"Huh?" a puzzled Rob responded.

"Democracy," I repeated, still working to get my hair just right. "Tomorrow, the whole class gets to vote on the Senior song."

"So, what's the competition?" Rob asked as he zipped his fly.

"That stupid, bubble gum song, 'I Can See Clearly Now'," I whined apologetically.

"No problem," Rob smirked confidently as he checked his look in the mirror. "We'll just have to do a little old-fashioned influence peddling. Like they say, some people are born to democracy while others have democracy thrust upon them."

"And you're just the guy to do the thrusting," I snickered.

"Watch and learn, buddy boy," Rob assured. "Watch and learn."

All day Thursday, the Studs campaigned vigorously for our song, buddying up to kids for whom we'd previously never had the time of day, making promises we had no intention of keeping. Our eyes were set on the goal; the end justified any means necessary. We walked that fine line between persuasion and outright intimidation and, by the end of the day, we were convinced that both the song and the Studs were on the verge of making K-town history.

By the next morning, we had discovered our place in history … right alongside Napoleon at Waterloo. "He Ain't Heavy, He's My Brother" had lost by an almost two-to-one margin. Sure, I was disappointed by the fact that my choice for Senior song had lost, but on a deeper level, I was disappointed in my class.

As in past crises, the Studs and Duds would convene at our statue to mull over the loss, mutter expletives about our unappreciative classmates, and plan some sort of response action. Although I usually loved these "search and destroy" bull sessions, I just wasn't up to it right now. I needed to talk to someone who could appreciate how I felt, someone who might offer not only words of consolation, but also some sort of perspective on this put-down … someone like Mr. Dwight.

I knew that Mr. Dwight had a free period, so I skipped English Literature and made a beeline for his class. When I entered the room, Sam was leaning back in his chair, reading the *Stars and Stripes*. "What do you think about all this Watergate stuff, Mike?" he grinned as he folded the newspaper and laid it on his desk. "I think Tricky Dick's in on the whole thing," he continued, without waiting for a response from me. "Never did trust that guy."

"Uh, Mr. Dwight," I began softly as I sat on the comer of his desk.

"Sam."

"Sorry … Sam. You got a minute?"

"Several," Dwight smiled and sat up in his chair. "Next class doesn't start for almost an hour. What's on your mind?"

"I guess you heard what happened with our class song contest," I mumbled.

"Yeah, tough break. For what it's worth, I was rooting for you guys."

"Really?" I responded with surprise. "I thought you didn't appreciate our little club very much."

"Well, you've got great taste in music, so you can't be all bad," Dwight smiled as he again leaned back in his chair. "How are the other guys taking it?"

"I don't know, I'm sure they're pissed off."

"And you?"

Without replying, I hopped off the desk and sulked over to the table where Dwight kept some back issues of news magazines. "Well," I muttered while nonchalantly flipping through the stacks, "I'm more … disillusioned."

"Ahhh," Dwight grinned. "I get it … you guys practically run the school so you assumed …"

"That's not what I'm talking about," I snapped. "It's not about the Studs."

Mr. Dwight sat motionless behind his desk, a pensive look filling his deep-set, brown eyes. "Okay," he finally responded, "lay it on me, Mike. What's bugging you?"

For the next several minutes I bared my soul … my peers—kids weaned in a world filled with racial injustice and social unrest, a generation who had experienced first-hand the assassinations of Bobby Kennedy and Martin Luther King, teenagers who wore Vietnam P.O.W. bracelets with pride and compassion—had chosen to have their moment in time represented by a light, cheery, self involved, bubble gum tune over a song that had substance and meaning, and spoke of concern for one another's welfare. I just didn't understand it.

Mr. Dwight sat quietly through my cathartic discourse, his attention occasionally accented by a nod of his head and a knowing smile, and as I finished my indignant soliloquy, he rose from his chair and walked over to where I was standing. He picked through the clutter of magazines until he located a copy of *Time* with President Nixon's face emblazoned across the cover, and bearing the words: "Should he resign?"

"How do you think he'll be remembered?" Dwight solemnly queried. "It's a great concern of his, you know, and one that motivates most politicians … their place in history. Right now, ol' Tricky Dick is sweatin' bullets, not because of what he's done, but because of Watergate's impact on his legacy. He's afraid that when all is said and done, people won't remember that he opened the door to China, or achieved détente with the Soviets, or possibly even ended the war in Vietnam. They'll just remember Watergate." Dwight smiled and tossed the magazine on the table. "Maybe that same concern is bugging you, Mike."

"The Nixon analogy ain't working for me, Sam," I glumly replied.

Ignoring my self-pity, Sam continued. "Consider that song you chose to represent your class, your legacy, as it were. I understand it also happens to be the theme song for you and those guys you hang around with … the Studs."

"Yeah, it is. But that doesn't change the song's message."

"That's true," Dwight agreed as he returned to his desk, "but it does add to your disappointment that your song lost."

"I'm still missing your point," I sighed, taking another glance at

Nixon's picture.

"My point is the importance that humans place on historical retrospection. In years to come, whenever people hear the name Nixon, their first thoughts will be of political corruption. If 'He Ain't Heavy, He's My Brother' had won, the Studs' domination of the class of 1973 would have been set in stone, and the memory of you would be forever linked to the sentiments expressed in that song." Dwight leaned back in his chair, clasped his hands behind his head, and drove home his assessment. "But, without that linkage, the Studs might be remembered ..."

"As a bunch of skirt-chasing guys who threw great parties and erected an icon to themselves in the student park," I completed his thought.

"Maybe," Dwight smiled, "but who knows? And why do you care?"

That was the real question. I understood what Dwight was saying about historical linkage, but my concern ran deeper than how my friends and I would be remembered. Oh, that was important to me, to be sure, but as graduation loomed ever closer I couldn't escape the feeling that more than my high school days were coming to an end. The class had chosen a song riddled with references to "I" and "me" that, at least in my mind, signaled more than a repudiation of the Studs. During the '60s, kids my age had watched anxiously from the sidelines as the battles over peace, brotherhood, and equality had been fought. We were a generation nurtured on the premise that united we'd stand, divided we'd fall, and yet, now that it was our turn to carry the banner, it seemed that the era of "togetherness" was being supplanted by "it's every man for himself." It didn't have a name yet, but the birth of the "Me Generation" was at hand, and with it came the premature death of ideals that I had always assumed would flourish throughout my lifetime. I was slowly coming to the realization that my peers were merely stepchildren of the '60s, too young to fight for the cause but, I thought, old enough to embrace the message.

Unfortunately, I was naive enough to believe that everyone thought the way I did.

"You know, Mike," Dwight softly broke my concentration, "the ideals you champion, like the sentiments expressed in the song, are admirable. But they're ideals that you inherited, values forged by the vision and passions of the generation that preceded you. You guys are more like the second line of defense. The principles born in the '60s have been shoved through a filter ... some of them got through, some of them didn't. If your generation isn't living up to your expectations, perhaps you shouldn't have so many. Besides, I'd say your classmates embraced at least one of those ideals you hold so dear …"

"Yeah?" I said incredulously. "What would that be?"

"Free thought … they've learned that they can say 'NO'," Dwight stated simply.

"To what?" I shot back defensively.

"There's a whole myriad of possibilities." Dwight broadly smiled, his pencil-thin lips stretched like a rubber band across his face. "Anything … everything … maybe they're saying no to the song, maybe they're saying no to the whole process … or maybe they're just saying no to you."

I knew he was right, I'd really known it all along. Instead of promoting the song on its virtue as a hymn for our generation, my friends and I had made it personal. The song's message had taken a back seat to its reputation as Stud Anthem, turning the adoption of Senior Class song into a contest of wills, and our classmates had rejected the whole process. Ironically, I really believed the message of the song, but had put my true motives aside. I wanted to be part of a generation who thought that the highest form of personal gratification lay in an act of kindness towards another human being. What's more, I wanted everyone to know that I felt that way, and I wanted to believe that my peers felt that way, and that we were proud that we did. But now, all I felt was disheartened.

Dwight, almost sensing my discomfort, ended the awkward silence. "Anyway, that's just my opinion …"

"No," I interrupted, "you're right. They were saying no to us … it was the right answer to the wrong question."

The look on Dwight's face made me feel a little better; he was wearing one of those tilted-head "you're growing up" approving smiles that parents cast at their kids on special occasions, like the first time they use the toilet without the safety net of a potty seat. "So," he grinned, "where do you go from here?"

I smiled cryptically and headed toward the open classroom door. "Out to change history, Sam," I declared, "out to change history."

The gang was right where I'd expected to find them, gathered around Stud statue, commiserating among them.

"There you are," Rob chastised as I neared the statue. "Where've you been?" I started to respond but, before I could get a word out, Rob proceeded, his words laced with anger and humiliation. "Listen, man, we've got to come up with a plan, something that will show these pukes that the Studs are a force to be reckoned with. Tim's got this great idea about how we could sabotage the prom."

"Yeah," Tim chuckled from his perch at the top of the statue. "You're in charge of getting the band, Ritter, so I was thinkin', like you get the worst band in the world, and ..."

"And what do we dance to?" I posed. "Portable radios?"

"You got a better idea?" Rob huffed.

"Yeah," I said while straightening a bent cigarette from the wrinkled pack that had been stuffed in my back pocket. "I think we should throw them a party."

"A what? " Rob bellowed. "Tell me you didn't just say we should throw them a party."

"That's what I said," I calmly confirmed. "I think we should throw them a party."

Rob raised his arms in the air, as if requesting divine guidance. "Sure," he said sarcastically, expressing the word in four separate syllables, "why don't we take them all out to dinner, too? And a movie! You think they'd like that, Mike?

"Probably," I smiled.

"Man, have you lost your friggin' mind?" Tim snarled as he shimmied down the statue. "These clowns insult us and you wanna throw them a party? Forget it! These suckers must pay!"

"They will," I agreed, "I'm thinking about five bucks a head."

"Forget it," Tim insisted, too angry to hear what I'd said.

"Wait a minute," Rob commanded, his tantrum momentarily thwarted by the prospect of making some cold, hard cash. "Keep talking, Ritter."

"Let's throw a Senior Class party," I proposed. "It's the last thing they'd expect us to do. We rent some space, buy a few kegs, hire a band, charge people five bucks to get in, and it's a party."

"I dunno," Tim huffed, "sounds like—"

"A great idea," Rob blurted. "Outstanding! We throw the party, we make some money, we look like heroes, and they all feel guilty for rejecting our song. Payback with real pay ... it's perfect, Ritter. I knew I wasn't wasting my time on you."

The girls, led by Jessie, as usual, weren't quite as enthusiastic. "This sounds like a lot of work," Jessie protested. "The prom's in a couple weeks, not to mention all the other stuff I've gotta do before graduation."

"Fine," Rob responded, his eyes twitching as he silently recalculated his percentage of the profits. "There'll be fewer people to split the pot. Any of you other girls want out?"

"It's not that I'm against it," Sean remarked, "I just don't think we can pull it off. Hell, half of the kids in the class aren't even old enough to drink."

"Never stopped any of us," I grinned.

Willie was nervously pacing the ground. "Yeah ... and what about their folks? What if some kid gets drunk at the party and their parents find out. Who do you think they're gonna blame?"

"Us, of course," Rob scoffed, "but, so what? It's not like they can get us kicked out of school, or anything. We've got nothing to lose here. Jesus, Pickett ... show a little backbone, will ya?"

"Screw you, Mathison," Willie huffed. "I didn't suffer through twelve years of school just to blow it this close to the finish line. The last thing I need right now is a black mark on my record."

"Listen to yourself," Rob scolded, "this is our chance to go out in a blaze of glory, and you're still worrying about getting into trouble. You'll make a good husband, Pickett," he continued mockingly. "I can just hear it now... 'Honey, if I promise to be home early will you let me play poker tonight with some of my buddies?' Man, what a wank."

"So I'm considerate of others, so sue me," Willie rebutted, in an ill-fated attempt to salvage his dignity.

"You're not considerate," Rob snarled. "You're just plain scared."

"I am not!" Willie exclaimed.

"Yes, you are," Rob shot back. "You're scared of your folks, your teachers, the police ... Hell, Pickett, you're even afraid of yourself."

"Leave him alone," Jessie admonished as she shoved Rob in the back. "Maybe he's just more sensitive than you are. For that matter, Hitler was more sensitive than you are."

"Don't help me, huh," Willie uttered quietly, amid a background of muffled giggles.

Rob sauntered over to Willie and took a few deep breaths, before speaking again. "This isn't about Willie," he said softly, his angry demeanor suddenly replaced by a more introspective posture. "This is about us ... all of us. This is it ... the last hurrah before we ride off into the sunset. Don't you guys get it? When they voted against our song, they voted against us. That's okay, now we know we're all we've got, we're all we can depend on. But," he continued, his voice at once both mischievous and sincere, "we can still show this school that we're not defeated, and throw a party that nobody will ever forget. We need to let them know that we're together on this ... that the Studs and Duds will not be daunted, that it'll take more than a song rejection to knock us down. It's important ... it's important to me."

And we could see that it was. Rob's remarks were as close as he would ever get to letting us know how he felt, how much we meant to him, and how much he'd miss us when we all went our separate ways.

"I'm in," Willie declared. "You can count on me, Rob."

"Me, too," Tim chuckled. "Just don't start cryin' or anything, okay, Mathison?"

One by one, we each signed on ... even Jessie who said she'd manage to find some time in her hectic social calendar to help out. And while it was my idea, it was definitely going to be Rob's show. "Then it's settled," Rob chirped as we headed to our next class. "We'll meet at my place tonight and work out the details."

On Friday nights, we often congregated at Rob's house. His young stepfather and hot-to-trot mom were usually going out, giving Rob free reign over the place. They always had an ample supply of beer in the fridge, and didn't even mind if we partook of their supply, as long as we promised to stay off the streets and not tell our folks where we got it. I loved hanging out at Rob's place; his almost-too-hip folks were more a part of the gang than parents, and it was a welcome change from the judgmental tension that had, over the past few years, taken hold of my own home. Rob's folks never seemed to ask him "why" (the first word in my parents vocabulary), and while their reasons may have run closer to disinterest than trust, I envied Rob's freedom to explore new things, to search for his own answers to life's questions, without having to validate his ideas and feelings by filtering them through parental agendas. Rob's folks had given him a gift that I'm still not sure he fully appreciated ... he was given the freedom to fail without fear of recrimination. He was the first kid I'd ever known who was truly his own person and, while he did have a penchant for irritating the shit out of people, he was honest about who he was. If you didn't like him, that was your problem, not his, and I admired his confidence in his own, seemingly innate desire to forge new boundaries of acceptable behavior.

So, at Rob's place that Friday night, we divvied up responsibilities for the party, between Yard-of-Ale chugging contests. Rob and Willie would procure the beer, the girls would be in charge of advertising and selling tickets, and Tim, Sean and I were handed the charge of booking a band and finding a place to throw the shindig. With only a few weeks remaining before graduation, we knew our missions would be challenging, but not impossible. After all, we were the Studs ... accomplishing the impossible was right up our alley.

An unequivocal, optimistic energy surrounds graduation from high school that seems to leave a lasting memory in people. Whether it be the relief of life unbound from required schooling, or the courageous, youthful anticipation of a major life change, people never seem to forget that magical time in their lives. As we set plans for the party in motion, the adults we called upon for help were more than willing to lend a hand, as if their willingness to be a part of the process rekindled fond memories of their own fearless days of innocence and endless possibilities. My dad's brief stint as a bouncer at the Airman's Club gave me an "in" with the club's manager, and we were able to reserve the club for the Friday before Tuesday's graduation. Willie worked part-time at the Class Six, military jargon for liquor store, where his boss agreed to front him five kegs of beer "on consignment." Tim's friend was the drummer for the local band, Dr. Pig, who collectively "oinked" their promise to play for a percentage of the take at the door. And, in the small amount of available time that Jessie had to contribute, she was able to use the copy machine in her father's office to print the tickets. The party to end all parties was taking shape, and it wasn't costing us a dime.

By the time the Senior Prom rolled around, just a week-and-a-half before graduation, we'd already sold over one hundred tickets, at five bucks a pop. Willie guarded the cash and, like teenage Shylocks, we'd gather at the Youth Center every night to go over the daily totals, and marvel at our ability to extract tiny pieces of flesh from our naive classmates.

The Prom came with the usual fanfare, and we were all decked out in the finery of the day, pastel-colored tuxedos with frilly shirts and ruffled cuffs. In hindsight, our evening attire made us look like a cross between James Brown and Bozo the Clown. I wore a white jacket with a black collar and black pocket trimmings, and made my date look all over Germany for a black carnation to finish the ensemble. In the excitement of planning the Stud party, I'd forgotten to book the music for the Prom until the last minute, and had to settle for a band called Atomic Rooster that I'd never seen or heard. Their repertoire was largely acid rock, a stark contrast to the "Land of Oz" theme of the dance, but under the seductive lights of a spinning, mirrored ball, the crackle of taffeta and murmur of romantic conversations somehow muted the heavy metal opus.

By party day, the following Friday, the buzz around school was that the Stud graduation blowout was going to be the place to celebrate the right of passage. The jocks, the freaks, the juicers, even the members of the Glee Club lined up to buy tickets, and by the time we left school on Friday afternoon, we were up almost eight hundred dollars.

We arrived at the Airmen's Club about an hour before the party was scheduled to start, and we busily prepared for our history-making extravaganza. Once the kegs were tapped, the music keyed up, and the lighting set, Rob assembled us at a table that he'd cordoned off with velvet ropes. Carefully positioned on the white tablecloth was a sign that read "Reserved for The Studs", and a bottle of champagne on ice sat next to the table. We all took our places while Rob, much like the proud father of a new bride, wordlessly poured glasses of the bubbly elixir and relayed them around the table to each member of the "family".

"Ooooo," Jessie cooed, "champagne ... I simply love champagne!" Holding the glass with both hands, she raised it close to her face to savor the bouquet, as the alcohol-laced effervescence danced around her nose. Then, cocking one eyebrow and peering over her glass at Rob, she grinned. "Where'd you get the money for this, Mathison? It'd better not have come out of our profit margin."

Rob ignored Jessie's insinuation and smiled broadly, raising his glass in the air. "Here's to us," he announced, the sentimental glow in his eyes belying the common start of his salute: "To tonight, to all the yesterdays, and the tomorrows. You guys are the best thing to ever happen to me, and I'll cherish the memory of you and our time together for the rest of my life."

It was a wonderfully awkward moment. We all knew it took every ounce of Rob's courage to open up to us like that, and the unusual tenderness left us each searching for a response. Finally, Jessie broke the fidgety silence. "To you, Rob," she affectionately giggled, "our favorite jerk."

Rob insisted that he take the first turn collecting tickets at the door, perhaps because he viewed each ticket as both a tribute to, and a vindication of, the friends he held so dear. For the next five hours, we partied like there was no tomorrow, the Stud graduation festival exceeding our wildest expectations. It was two in the morning when the last reveler stumbled out the door. Our private table was awash in empty, plastic cups and cigarette butts, and as I looked at the faces of my exhausted chums, I was overcome by a sensation of warmth and satisfaction. We had done it, we had made K-town history.

Three a.m. came and went, and we were still sitting amidst the marvelous mess, trying desperately to hold onto the moment for as long as we could. Eventually, it was Willie who raised his head from the beer-soaked tablecloth and murmured, "I've gotta go home, guys. My mom will be worrying about me."

Willie's comment sent laughter ricocheting around the table. It was classic Pickett, and the perfect setup for one of Rob's sarcastic retorts. But Rob simply smiled, rubbed his bloodshot eyes, and helped Willie to his feet. "Okay, Pickett ... c'mon, we'll all walk home together," Rob yawned.

The cold, early morning air was invigorating, and as our rumpled troupe zigzagged its way back to the housing area, several of us felt the need to pause now and then to empty our stomachs the hard way—not exactly a trail of bread crumbs! One by one, we each went our separate ways, until only Rob and I remained standing in front of my apartment building. "C'mon down to my room," I beckoned, "unless you think your mom will be worried, too."

Rob flopped down in my rocking chair as I flicked on the stereo.

Quite a night," he smiled contentedly. "Guess we showed them who runs the Senior Class."

"Yeah," I replied softly, "something like that."

"What do you mean, 'something like that'?" Rob slurred.

"We're the best, man. We're the Studs. They'll never forget us, now."

"I know, I know," I answered, "but ..."

"But what?" Rob rebounded.

Calculating my words, I waited several seconds before responding, "Well," I finally revealed, "maybe 'He Ain't Heavy, He's My Brother' means everybody ... not just our circle of friends. Wasn't that the point?"

I wanted desperately for Rob to agree with me: I needed to know that he saw the big picture, that he could see beyond his self-satisfaction to our greater act of kindness toward our fellow classmates, and that he understood that the concept of brotherhood extends beyond the boundaries of comfortable acquaintances. But Rob's flippant remark again reminded me that expectations usually end in disappointment. "It's just a song, Mike," Rob advised as he got up from the chair. "Nothing to get worked up about."

Forget it, I thought, he didn't understand. Rob was Rob, my friend, and that was all I could, or should, count upon. After all, he had always been there for me, ever since he came to my aid after that humiliating fight with Greg at the Youth Center last year. Hell, when that happened we weren't even friends yet, but ... that's right, that had happened before we were friends! What a fraud! All along, Rob had gone out of his way to cultivate a reputation that really didn't reflect the charitable person whom I had experienced, firsthand. Jessie was right, Rob was full of shit. For whatever reason, he wanted his image to be that of an unfeeling smartass. And, for whatever reason, that's how we accepted him.

"It'll be dawn soon," Rob added as he opened the door, unaware of my silent epiphany, "and I've gotta go back to the club and clean up the mess. Wanna give me a hand?"

"Sure," I smiled, "your mess is my mess."

We'd made plans to go swimming the next day so, with little sleep and throbbing heads, we all met at the Snack Bar at noon on Saturday. Before making tracks for the pool, we divvied up the fruits of our labor; expenses aside, we'd managed to rake in $650, which netted us about 59 smackers each. "There's an extra dollar here," Willie smiled, waving the bill in the air. "I'll take that," Rob replied as he snatched the dollar out of Willie's hand.

"How come he gets the extra buck?" Willie protested.

Jessie hummed as she again counted her take of the cash. "Lay off Rob, will you, Willie?" She chirped. "This incessant whining of yours is really getting on my nerves."

"Ah," Tim grinned at Jessie's sudden turn of support, "the power of money..."

"Makes strange bedfellows doesn't it, Jessie?" Rob leered.

Jessie tapped her money against the tabletop until the bills formed a perfect stack. "I'm rich," she dryly proclaimed, "not demented."

"Speaking of demented," Cissy interjected, "are you guys really going swimming? It's, like, sixty degrees out there today. You know, my dad, the Colonel, says it's not healthy to swim in cold weather. Actually, it's when you get out of the water that you really have to watch it, that's when ..."

"Are you kidding me?" Rob howled. "C'mon, babe ... it's adult time, time to give up this 'Colonel' jazz. You're hours away from graduation, you've got fifty-nine tax-free dollars," he reached across the table and took Cissy's hand, "and my attention. Besides," he paused and leaned in closer, "your nipples get really hard in cold water ..."

"That's disgusting," Cissy yelped and yanked back her hand.

"They're your nipples," Rob lasciviously stated. "Guess you'd know."

"Rob," Jessie groaned as she struggled to stuff her wad of cash into the front pocket of her jeans, "why, why, why do you have to go so far out of your way to be an asshole?"

"I don't think he puts that much effort into it," moaned Tim, without lifting his head from the table—he was nursing a gargantuan hangover. "He just comes by it naturally."

"Oh, come on, Jessie," Rob laughed and leaned back in his chair. "She knows I'm just kidding. Making it with Cissy would be like … making it with my sister."

"I didn't know you had a sister," Tim wheezed.

"Me neither," whispered Willie as he elbowed Sean in the ribs. "Do you think she looks anything like his mom?"

"You really think of me as a sister?" Cissy sweetly inquired, the surprise in her voice causing each word to rise as she spoke it.

Rob rarely revealed his true feelings about anything. Granted, I get choked up by "The Star Spangled Banner," so I may not be the best judge, but I'd have bet my whole 59 dollars that at that moment, Rob was conjuring up some smartass response rather than letting himself admit that he thought of our female companions as anything other than a harem of potential conquests. But much to my surprise, and with all the sincerity he could muster, Rob smiled and leaned forward, resting his elbows on the table and his chin on his hands. "I think of all you girls that way," he softly confided.

I owe myself fifty-nine dollars.

"Really?" Cissy sighed.

"Sure," Rob chortled, "otherwise, I'd have nailed you all by now."

Called that bet too soon.

"So, we going swimming or what?" Rob quickly changed the subject as he stood up and edged toward the door. "C'mon, you guys. I'll pay the admission."

"That's nice," Cissy smiled, choosing to ignore Rob's addendum to his original, endearing words. "Thanks, Rob."

"Admission's free," Jessie muttered as she slid from behind the table and attempted to nonchalantly push the bunched-up material of her skintight jeans down her legs. On that note, we lifted Tim and exited for the pool.

The day was warm by German standards, and we lazily walked the three miles to the pool. When we finally arrived, Rob insisted that, for the girls' convenience, we position ourselves close to the ladies' restroom, but no one was fooled by his gallant suggestion. We all knew that the location provided Rob with the best chance to "check out the talent."

Nobody really wanted to go in the water … except Rob, of course. Tim immediately stretched out, face down, in the grass, his crumpled towel serving as a makeshift pillow. Jessie, Cissy, and the rest of the girls were in a circle, chatting about all the clothes they were going to buy with their newfound wealth. Which left us guys with little to do but ogle girls as they made their way to and from the showers. Rob was a master at the art of inconspicuous leering, and it didn't take long before his attention was captured by a petite brunette in a bright-yellow bikini who, much to our amazement, seemed to be returning his lusty stare. "Do you see that?" he breathlessly whispered out of the corner of his mouth. "That chick's giving me the eye."

"Maybe she's blind," Willie chuckled.

"And maybe you're not an idiot," Rob speedily returned, "but I don't have time to find out." With that, he grabbed his towel and strutted off in the direction of his admiring, albeit quite gullible, quarry. While Willie struggled to understand the double-negative aspersion on his mental capacity, we watched in collective disbelief.

"This oughta be good," I grinned, as I peered at Rob over the top of my sunglasses, "five bucks says he blows it." With our gazes burning a hole in his back, Rob sauntered up to the little brunette and kneeled on her blanket.

"What do you think he's saying?" Willie wondered aloud, his eyes fixed on Rob. "Your little sister's deaf, Ritter, can't you read lips?"

The only thing more preposterous than that question would have been my taking the time to untangle Willie's twisted logic, so I played along with his backward supposition. "Let's see," I pondered, squinting my eyes for dramatic effect, "he's saying ... oh, that guy ... that's Willie ... yeah, he's okay ... for a fag."

"A fag!" Willie shrieked over our raucous laughter, "did he really say that?" Even Tim, from his face-down position on the ground, managed a muffled giggle.

"Oh, yeah," still staring at Rob, I prolonged the prank, "now he's calling you a little prick ... no, sorry, my mistake, he said you have a little prick."

"I'll kill him," Willie hollered.

"Will you cool it, Pickett," Sean chuckled, "Mike's just toolin' you."

For the next few minutes, our attention was riveted on the romantic drama unfolding a few yards away. Then Rob, with his latest conquest in tow, headed toward the pool. "Say what you will about Mathison," I smirked, "the guy's got balls."

Rob was loving life; not only did he have the full notice of his bikini babe while he showed off his aquatic skills and cut up by the pool, but he was also aglow in the triumph of winning her over, under full scrutiny of his less-fortuitous friends. A short time later, Jessie broke ranks with the female gabfest and walked over to where Willie, Sean and I were playing cards. "Where's Rob?" she asked.

"He's screwing around by the pool," I answered, without looking up.

"I don't see him," was Jessie's puzzled response as she searched her purse for a cigarette.

"Then, I don't know," I replied indifferently, more interested in the inside straight draw I held in my hand than in Rob's whereabouts. "Last I saw of him, he was showing off for some chick by the pool."

At the time, I had no idea how prophetic my words were. The next few hours were a blur of tears and panic, ambulance lights and life support, culminating in the shocking realization that Rob, our indestructible friend, was dead. He'd broken his neck by diving into the shallow end of the pool, and died on his way to the hospital.

I spent that night in my Maid's Room, sitting alone in the dark, listening again and again to "He Ain't Heavy, He's My Brother" playing on the stereo. My mother came to my room several times, each time rapping gently on the door, but I didn't answer her. I was numb with disbelief, engulfed in thoughts of Rob, overwhelmed with grief at the loss of my friend, and ultimately returning to the same, unanswerable question, "Why?" At daybreak, I dressed in my grey suit and, without saying a word to my family, walked alone to the church and Sunday services. I wasn't particularly religious, it just seemed like the place to be, and as the pastor greeted the congregation, I sat down in the back pew. I took some consolation from the rows of smiling people that filled the church, and when I more closely examined the faces around me, I spied Jessie and Cissy sitting just a few rows up, their arms around one another. To my left, closer to the front of the church, sat Willie, his head bowed as he massaged the back of his neck. The church door opened and I turned to see Tim and Sean standing in the doorway, their plaintive expressions revealing unspoken sorrow. And all at once, my heavy heart felt a bit lighter as I realized we were all there, not in some organized tribute, but as individuals mourning the passing of a dear friend.

When the service was over and the church emptied, we each acknowledged one another but, surprisingly, did not congregate outside the building. I guess we just didn't feel like being together, as if we individually understood that the loss of Rob would only be amplified by his absence. There would be time to mourn collectively, but at that moment, each of us just wanted to be alone with our reflections. I walked the five blocks to Rob's apartment and stood facing his front door for several minutes, mustering the courage to knock. Rob's mother answered the door, and when her red-rimmed, sorrow-laced eyes met mine, we hugged and cried together. "He thought the world of you," she tearfully whispered in my ear.

"Is there anything I can do?" I sobbed as my grip on her tightened for support.

She pulled back and smiled, gently wiping a tear from my cheek. "You already have," she softly consoled, "you gave him your friendship, you treated him like a brother, and I thank you for that."

I returned to my Maid's Room, lay down on the bed, and stared at the ceiling until my anguish gave way to exhaustion, and I drifted off to sleep.

By Monday morning, word about Rob's death had spread throughout the school. Amid an air of uneasiness, we went through the motions of enjoying our final days of high school, but it was next to impossible. Our victorious Senior Class party seemed a distant memory, practically forgotten in light of what had happened. We were finished with classes, and the day was devoted to rehearsal for Tuesday's commencement ceremony. My friends and I huddled joylessly in the gymnasium while Ms. Young issued inane instructions on how to line up and walk. As we fought back feelings of anger toward what had become, for us, an empty exercise, our classmates seemed too wrapped up in their own joy to indulge our grief. In fairness, I couldn't really fault their excitement; their lives would continue even if Rob's would not.

Graduation day arrived, and I made every effort to check my feelings of sorrow and appreciate what the milestone meant to my folks. The commencement would begin at six in the evening, and my pre-graduation hours were occupied with ironing my bright red robe, taking obligatory pictures, and enjoying the excitement and pride of my parents and siblings. Shortly after five, the whole family piled into the car, in order to get me there in plenty of time for the festivities. When we got to the school, I joined my classmates in the student park, where we waited in anxious anticipation. As we lined up alphabetically to parade before our teachers and families, the atmosphere was almost surreal. I felt like a new foot soldier decked out in my red uniform, about to keep my date with destiny. My friends and I exchanged a few friendly glances, but made little contact, the joy of the event being subdued by bittersweet memories. At five-thirty a whistle blew, and we marched into the gymnasium to collect our diplomas and revel in our moment.

Inside, the gym was packed with friends and family. Red curtains hung loosely on either side of a hardwood stage where faculty and guest speakers were seated. As vice president of the Senior Class, I had fought and won an uphill battle to invite Herr Leo Grzenia, a German national who taught foreign language, to give our commencement speech. Herr Grzenia was an older man who stood about five-foot-nothing. He had lived through the ravages of the Second World War, and I thought that, as guests of the country, it was appropriate that we honor a representative of our hosts. Moreover, I was certain we would all benefit from the wisdom of a man who had known the world as both a beautiful and horrific place. But if he did impart any profound messages, they were lost somewhere between the thick, German accent and the acoustics of an old, Army surplus gymnasium.

Herr Grzenia's lengthy, incoherent address finally ended, and the time had come for Liz and two other girls to sing the class song. I had been dreading the moment. I glanced around at the Class of 1973, pausing for a moment each time my gaze fell upon one of my closest friends. My thoughts were interrupted by the hum of the microphone as the trio took the stage and prepared to sing our class song.

As the pianist started playing, a hush came over the crowd and I held my breath, saying a silent apology to Rob. A few, unexpectedly familiar notes gently filled the room as Liz began to sing:

"The road is long, with many a winding turn, that leads us to who knows where, who knows where …"

She was singing our song! All around me, my fellow graduates were turning in their chairs and smiling their approval of Liz's tender-hearted decision to change the program. In that split second, the Studs' collective burden lightened, and our sad thoughts of Rob melted into feelings of joy and gratitude.

"… so on we go, his welfare is my concern, no burden is he to bear, we'll get there …"

I was surrounded by the smiling faces of my peers, swaying slowly in their seats to the rhythms of our Stud anthem. The place was packed to the rafters with adoring parents who looked down proudly at their children. It was coming true, Rob's vision was coming true!

"… while we're on the way to there, why not share. And the love, doesn't weigh me down, at all. He ain't heavy, he's my brother."

At the conclusion of the song, Liz softly added, "That was for Rob

Mathison, our friend. We'll miss him." Goose bumps danced across my skin, and I knew, I just knew, that Rob was with us ... definitely smiling, and probably dreaming up some smartass response.

Chapter Twelve
FROM THE REARVIEW MIRROR

The days immediately following Rob's death passed very quickly, much as I wish they hadn't. It's not that we had prematurely healed from the loss of our dear friend, but as they say, time marches on, and so does the Air Force. Within two weeks of graduation, four of my friends had already boarded the metal birds that would wing them back to the "world," and with each departure, one more chapter of the Studs saga came to a close. In another ten days we'd all be gone: Tim had enlisted in the Navy; Willie would head back to Goosetown, Tennessee, to attend junior college; Jessie had enrolled at the University of Maryland, in Munich; Cissy's family had been transferred to South Carolina; Sean, whose old man was retiring to Miami, Florida, would accompany his father back to the States and, in a few months, would don the uniform of the Air Force's Elite Guard; and I, still choosing to keep my options open and take one day at a time, had decided to postpone higher education and tag along with my family to Dad's next assignment, someplace called Austin, Texas.

To be honest, I was a little bummed. I'd looked forward to saying adios to school for so long, yet now that the time had come, real feelings of confusion and loss had settled deep in the pit of my stomach. In ten days that would speed by all too soon, Ramstein, K-Town, Maid's Rooms, and the best year of my life would become history, and when enough yesterdays pile up, even the memories fade. Although I did understand that the life of a military brat came with a "don't get too attached" clause, this move seemed different somehow; it hit harder than any other. This time, I was saying goodbye to much more than an Air Force base.

I was preparing to meet the rest of the guys at the Rome Inn for some pizza and beer, a nightly ritual since graduation. Night after night, we'd gathered to reminisce and bid farewell to another of our brethren— tonight's casualty was Tim. As I fumbled through my near-empty closet, searching for a decent shirt that had made it past Mom's packing frenzy, the sour odor of fresh paint filled my nostrils, driving home the fact that the glory days were coming to an end.

My Maid's Room had been totally stripped of its character; fresh, white paint glistened from walls once covered by rock band posters, political slogans, beer signs, and centerfolds. My record collection sat in two boxes marked "Medical Equipment – FRAGILE." Posters were neatly rolled and stacked in the corner, and at the foot of the bed sat Dad's old footlocker, packed to the brim with priceless memorabilia from moments in time that I not only lived, but that lived in me.

When I emerged from the dark, dank hallway through the metal doors that led from the stairs into the late-Spring night, cool, fresh air enveloped me, and I smiled as I gazed at the stretch of olive-colored buildings that lay before me. For the past three years this had been home, and with a deep, satisfying breath I soaked up the view, realizing, perhaps for the first time, just how beautiful and tranquil it truly was. The illumination from the tall streetlights lit up the buildings, reflecting off the windshields of countless cars that filled the parking lot and casting eerie beacons down nearly deserted streets. The stacks of apartments that peppered the blue-black night sky were aglow from the light of a hundred living room lamps, their radiance twinkling behind off-white, government-issue curtains.

"Nice night, isn't it?" a voice from behind me suddenly stated.

I spun around, startled by the abrupt intrusion on my sentimental musing, to see Dad, standing alone on the balcony above me. "Wonder what the weather in Texas is like this time of year," he continued as he leaned gently forward, resting his elbows on the handrail and folding his hands.

"Probably hot," I smiled.

"Yeah," the old man grinned, "probably."

"Yeah," I chuckled and nodded my head in agreement, "probably hot."

"I always wanted to live in Texas," Dad confided. "Did you know that, Mike?"

"No, Pop," I answered, "since when?"

"Oh," the old man reflected as he shifted to lean against the railing, and folded his arms across his chest, "for years now. Hell, since I was a kid watching those Saturday morning westerns at the movies."

"Now that you mention it," I smirked, "I do recall some furniture we had with saddles and horse heads on it."

"Yeah," Dad laughed and shook his head, "your mom really hated that stuff, didn't she? Seriously though, I've always had this fantasy of driving one of those long Cadillac convertibles, with a huge set of longhorns mounted on the hood, my ten-gallon hat flapping in the breeze while I speed down a winding, dusty road that leads to the R-7 Ranch."

"The R-7 Ranch," I moaned. "What's the R-7 Ranch?"

"Just a dream of mine," Dad smiled. "There are seven in our family ... seven Ritters ... the R-7 Ranch, get it?"

"Oh, I get it," I grinned, "kind of like the movie Giant, with you in the Rock Hudson role."

"Hey, if the boots fit ..." Dad returned. "Guess I'm getting too old to dream, huh?"

"Naw," I chuckled as I started to leave, "you'll never get old."

"We all get old, chief," Dad replied.

"Not you, Pop," I shouted over my shoulder. "Mom won't let you."

I walked alone for several blocks, heading toward the Four Corners, a main intersection on the base where the movie theatre, base exchange, Youth Center, and church occupied opposite corners ... hence, the name. It was Ramstein's version of a shopping mall, and usually a hub of activity. As I approached, the movie was just letting out, and the street filled with chatting patrons, strolling to their cars or standing in small groups, talking leisurely about the movie they'd just seen. While scanning the crowd, I noticed Hank and a few other guys standing in a semicircle, taking turns excitedly reliving choice parts of the feature film, Bruce Lee's Enter The Dragon. My first instinct was to cross the street as nonchalantly as possible, a discreetly desperate attempt to avoid being sucked into one of Hank's infamous, long-winded, blow-by-blow retellings of the movie. Nonetheless, I continued on my path, stopping right behind Hank just as he spun in place amid a flurry of Kung Fu hand gestures, undoubtedly reenacting his favorite scene.

"Hey, Ritter," Hank grinned from his crouched, martial arts position, "almost gotcha there. Did you see the flick?"

"Yeah," I smiled, "great movie."

"Did you see the part where Bruce Lee jumps straight up into the air and lands in that tree?" Hank breathlessly continued.

"Yeah, Hank," I acknowledged, "I saw it ... great scene."

"And when he was giving that kid Kung Fu lessons in the beginning?" Hank persisted.

"Yeah, Hank," I replied petulantly, "I remember."

Hank sidled up next to me and placed one hand on my forehead as he pointed at the distant sky, mimicking in his worst Chinese accent a line from the movie: "Don't concentrate on the finger or you'll miss all that heavenly body."

"Nice Bruce Lee imitation," I smiled, taking a step back. "Sounds just like him."

"Words to live by, Ritter," Hank grinned, "words to live by."

"You bet," I confirmed, backing away in an attempt to extricate myself from the situation, "and I wish I had more time to talk about it, but I'm already late."

"Yeah, okay," Hank sighed, a little disappointed at my abrupt termination of his impassioned narrative. "Meeting up with Sean and Willie and those guys?"

"Uh-huh," I called back, resuming my journey, "over at the Rome Inn."

"Maybe I'll catch up with you guys later," Hank shouted as I turned to cross the street. "We can talk about the movie some more."

"Wonderful," I muttered while jogging through the intersection, grimacing. "I can't wait."

I climbed the hill to the Youth Center where the first dance of summer break was taking place. The grassy hillside was partially lit by the bright light that spilled from the Center, casting long shadows across the sloping terrain. A group of kids had gathered by the front door, taking quick drags off stolen cigarettes and joking around. Through the windows, I could see kids dancing to the music of Dr. Pig; I'd heard it was the band's last gig before the drummer went off to college at Ball State.

Behind the Youth Center lay the Commissary. Its long loading dock was deserted now, but signs of earlier enterprise remained in the smattering of empty chocolate milk cartons that littered the aging, wooden planks. Climbing a short set of metal stairs, I sat down on the splintered floor, in the glare of a harsh, yellow light that hung tenuously above the large, metal bay door behind me. Dangling my legs over the side of the dock, I lit a cigarette, took a deep drag and leaned back, resting comfortably against my elbows. For the next few minutes I just sat there, blowing translucent smoke rings into the cool, evening air, and drinking in the quiet. While running my fingers over the weather-beaten timber, I discovered something etched into the rotting wood. I took out my Zippo lighter, crouched on my knees, and held the flame close to the weathered engraving. There, gouged into the boards, were jagged letters that read, "Space Child Wuz Here."

I smiled and resumed my position on the dock. My thoughts effortlessly returned to those days when I worked at the Commissary warehouse, and I wondered if the guys who work here now were building forts out of Kotex boxes. Suddenly, my thoughts were interrupted by a burst of blinding light that flashed in my face. "Hey asshole," I yelped, "what're you doing?"

"The question is," a voice boomed from behind the intrusive high beam, "what are you doing?"

By shielding my eyes, I could barely discern the blurry but unmistakable outline of an M.P. standing next to a jeep, his hand steadying a floodlight on me. Speechless, I could only stare into the light, like a grade school kid who forgot his lines during the class Christmas pageant.

"Well?" the officer insisted.

"I'm trying to come up with an answer," I finally muttered.

"How 'bout coming up with some ID?" the M.P. impatiently ordered as he approached me.

I hopped down from my perch on the dock and fumbled with my back pocket, trying to produce my wallet and that all-powerful little, green card which proved that, while I may be a trespasser, I was an American trespasser. While the officer examined my right to exist, a familiar chugging sound filled the air, clearly the strained efforts of an abused engine desperately climbing the hill from the Four Corners intersection. I looked up to see Jim Bronson driving slowly by in his Volkswagen bus, the engine burping like a fat man at a chili eating contest.

The cop noticed Jim, too. "Okay," he blurted, "I'm letting you off, kid. You're just lucky that VW came by. That sucker's got a ticket coming."

Thanks, Jim, I thought to myself. Sorry about that, buddy ... I owe you a beer.

I continued my meandering journey to the Rome Inn, arriving about ten minutes later. My friends were sitting around a table, eyes glued to the television. "Hey, guys," I grinned, "what's happening?"

"Shhh," Tim hissed, "check this out."

Although slightly perturbed by Tim's shushing, I took a seat next to Willie who was staring so intensely at the TV that I thought perhaps the Air Force was piping in a porno movie from France. Anticipating aberrant behavior on the screen, I was disappointed to see only a young Airman, delivering the nightly news. "And on the campus of Ohio State University," the tinny sounding Airman continued, "the naked truth was exposed—along with a few other things—when a lone streaker, dressed only in a pair of Mickey Mouse ears and tennis shoes, interrupted the school's graduation ceremony when he dashed across the stage, displaying his wares to a startled audience."

"Oh, man," Tim laughed as he slammed his beer down on the wrought iron table, "now, that guy has balls."

"No shit," I chuckled, "and it looked like he was pretty proud of them, too."

"We should do that," Willie nonchalantly commented.

"Oh yeah, right," Tim scoffed. "That's gonna happen. This from a guy who gets dressed in his closet."

"Laugh if you want, smart guy," Willie shot back. "I'll do it if you'll do it."

"Watch out," Sean cut in, "that sounds like a direct challenge, Timmy."

"Yeah," I chimed in, "c'mon, Tim, show Willie that you're not afraid to let it all hang out."

"I've seen him naked," Jessie snickered as she nudged Cissy in the ribs, "and there's not that much to hang."

"Really?" Cissy goaded. "Tell me about it."

"Well," Jessie cackled, continuing the provocation, "remember your old Ken doll? He could give Tim something to hope for."

"Jessie, you are such a bitch," Tim returned fire as he jumped up from his chair, "and you've only seen me naked in your dreams." He suddenly stopped short and a smile crept across his lips. "Okay, okay ... I'll do it ..." he surrendered before adding the inevitable ultimatum, "but you girls have to do it, too."

Jessie was the first one to take up the gauntlet ... and heave it back at Tim. "Not me," she defiantly stated. "No way ... not in this lifetime. I don't flash these babies for just anybody," she smiled and cupped her breasts with her hands. "Me neither," Cissy agreed while trying to mimic Jessie's gesturing, but the impact was lost as Cissy's hands flattened against her chest.

Perhaps the fact that I'd be leaving in a few days made me feel as though I had nothing to lose, or maybe some part of me wanted one last hurrah, a way to go out in a blaze of glory. Whatever the reason, before common sense could get a toehold, I exclaimed, "I'm in."

We all looked at Sean, knowing, perhaps praying, that he'd turn down our invitation to show the world his better side. He was going into the Air Force in a few months, and we figured he wouldn't do anything to jeopardize his chance to become one of the Elite Guard. He'd been lusting after those damn blue berets for months now, so there was no way he was going to risk his opportunity to wear one. Sean debated with himself for several seconds, then articulated the words that have been a battle cry for teenagers since the first one swallowed a live goldfish. "What the fuck ... I'll do it."

"What about the Elite Guard?" a suddenly less-than-enthusiastic

Willie appealed.

"I'll wear a mask," Sean calmly responded, "nobody'll know it's me." Then, looking sternly around the table, he added, "And nobody better ever find out."

"Not a problem," I jokingly assured him. "I'm not that proud of my body."

"How 'bout you, Pickett?" Sean cross-examined.

"Maybe we should give this some more thought," Willie apprehensively suggested.

"I knew you'd chicken out, Pickett," Tim smirked, taking a swig from his Heineken. "All talk."

Willie had been wearing the "weak link" moniker forever. He was the one who always had to be dragged, kicking and screaming, into our misadventures. Rob had ragged him mercilessly about it, we all did, but now he surprised us. "Just name the place," Willie unflinchingly challenged Tim's ridicule.

The dare had been volleyed across the table, and it was again Tim's turn. "Okay, tough guy," he snapped, "the miniature golf course."

"Ha," Willie scoffed, "nobody there but kids ... why don't we just streak my little sister's Brownie meeting?"

I was also uneasy about flashing an audience that consisted primarily of nine-year-olds. "If we're going to do this," I interjected, "let's do it right. There's really only one place worth considering ... the Four Corners, right when the movie lets out."

Willie audibly gulped. "The Four Corners ... we'll be facing hundreds of people there!"

"And each one of them looking at you, Willie Boy," Tim jeered. "Or I should say, looking away from you."

"The Four Corners," Willie dreamily reiterated, "tomorrow night."

"Okay, here's the deal," Sean affirmed, "we wear masks so nobody knows it's us."

"And shoes," Willie added, "we can wear shoes."

"Only on your feet," Tim was quick to clarify.

"I'm bringing a camera," Jessie threatened between giggles.

"No!" Sean protested, "no cameras. I'm not kidding you guys ... if anyone hears about this before tomorrow night, I'm not doing it."

"Yeah," Willie concurred, grasping for any possible way out. "You know," he continued, "we've got to be careful. I mean, what if some woman faints or something?"

"They might fall down laughing," Tim grinned, "but I doubt anybody will faint."

Our enthusiasm mushroomed along with our plan. We decided we'd meet behind the commissary at 9:45 p.m., fifteen minutes before the movie lets out; at exactly 9:55, we'd strip down. The girls, driving the getaway car, would take our clothes and station themselves just behind the Snack Bar, a direct line between our point of departure and landing zone. The whole run would take about thirty seconds, but we hoped the legend would live on for years, with generation after generation asking the same burning question: "Who were those crazy, naked guys?" And it was crazy. In truth, the streak was not meant to shock or offend, we were just doing it to be absurd. It was silly and asinine and infantile ... and we couldn't wait.

When I got home around midnight, my brother was still awake and watching television. Without acknowledging his presence, I went into the kitchen, fixed myself two bologna-on-buttered-toast sandwiches, poured a big glass of milk, and sat down at the dining room table with the most recent issue of Conan the Barbarian comic book.

"What'd you do tonight?" Mark queried from his position on the floor.

"Nothin'," I responded, my focus still fixed on Conan's latest adventure.

"That's funny," Mark smirked. "I heard you guys were planning to streak the Four Corners tomorrow night."

"What?" I choked, jumping up from my seat as I spewed milk through my nose and all over my plate of crispy, bologna sandwiches. "How'd you know that?" I gagged.

"My friend, Rusty, told me. He was sitting next to you guys, having a pizza," Mark gloated, "he heard you."

This was trouble. I was almost sure I could buy or threaten Mark into keeping his mouth shut, but I had no such control over this Rusty kid. He could tell somebody ... everybody. My mind raced ... Shit! Now what? If I do the honest thing and tell the other guys, particularly Sean, the whole thing will be called off, and that's probably what I should do. But if I clam up, our chance of passing into the realm of legendary folk hero is alive, which is more than I can say for myself if the guys ever discover that I knew upfront that our cover was blown. But if nothing does go wrong, if Rusty does keep his trap shut, we'll live forever in fabled renown. My choices were clear ... faithful, vigilant friend, or celebrated, fearless, naked warrior. I made my decision ... I gave Mark ten bucks and told him to split it with Rusty.

The next morning, I awoke under a covering of heavily starched, white sheets, a loan from the military since all our bedding was bundled for passage to the States. The stiff, cotton fabric literally crunched when I sat up; apparently, the military wants everything under its domain, including the linen, to be permanently in a state of attention. Immediately, my nose was overwhelmed by the sour odor of fresh, white paint that, in harmony with the white industrial sheets, gave the room a look befitting a mental institution. But considering what my friends and I were going to do in just a few hours, perhaps that is where I belonged.

The hours preceding my impending lunacy would be occupied with the big move ... at any moment, Global Van Lines would descend upon us to pack up and haul away all our worldly possessions. My charge would be to help Dad keep Mom from over supervising the movers. Our possessions weren't much, but just the same, Dad was determined to ensure that Mom's inevitable, albeit well-intended need to oversee the men didn't result in retaliation against our household goods.

We'd already been through this ordeal a couple of times, when we'd moved from Germany to California, and then back to Germany again, so we knew the drill. Within the hour, a truck and three or four burly German guys would show up and swarm over our belongings like locusts in some biblical parable, clearing everything in their path. And I do mean everything. When we'd arrived a few years earlier, we'd unpacked ashtrays with cigarette butts still in them, and paper plates with half eaten, petrified sandwiches, so this time, Mom piled our personal belongings in a corner and, lest they get tossed onto the truck, guarded the mound like a true soldier ant.

When I arrived at the upstairs apartment, my siblings were standing in the kitchen, juggling bowls of Cap'n Crunch cereal, sloppily attempting to slurp down breakfast while my anxious mother coached from the sidelines. "Hurry up ... I want to get those bowls washed and into a box before the movers get here," she impatiently urged.

Yep, the countdown had begun, all hands were on deck, the circus was in full swing. The cereal bowl juggling act left center stage, Ringmaster Mom cracked her imaginary whip and, on that cue, we all took our positions, each member of the troop having been assigned a particular part in the show. Of course, I wanted to do my fair share; as the oldest, I understood that my commitment to the task would set an example for my younger siblings, and would therefore be a pivotal factor in how smoothly this difficult, tense intrusion on our lives would unfold. "See ya," I waved as I sauntered toward the front door.

"Where's he going?" Mark yelped. "Man, if Mike doesn't have to help, then I'm ..."

"He's going out to meet the moving van," Mom scolded, "now go check your closet one more time and make sure you've cleared it out."

"Mom," Mark huffed, "there's nothing in my closet, I swear ... nothing. Just air and a few hangers."

"Are they good hangers?" Mom quizzed.

"Good hangers? What are good hangers?" Mark returned.

"Good enough to ship to Texas," Mom curtly replied.

"I don't know," Mark sighed, his shoulders slumping forward, "they're hangers ... wire hangers ..."

"We don't need them," Mom hastily confirmed. "I told you kids, these guys will pack anything that isn't nailed down. Honest to Pete, sometimes I think ..."

"I was just going to throw them out," Mark moaned as he shuffled off to his room.

Mom's at her best in a crisis; since she views everything in her life as a crisis, she's had a lot of practice. But sometimes she gets a little too ... perplexed, like this moment, when she was doing breaststrokes in the stress pool. Mark was just unlucky enough to be the first one to dip a toe in the water. He usually was ... the guy had a real knack for being in the wrong place at the wrong time. No matter how much he jumped and danced, he always seemed to land smack dab in the line of fire. Momentarily, I felt sorry for Mark—until I remembered the ten bucks.

Allow me a brief detour while we're on the subject of Mom and her perpetual crisis. It is only through the lens of hindsight that I have grown to appreciate why Mom chooses to walk barefoot on a carpet of pins and needles ... it's her means of survival. I'll admit that, at the time, her obsessions really bugged the shit out of me. I never understood why she found it easier to worry about things than to just let the chips fall where they may. For me, the former takes work, effort, a driving desire to examine all situations for potential peril, real or imagined. But the latter is effortless, almost joyful ... just whistle your way through life and the good and bad moments will inevitably balance themselves out. What I didn't understand then, the piece of Mom's puzzle that was missing or ignored, was that she grew up with her mom, and my grandmother, my wonderful, caring, big-hearted, screaming-liberal grandmother, put the "worry" in "worrier".

In truth, Grammie did worry big—she was partial to the large causes:

war, hatred, social injustice, government corruption, civil rights … the really big-ticket items. I do believe if she could have chosen her lot in life, it would have been Ambassador to the United Nations, delivering a whole world and its troubles to her doorstep. But Keokuk, Iowa, is a far cry from the international fervor of New York, so Grammie channeled her ample capacity for concern into local issues where, I've heard more than one person say, she had a profound, positive effect on the lives of many people.

Even so, the handmaiden of worry is preparedness; that is, expect the worst and you'll never be disappointed. I can't count the times my grandmother told me the story of the grasshopper and the ant. The gist of the story is that the grasshopper spent his days lazing around, while the ant laid in supplies for the bleak times ahead, and when insect Armageddon came to pass, the grasshopper died, bemoaning his shortsighted ways, while the ant confidently hunkered down in his well-stocked, underground shelter. A perilous parable, to be sure—at least that's the way Grammie meant for me to hear it. I, on the other hand, heard a story about a happy grasshopper who enjoyed every day of his life, basking in the brilliance of God's sun and appreciating the many wonders of the planet, while the ant wasted his days, preparing for an end that he, owing to his own pessimism, was determined to create. I never told Grammie my interpretation of the fable—she had enough to worry about.

Anyway, Mom inherited this imbalance, often allowing the anticipation of disaster to outweigh her expectation of good fortune. In some ways, fear served her well over her many years as an Air Force wife, when the unimaginable can quickly become just another part of life. Hell, we all survived many an uncomfortable moment thanks to her proactive worry, and even though I never appreciated it at the time, I have come to respect her resolve and to value all that she did for us.

It was 7:30 in the morning, and the dew on the grass glistened in the bright glare of the new sun. Gazing down the street, I spied a large truck headed toward my apartment building; as it neared, through the dusty cab window, I recognized the familiar grimace of my boss-for-a-day, Helmut. I hadn't even thought of Helmut since last summer, when I endured my brief and notorious tenure as apprentice crate-builder for Global Van Lines.

The van squealed to a stop, and slowly backed up until its rear wheels bumped against the curb. The passenger door opened and Helmut hopped out, holding a clipboard and studying whatever was written on the sheet of paper fastened to it. Without looking up, he headed in my direction. "Gut morning," he muttered indifferently as he extended his hand.

"What's happening, Helmut?" I chuckled and grabbed his hand. Helmut finally looked up from his clipboard. "Haff we met?" he skeptically queried.

"Only once," I grinned. "It wasn't very memorable. So, you're going to cram all our stuff into these crates, huh?"

"Ya," Helmut brusquely responded. "Where's your poppa?"

"In the house ... he'll be out in a minute," I readily volunteered. "These crates must be very strong ... well built ... sturdy wood," I continued.

"Ya, ya," Helmut irritably acknowledged, "we build zem good."

"I'm sure you do," I confidently conceded as I walked over and patted one of the large, blue, wooden trunks. "It'd be a real mess if one of these babies broke open in transit and somebody's belongings bit the dust. Yes sir," I chuckled, "a big mess."

"Never happen," Helmut huffed, still oblivious to our inauspicious affiliation. "Now, please, you go to get," he paused to look at his clipboard, "Master Sergeant Ramon W. Ritter."

I wasn't sure whether he was incredibly dense and really didn't recognize me, or was just a proud, stubborn German, but I decided to end the cat-and-mouse game. "Hey, Pop," I yelled, "it's pack-up-your-cares-and-woes time. Moving guys are here."

Dad came bounding out of the apartment like an excited puppy who thinks he's going for a car ride. "Good morning, fellas," he smiled, taking the clipboard from Helmut and scratching his name across the dotted line. "Everything's all set. We'll just stay out of your way."

"Gut," Helmut mumbled as he motioned to his cronies, still standing by the van, "it will go much faster that way."

"Ray," Mom called from the balcony, "just go ahead and send them up. I'll take it from here. You ... the one with the clipboard," she added, pointing at Helmut, "don't dawdle, there's lots to do."

"Looks like everything's under control," I smirked as I turned to leave. "I'm outta here."

"Hold it, chief," Dad stopped me mid-step, "I thought you were going to help out today."

"But I am helping," I countered, "I'm staying out of the way, just like you promised Helmut. I can't get much more out of the way than the Snack Bar, can I?"

"Always willing to do your part, right?" Dad sardonically commented.

"That's right, Pop," I laughed, "you can always count on me."

I spent the afternoon with my buddies, hashing over the plans for that evening's caper, cheerfully recalling bygone days of high school and Rob, and confidently creating promising scenarios for endless tomorrows. It was close to 4:30 p.m. when I decided I'd best report back to the home front to see how the move was going. "Gotta split," I announced, scooting my chair away from the table that was littered with empty glasses, mounds of twisted soda straws, shredded paper napkins, and half-eaten plates of cold, gravy-soaked, French fries. "They're packing up our stuff today, so I guess I should make an appearance. Besides, it's only four hours 'til the Studs' production of Hair hits the streets, and I need some time to get ready."

"What do you need to do to get ready?" Tim snickered. "Let's see ... take shower, put on shoes ... well, that about covers it."

"We're gonna be naked," Willie softly mumbled, looking as though he had just figured it out. As I made my way past him, he grabbed my arm, "Naked, Ritter ... naked!"

"That's right, Willie," I grinned, gleefully exploiting his rude awakening, "nude ... in the buff ... au naturel ... in our birthday suits ... dicks-dangling-in-the-breeze, stripped down, stark naked."

"A little louder, guys," Sean interjected as he leaned across the table and popped Willie on the forehead. "I don't think the people outside heard you."

Jessie stood up, and with a sweeping, circular motion of her hand, she announced, "They are going to be naked. I, on the other hand, will not," she clarified for anyone who may have overheard.

"You see?" Willie stammered. "Man, everybody's gonna know."

Jessie laughed and slid back onto her chair. "Nobody's listening, Willie," she giggled, "and if they were, what makes you think they'd stand in line to see you naked?"

"Jessie's right," I agreed while continuing toward the door, "on the other hand, getting a glimpse of me ... well, that might draw a crowd."

"In your dreams," Cissy chuckled as she bounced a chunk of ice off the back of my head.

"See you tonight," I chirped. "I'll be the one wearing ... a smile."

When I arrived at Move Central, Mom was standing in the front yard with Helmut, pocketing what was undoubtedly her twenty-seventh reassurance that our belongings would arrive in the States in good condition. "Please," Helmut was pleading, "I promise you, lady, if your things break, I will fly to America and fix zem, myself."

"So you do think something might get broken?" Mom huffed.

"*Ach du liebe* ..." Hemut softly moaned, gripping his forehead, "nothing vill be broken." He glanced at me as I approached and, without skipping a beat, added, "Your son didn't build zees crates."

The old S.O.B. knew all the time, I thought; but rather than stick around and be roped into explaining to Mom what Helmut meant by his remark, I made a quick U-turn and headed toward the apartment building. I moseyed up the stairs and waltzed into our hollowed-out apartment, in search of less-threatening discourse.

Inside, Dad was sitting in the middle of the living room floor, surrounded by my brother and sisters. They were rummaging through an old footlocker, its weathered top hanging by one rusty hinge, and scattered across the carpet were small piles of pictures. "This is you when we lived in Clovis, Cyndy," Dad said as he held up a crumpled, black-and-white photograph. "Do you remember that Easter dress? I swear, I've never laughed so hard as I did when I saw you trying to walk in that thing. You must have been all of two when this was taken."

"Yeah," Cyndy grinned, "I remember ... I think."

"Where's one of me, Daddy?" Ruth Ann implored, positioning herself closer to the deep, tattered trunk and the mound of Instamatic memories.

"Here you are, baby," Dad smiled, "you and Connie ... going to ballet class in California."

"Here I am," Mark giggled, "I remember the Christmas I got that Captain Orbit space suit ... man, I can't believe you actually bought me that."

"We didn't," Dad reminded him. "Santa brought you that."

"Oh, yeah," Mark knowingly agreed, "it was kinda cool."

Actually, this whole scene was kinda cool—the old man strolling down memory lane with his kids, on the eve of our new life in Texas ... another Kodak moment in the making. But, the moment was abruptly suspended by, "Well, something's going to get broken, I just know it."

No, I thought, not now. C'mon, Mom, give your pessimism a rest for a minute, will ya?

"Who's this?" Ruth Ann asked, handing Dad a faded, eight-by-ten, color photograph.

Dad took the picture from Ruth and held it for a few seconds, his smiling eyes scanning its subject. "That's your mom," he sublimely grinned.

"Nuh-uh," Connie declared as she snapped the picture from Dad's hand.

"Uh-huh," Dad jovially shot back, playfully tickling Connie. "That's how she looked when I met her. In fact," he continued as he turned to glance at Mom, "that's how she still looks ... to me."

"Oh, Ray," Mom tittered, "here, let me see that."

Alright, Pop! A quick compliment and, poof, instant tranquility ... collision averted. Truth be told, I knew the old man was sincere and, through his eyes, Mom really did look just as she had almost twenty years earlier. It was sweet, but at the same time, a little creepy; kind of like Kim Novak casting a love spell on Jimmy Stewart in the movie *Bell, Book and Candle.*

Mom knelt on the floor next to Dad and held the picture out in front of her. "Jesus, Ray," she beamed, "it seems like this was just yesterday ... but it feels like a hundred years ago. We've sure been through a lot together, haven't we, Ritter?" She delightedly threw her arms around my dad, and hugged him hard. "Nobody can say we haven't paid our dues, that's for damn sure."

"Any regrets?" Dad softly posed.

"You must be kidding," Mom giggled girlishly as she looked around the vacant apartment. "Miss out on all this fun?"

I was suddenly aware of overwhelming feelings of contentment rushing through me. This tender family scene was one of those moments that comes along once in a great while, a tiny event that settles deep in the recesses of the mind until, over time, it's actually absorbed into your being and becomes a part of who you are. The really cool thing is that it always comes out of nowhere, so the sheer weight of the unexpected pleasure helps to root the moment in your existence.

"Come over here, Michael," Mom coaxed, "this trunk is loaded with pictures of you." The funny thing was, I really wanted to join them but something inside held me back. A certain awkwardness always plagued me at those moments, which is odd, because I'm truly a sucker for sentimentality. I still get downright choked-up when I hear the national anthem, and I can't help but smile when I see an old couple, hand-in-hand. In fact, the description "warm and fuzzy" only scratches the surface of my sensibilities when, each Christmas, the Grinch's heart grows three times its size. But as a teenager, those feelings were personal and guarded, emotions I was unwilling, or afraid, to reveal. And while I drew personal enjoyment by spurring others into sentimental situations, I was more comfortable as a spectator, deeply appreciating the emotional moments, but only, and always, from a safe distance. So even though I was a few hours away from exposing myself to the world, literally, I couldn't muster the courage to participate in my family's journey down memory lane. "Uh, okay, Mom," I nervously stuttered as I crossed over and took a seat near the trunk, "but only for a minute."

The sun had already set when the moving van, laden with the Ritter's whole kit and caboodle, wobbled away, and we were left with only the personal items that we truly couldn't do without. "We're going over to the Rome Inn for some pizza, Mike," Dad said as we watched the truck chug slowly away. "Why don't you come with us?"

"Maybe I'll meet you there later," I quickly responded, "there's something I've gotta do first."

"Take a jacket," Mom cautioned. "It's supposed to get cool tonight."

"I won't need it," I called from the doorway, and not wanting an argument, I hastily disappeared down the stairs.

"Maybe you should tie it around your waist," Mark mirthfully yelled from the balcony, "just in case you feel cold later." As I slid into my car, it occurred to me to go back and threaten my little brother, but I glanced at my watch and decided I'd have to rely on the ten-dollar bribe, and Mark's fear of a potential pummeling, to keep him quiet.

While speeding along, I suddenly realized this would be my final night in the "Cream Machine." I'd already sold it for three hundred bucks to one of Jim Bronson's GI friends, and the guy was picking it up in the morning. I knew I'd miss the car. It was a hunk of junk, to be sure, but it was my first car, and a guy's first car is like his first sex ... no matter how rough the ride, he never forgets it. And yet, when I pulled into the parking lot behind the Youth Center and saw my cohorts laughing and cutting up, all fond reflection on the old VW was instantly left behind.

"Cavalry's here," I excitedly proclaimed while climbing out of my car, "are we all ready to charge down Four Corners hill?"

Tim leapt toward me, thrust a beer into my hand, and howled, "Here's to the charge of the nude brigade! Man, this is gonna be great! A first! I can see the headlines now, 'Streakers Strike Four Corners!'" He held his beer bottle up to my mouth, simulating a microphone. "Tell me, sir," he parodied, "what did you see? Were they actually ... naked?"

"They sure were," I played along, "grown, runnin', naked men. I did two tours in Vietnam, and I tell you I never saw anything as shocking and sickening as what I witnessed here tonight. Jesus Christ, the whole thing's just disgusting!"

"And you, madam," Tim persisted as he swung the beer-bottle microphone around, and resumed his mock interview with Jessie, "did you see anything ... peculiar?"

"Oh my, yes," Jessie sniffled, "these ... these naked boys, with their ... their ... things just exposed like that. And ... and ..." she shuddered while tightly clutching her blouse, "I think one of ... the things ... actually brushed against me when the boys ran by!"

Willie was already hunkered down behind a bush, his eyes riveted on the movie theatre that sat just two hundred yards away, at the bottom of the hill. "Shhhh," he hissed, "somebody's gonna hear you."

"You guys are really going to do this," Cissy dubiously asserted.

"And you, sir," Tim carried on with the gag, as he sat down on the curb and jammed the bottle in front of Sean, "any thoughts on what happened here tonight?"

Sean had been sitting silently on the curb, focusing his complete attention on lacing up his track shoes. "I don't want to play," he somberly replied.

Tim, taken aback by Sean's reaction, stood up and held the empty bottle to his own mouth. "Oh, you don't want to play," he sneered. "We're all here to play, man. Why don't you just lighten up!"

I grabbed Tim's shoulders from behind, while Sean calmly completed his task. "He's psyching himself out," I loudly whispered in Tim's ear, "like he does before a big track meet."

"Oh, sorry," Tim moaned. "Didn't know I was intruding on his cosmic oriental meditation."

Ignoring the sarcasm, Sean stood up and started doing leg stretches. "It's called 'focus'," he coldly remarked, "I'm getting my mind set on the finish line."

Tim wouldn't let it drop. "Getting your mind set?" he spouted. "This isn't a race, you know. It's fun, man ... not a competition."

Sean stopped exercising and pointed his finger at Tim. "It's more than a race," Sean stated, "it's four guys running naked through a crowd of unsuspecting people. I'm streaking tonight because I said I would, and I never welsh on my word, but I'm going through straight and I'm going through fast, even if I have to run over you to do it."

Willie pounced on the prospect of a reprieve. "Maybe we should call the whole thing off," he championed from his position behind the bushes.

"No," Sean sharply rebuffed, "we're doing this. We have to."

"Oh, man," Tim scornfully returned. "Have to? I'm doing this because I want to. Does everything have to be a challenge with you, Sean? Do you do anything just for the shits and grins of it?"

Sean quickly approached Tim and barked, "I could kick the shit out of you and grin about it later."

"I win," Jessie coolly proclaimed as she casually inserted herself between Sean and Tim. "You owe me five bucks, Cissy."

"What's this?" I probed, seizing the break in hostilities to change the subject.

"Jessie said you'd find some way to weasel out," Cissy sighed, her words laced with disappointment, "so, I bet her five bucks that you guys would go through with it."

I took a few steps back to get a clear view of the tapestry unraveling. Sean and Tim were at each other's throats, Willie was shaking in the bushes, and Jessie was exhibiting her unwavering support by betting against us. Several strained seconds passed before Sean broke the suspense. "Hold on to your money, Cissy," he advised, "nobody's weaseling out of anything."

"That's right," Tim exclaimed, raising his beer-bottle in a salute, "we're like the Three Musketeers ... and Willie ... one for all and all for one."

"Right on," I heartily agreed as I crossed the neck of my beer-bottle sword with Tim's, "one for all ..."

"... and all for one," Sean completed the covenant.

"Uh, before you guys race off to save the Queen," Willie reported from his lookout in the weeds, "you might want to check this out. Ritter, isn't that your little brother there, on the corner?"

I crouched down and peered over the dark foliage. It was Mark alright, standing under the streetlight, accompanied by a few of his buddies.

Besides my brother, I could only recognize one other kid, and unfortunately it was Rusty. This was not good ... not good at all. I'd determine how to kill Mark later, but at that moment, the inflated ball of nervous nausea in my stomach told me I had a bigger decision to make. Should I confess that our scheme had been overheard, and our identities were in real jeopardy of being revealed? The potential for disaster was enormous, and my mind shifted into overdrive. How many other kids did Mark tell? What if, somehow, the police know that we're planning to streak? Wait ... don't panic. Stay calm. Maybe Mark is just meeting some friends, to go see a movie. Sure, that's it, he's much too afraid of an ass-kicking to risk ratting me out. He's just going to the movie. Of course, nothing to sweat about.

"Yeah," I answered, trying hard to feign indifference. "That's him. So what?"

"So, nothing," Tim huffed as he started to unbutton his shirt. "Quit stalling, Pickett, it's rock-and-roll time."

"Oh my gosh," Cissy cooed, taking Tim's shirt from him and draping it across her arm, "they're really going to do it."

In the shadows of the parking lot we silently undressed, until all we wore were our underwear and sneakers. The girls stuffed our clothes into my Volkswagen, and climbed into the front seat. It was almost time for the movie to let out, and the show to begin.

We had each come prepared for anonymity: Tim put on his rubber Nixon mask; Willie sported a cowboy hat and a Groucho Marx nose and glasses; Sean tucked his long hair under a baseball cap and hid his face with a surgeon's mask; and I stretched a pair of my sister's pantyhose over the top of my head, concealing my face with one of the legs while the other hung limply off my shoulder, like a dehydrated snake.

Sean leaned through the driver's window of the car and spoke to a giggling Jessie, sitting behind the wheel. "Okay, girls," Sean mumbled from behind his medical disguise, "you know the drill. You take our clothes and drive over to that dark area behind the snack bar, where the streetlight is burned out. It's a straight shot from where we are, through the intersection, to where you'll be waiting. And remember to leave the engine running! Now, you got it?"

"Sure, sure," Jessie snorted, "we've got it. But, enough of this chatter … boys, hand over that underwear!"

Tim whipped off his jockey shorts and sling-shotted them into the car, hitting Cissy in the face; she squealed, and flung the tattered, grey briefs into the back seat. We all followed suit, albeit much more modestly, and were finally left with only our tennis shoes for warmth.

"Ta, boys," Jessie waved, and off they drove, leaving us standing alone and naked on the asphalt, with no way out but through. The movie would be over in a matter of minutes, so we crouched together in the brush overlooking the Four Corners. My brother and his friends were still stationed under the streetlight, and seemed to be scanning the horizon. Not a good sign, but at least the crowd didn't seem to be expanding.

Now, crouching naked is not one of the most comfortable things in the world, but crouching naked in a bush, with three of your buddies who are also naked, is downright annoying. "This is great," Tim chuckled, and swigged the last of his beer. "I feel like Tarzan or something out here."

"Well, I think you feel more like Cheetah," Sean complained. "Get your hairy leg off me!"

Minutes seemed like hours while we impatiently waited in the darkness, our collective view focused on the intersection.

"There's Jessie and Cissy," Willie whispered, pointing toward my car as it turned the corner and disappeared into the shadows.

"When's that damn movie supposed to let out, Ritter?" Sean anxiously snapped, once again tugging on his shoelaces for assurance.

"Any second now," I muttered, "keep your shirt ... I mean, your pants ... shit, keep your shoes on."

The scene was set, all systems were 'go,' nothing between us and infamy but a few hundred yards of concrete and ... wait a minute, what's this? Mark's circle of friends had suddenly quadrupled in size, and there were now thirty or more people gathered on the corner. "Ritter," Willie hissed, "your little brother sold us out, which means you must have told him."

"No he didn't, I mean, I didn't," I nervously responded. "He doesn't know all those people. It's just a coincidence, man."

"Then, why's that kid holding up a sign that says, 'RUN, STUDS, RUN!'?" Sean growled. "Damn it, Mike ..."

"The movie's letting out," Tim cheered, "let's go!"

"Forget it!" Willie screeched. "Are you out of your mind?"

"Okay," replied Tim, in a matter-of-fact way. "Stay here in the bushes." And with that, he lunged from our hiding place and dashed toward the meandering swarm of involuntary voyeurs, his enthusiastic screams muffled by the latex "Tricky Dick" that covered his head.

No words were spoken, no signal was given; pure resignation took hold, and without even realizing it, Sean, Willie, and I abandoned our leafy bunker and bolted after our maniacal friend, securing our disguises as we catapulted down the hill. I am now convinced there are such things as time warps, moments when objects actually enter a slow motion dimension. In that frenzied instant, everything around me blurred, and yet I could clearly discern my brother as he impassionedly yelled, "Here they come!"

Amazingly, we caught up to Tim, and the four naked horsemen of the apocalypse charged from the relative safety of the grassy knoll, across the harshly lit concrete crossroads, and into the throng of startled movie patrons. Flashbulbs popped, kids cheered, men laughed, and women screamed as we twisted our way through the flock of astonished, gawking onlookers, trying desperately to avoid colliding with anyone.

Sean led the way, his feet flying across the pavement so fast that they barely touched the ground, and I was right behind him, my pantyhose ponytail flapping wildly in the breeze. I assumed Willie and Tim were close on our heels, but didn't dare slow down to look lest I lose pace with Sean. All of a sudden we broke through the crowd and, in the distance, I could see the parking lights of my trusty Volkswagen.

While Cissy and Jessie stood nearby, laughing hysterically, Sean opened the car door and started flinging clothes onto the asphalt, frantically searching for his pants. I wheezed up next, and joined in the delirious clothing quest, pausing only long enough to watch Willie careen into the side of the car. "They're chasing us," he panted, "get in the car!"

Cissy and Jessie quit laughing and jumped in the front seat of the car. "Where's Tim?" I bellowed.

"Right here," a voice playfully revealed from behind me. "Man, was that a trip or what?"

I grabbed Tim and shoved him into the car, where he landed on Willie who was scrambling to pull on his underwear. Sean and I shoveled the remaining clothes into the car and squeezed our way into the backseat, with our two naked brethren. "Drive, Jessie, drive!" I shrieked. Jessie shoved the car into first gear and we began to lurch across the parking lot … and promptly sputtered to a stop.

Pandemonium erupted in the car. "Turn the key, Jessie, turn the key!" I screamed at our getaway driver, from my cramped position on the floorboard of the backseat.

"They're coming!" Willie screeched as he furiously rummaged through the pile of clothes, trying to find something, anything, to use as a cover.

"Wrong again," Tim howled, "they're here." Through narrow openings in the mound of twitching flesh and scattered clothing, I could see the faces of our tenacious posse, each struggling to catch a glimpse of us while pounding on the roof of the car.

Jessie was absolutely helpless in the driver's seat, a victim of incorrigible giggling. Cissy sat motionless, face buried in her hands in a foolhardy attempt to hide her identity.

"Damn it, Ritter," Sean hollered, "get this piece-of-shit car moving!"

I gripped the back of the front seat and inched myself up the tattered vinyl, until I could see Jessie's face in the rearview mirror. "Drive!" I wailed, "drive!"

"Okay, okay," Jessie cackled, "keep your pants on. Get it, Cissy?" she jested, with a slap across her co-pilot's arm. "Keep your pants on?"

"We all get it!" I screamed. "Will you start the damn car!"

By now, my little Volkswagen Beetle looked like a wounded bug being attacked by scavenger ants. The thin, metal body rocked from side to side, as the ravenous horde toyed with its kill. But just as suicide seemed the sole means of escape, the engine kicked over and Jessie turned to look at us, smiling proudly at her accomplishment. "Ta-da," she chirped.

"Ta-da?" Willie roared. "Ta-da? Get us the hell out of here!"

Using both hands, Jessie forced the car into gear. "To the Rome Inn, next stop on the Humiliation Tour," she chuckled as the car lunged forward, threatening the sea of startled spectators. Jessie gripped the wheel and promptly became Mario Andretti, squealing around corners and speeding down dark alleyways, narrowly avoiding several large dumpsters on her way to the main street. "Fasten your seatbelts, boys," she warned, and propelled the car over a curb; we hit the road with such force that the hubcaps flew off and landed on the asphalt, causing a clamor that echoed in my ears all the way to the Rome Inn.

Don't ask me how, but somehow, in the cramped space of the backseat, amid all the laughing and cheering, we wrestled into our clothing. When we rolled into the Rome Inn parking lot we had all succeeded, all but Tim who, except for his Fritz-the-Cat T-shirt, was still naked from the waist down. "We're here," Jessie sighed as she fumbled through her purse for a much-deserved cigarette. "You can put your clothes on now, Tim."

"I can't," Tim calmly replied. "And do you want to know why I can't? Because these," he smugly announced, holding up a well-worn pair of underwear, "are not my shorts."

"Oh my God," Willie gulped, "they're mine. That means ..."

"That's right, Willie Boy," Tim chuckled. "You're wearing my skid marks."

A mighty shudder shot through Willie; I could see the actual chill creep up his spine. I'd never seen a person literally shudder before, so it was with both intrigue and amusement that I watched while Willie's twitching intensified into a full-body spasm. His back stiffened, his legs trembled, his arms shook, and his head jerked as his mind short-circuited, unable to handle the surge of revulsion that swept over him. His response to Tim's proclamation was so severe that we were momentarily stunned, uncertain whether to burst out laughing or call an ambulance. But our passing concern was soon replaced with uncontrolled hilarity. Okay, so sympathy wasn't our strong suit ... but it was funny.

"I think I'm gonna be sick," Willie muttered, swaying back and forth.

"I don't blame you," Jessie consoled, while struggling to control her giggles. "You just go right ahead and throw up if you need to."

"Hey," Tim added from the backseat, "I'm starting to get a little offended in here."

As entertained as I was by the final act of the evening's production—the great underwear exchange, a performance worth any price of admission all on its own—I was still conscious of the feeling that this was it, our last curtain call before we went our separate ways. But the melancholy was fleeting, and abruptly gave way to more comforting emotions of satisfaction and delight. I actually felt good, special, and fortunate to be a part of something that was, in my history of friendships, unparalleled. These people were as close as family, and I knew I'd cherish the memories of our adventures for the rest of my days.

Once everyone's "boys" were housed in their proper apartments, we stumbled through the double doors of the Rome Inn and made our way to the open air of the beer garden, to bask in the glow of our latest stunt. Willie still clung to the hope that we had gone unrecognized, and cautioned us to hold our voices down as we passionately recounted our exploit. "Shhhh, you guys," he hissed, "you're gonna blow our cover."

"You mean our uncover," Tim howled, reveling in the obnoxious humor of his own pun. "Look, Pickett, it's over, quit worrying, nobody cares."

"Oh, yeah?" Willie retorted, "then what about all those people, just waiting for us? They had signs, for Christ's sake! I'm sure they're trying to find out who we are."

"I think they already know about you, Pickett," Sean smirked. "That stupid rubber nose and glasses you were wearing fell off right after we started running."

"Oh, God," Willie whimpered.

"Don't worry, Willie," Cissy comforted. "Later on, we'll go back and look for your costume."

"Well, I need a drink," Jessie resolved while reaching for her leather-fringed purse that hung haphazardly from the back of her chair.

I leaned over and gave Jessie an unprecedented smooch on the cheek; her delighted reaction to my kiss served to double the pleasure. "It's on me, babe," I grinned. "Any woman who can drive like that shouldn't have to pay for her own beer."

"Finally," Jessie beamed, "one of you guys shows a little appreciation. Thank you, Michael ... oh, and would you make that a rum-and-coke?"

"I'll have a piña colada," Tim mimicked, "oh, and would you make sure they put a little, pink umbrella in it, and, oh, those little fruits slices. I just love those little fruit slices."

"Got it," I assured them, "one rum-and-coke, and a pitcher of beer for everyone else."

I zigzagged my way through the packed dining room, heading toward the bar to place my order, when I noticed my little brother, standing near the front door. He was scanning the crowd as if in search of someone. I immediately changed course and came up behind him. "Looking for anyone in particular?" I demanded.

I expected him to fear recrimination for shamelessly ratting me out, but instead when he turned to face me, he wore a big grin and held a ten-dollar bill in his outstretched hand. "Here, man," he snickered. "It was worth it."

"I should pound you," I threatened.

"But you won't," Mark chuckled confidently, as he shoved the ten-spot into the pocket of his jeans, "because if you'd been in my place, you'd have done the same thing."

He was right, of course; in the Ritter family, blood ties don't hold a candle to the twisted satisfaction we get from watching a member of the family make a fool of themselves. To this day, one of us slams our head into an open cupboard, trips over a rug, or gets caught doing something really embarrassing, and it sends the rest of the family into stitches. So, while I could understand his amusement at my expense, this display of fearlessness was a new component, and I was both surprised and a little impressed by his daring.

I grabbed him around the neck in a playful headlock. "All those people waiting out there knew it was us?" I grilled him while buffing the top of his head with my knuckles.

"I swear," Mark elatedly professed, "I only told a few guys."

"Did you tell them to make signs?" I facetiously snarled as I let him go.

"No," Mark grinned, "but it was a nice touch, don't you think?"

"Yeah, nice touch," I haltingly admitted, placing my arm across Mark's shoulders and guiding him toward the bar. "We were kind of like the Beatles."

"Only, naked," Mark clarified. "Anyway, it was really cool. Everybody's going to be talking about this. You guys are heroes, man."

"Unless Mom and Dad get wind of it," I cautioned, "which would be a major drag. What do you think they'd do if they found out?"

Mark pointed toward the back of the crowded room. "Why don't you ask them, they're sitting right over there," he suggested. "I was supposed to meet them here for pizza." Just as I peered in their direction, Mom looked up and caught my eye; she waved for us to come over.

"Don't say anything," I mumbled to Mark, "let me do the talking."

We made our way to the table where my family was seated. Strewn across the checkered tablecloth were two, large pepperoni pizzas, and numerous red plastic tumblers of soda. My dad and three sisters were engrossed in a movie they were watching on the television set, that sat high on a shelf, in the corner of the room. "Hi, boys," Mom beamed, "isn't this nice? Come, sit down, have a slice of pizza. They're showing The *Incredible Mr. Limpet* on TV. It's almost over, but you can still catch the end."

"Actually," I sheepishly responded, "my friends are waiting for me in the beer garden, so ..."

"I'll have a slice," Mark gladly accepted, interrupting me mid-excuse. "Can I have a sip of your beer, Pop?"

"Yeah," the old man absentmindedly approved, immersed in Don Knotts' aquatic alter ego.

"You may not," Mom instantly inserted. "Who do you think you are, asking your father for a drink of his beer? Do you believe this kid, Ray? I swear, he's getting more like his brother every day."

"Thanks," Mark returned, as if receiving a compliment. He tore off a big chunk of pizza and shoved it into his mouth.

Until that moment, I really hadn't harbored any idea that Mark regarded me as anything more than his pain-in-the-ass, gets-everything-he-wants older brother. But there was a hint of admiration in his voice, like he believed I was actually worth emulating, and I was genuinely touched by his response to my mother's disparaging observation.

I again attempted to extricate myself. "So, anyway, Sean and the guys are ..." I started, but my pretext was interrupted by a voice coming from the television. "Good evening, I'm Technical Sergeant Lance McConnel, and this is The Ten O'clock News. NATO military exercises continued today, in the wake of unsettling developments in the Middle East ..."

"I've gotta go, Mom," I beseeched, "the guys ..."

Mom folded her napkin and tossed it on the table. "The guys, the guys ... would it kill you to spend one evening ..."

Being that I had heard this song before, I instinctively knew that if I agreed with her, it would cut short the lecture. "You're right, Mom," I broke in, "I should spend more time with my family, and I will. It's just that tonight ..."

"Hush a minute," Dad insisted, bringing a momentary halt to the debate. "I'm trying to hear the news, they're talking about Ramstein." At once, our attentions focused on the news report.

"The streaking fad has struck Ramstein Air Force Base," Sergeant McConnel's voice boomed from the TV.

"It was reported that four teenage boys, recent K-Town graduates, ran through a crowd of movie patrons just as the picture was letting out, wearing nothing but ... well, nothing. The manager of the Four Corners Theatre said ten people had complained about the event, but of those ten, six had complained that the boys ran so fast, they were unable to get a good look. The streakers themselves were unavailable for comment."

Mark looked at me. I looked at Mark. We both looked at Dad. We didn't have time to look at Mom. "Sounds like something you'd do, Michael," she dryly pronounced as she dipped the corner of her napkin into a water glass.

Defenses up! Watch your step here, boy, you're walking into a minefield! Could she somehow already know? Is this a setup? No, Marks a rat, but he isn't a fink, he wouldn't tell Mom. Play it cool.

"Yeah, right," I chuckled nervously. "I still have nightmares of showing up at school, in my underwear." Then, like an idiot, I overplayed my hand. "Took a lot of guts to do that, though ... run naked through a crowd of people, I mean."

Mom settled back in her chair and took a moment from her latest crisis, pizza sauce on my little sister's pants, to weigh her response. "All the same, it doesn't take too many brains."

It's all part of the game, don't make a big deal out of it. She's not calling me stupid, unless, of course, she knows it was me ... no, no, no ... the important thing is to get out, don't argue...

"I'd do it," Mark volunteered, while struggling with a string of melted cheese that hung from his lower lip. "I'd streak."

Alright, Mark! Nice deflection!

"You would not," Mom scoffed.

"She's right," I counseled, happy that the spotlight had shifted but preferring to drop the subject, altogether.

"Betcha I would," Mark asserted as he reached across the table for a soda. "Betcha ten bucks."

That's right, the bribe! He still has my ten bucks!

"You know," I said as I smacked his arm, "I don't think I'll take that bet. I believe you'd actually do it."

"Well, he has a qualified teacher," Mom knowingly remarked, as she pushed away from the table and stood up. She nabbed my little sister and trotted her off to the bathroom, for additional scouring.

Mom was actually letting it slide ... unbelievable. We both were definitely growing up. I sat down in her vacated chair and leaned toward Mark. "Man, she knows," I softly divulged.

"Of course she knows," Mark whispered back. "She's Mom. She knows everything."

Dad sat at the other end of the table, playing a game with my sister Cyndy, while my sister Connie cheered from the sidelines. They were engaged in a "football" match, a contest in which the contenders seek to finger-punt a triangular-shaped wad of paper over their opponent's "hand" goal. The three of them were oblivious to the melodrama that was playing out just a few feet away. "I'm gonna split," I told Mark as I eased away from the table. "Come into the beer garden and let me know before you guys leave. Oh, and you can keep the ten bucks."

"What ten bucks?" Mark grinned.

He'll go far, I predicted while winding my way back to the bar, where I picked up a pitcher of beer, some plastic cups, and Jessie's rum-and-coke. When I turned the corner to enter the beer garden, it was obvious that my family members weren't the only ones who were watching the news. My friends had been besieged by well-wishers; a crowd swamped the table, cheering and whooping it up, with congratulations all around. Jessie and Cissy were at the center of the pack, basking in the admiration while holding their own personal press conference. Cissy was nodding her head and grinning from ear to ear, as Jessie used an imaginary steering wheel to reenact her getaway skills. Sean and Tim were actively employing their newfound celebrity status to hustle dates; and Willie, petrified Willie, was engaged in carefree laughter, eagerly relating the misplaced underwear story. He stopped when he noticed me at the back of the crowd.

"Everybody knows!" Willie bellowed over the heads of his audience. "We're heroes ... isn't it great?!"

Apparently, this "happening" had the Studs' fingerprints all over it, because once the "streaking" story hit the airwaves, everyone seemed to unquestionably place the tribute or blame, as it were, on us. Maybe it doesn't speak well of one's reputation to be the first suspect when something really stupid goes down, but at that moment, the truth behind the recognition was secondary to the fact that we were receiving kudos. I waded into the throng, trying not to spill any beer as my exuberant cronies greeted me with a shower of pats on my back. Finally reaching the table, I set the pitcher down in front of him. "Mikey, baby," Tim laughed as he reached for a plastic cup, "quite the fanfare … maybe I'll just run around naked all the time."

"How'd they figure out it was us?" I shouted over the rumpus.

"Well," Tim began his casual confession, "I may have told a few people, and I know Jessie told some of her girlfriends and, of course, your brother …"

So, Mark wasn't the sole culprit; the knowledge made me howl with laughter. Tim squinted at me and shook his head, but didn't question my outburst. I guess he chalked it up to the fact that everyone was riding an emotional roller coaster that night—even him.

"You know, I'm really going to miss this," Tim blurted out, as if needing to complete his confession.

"Which part?" I quipped.

"All of it," Tim somberly replied. "This place, this time, these people. In twenty-four hours I'll be back in the States, at Navy boot camp. My hair will be gone, my friends will be gone … but no matter what," he rebounded, shaking off his dejection, "I'm not giving up my Fritz-the-Cat T-shirt!"

"Then, here's to Fritz the Cat," I toasted, raising my cup in salute.

"And his descendants," Tim added, and tapped his plastic cup against mine.

As I reached for the pitcher and a refill, I noticed Mark standing at the back of the garden, waving his hands and silently mouthing the words, "We're leaving now." I acknowledged his message, and returned my attention to Tim. "My family's here," I said as I firmly grasped Tim's lower arm, "I think I'm gonna go with them."

"You can't just leave," Tim gently protested, returning my grasp. "You've gotta say goodbye to everybody."

"We played our farewell performance," I merrily pointed out as I stood up and waved at Mark, who was now joined by the rest of the family. "How am I gonna improve on that?"

Tim smiled broadly and shook my hand. "Happy trails, buckaroo," he affectionately imparted, his voice shaking slightly, "may our paths cross again."

"Until that time," I smiled while fighting back tears. "Until that time."

And with that, I left. I didn't even turn around as I walked over to where my family was waiting. "All set?" the old man asked, placing his arm around my shoulders. "All set," I resolved, "let's go home."

The minute we walked through the door and into the cool night air, I suddenly remembered that my Volkswagen still sat in the parking lot, waiting for our last trip together. "Do me a favor, Pop," I proposed as I tossed Dad the keys, "take Mom and the girls and drive my car back for me. Mark and I can walk."

"Okay," Dad accepted without question, and a few minutes later my brother and I watched the Cream Machine, my pride and joy on wheels, chug into the distance.

"That was nice," Mark noted while gazing down the road at our parents' retreat, "I mean, letting Dad take the last drive in your car."

"Yeah," I admitted, "I'm a real sweetheart. Besides, the cops may have a description of the car."

And we walked together down the shadowy street, laughing about the possibilities.

* * *

The next twenty-four hours passed routinely. The excitement aroused by "The Great Four Corners Streak of 1973," as it would come to be called, died out quickly, eclipsed by summer activities and the inevitable changing of the guard. Tim was back in the States, no doubt giving the Navy a run for its money. And perhaps because none of us was really up to saying goodbye, the remaining members of the Studs never came by to see me before I left.

The Ritters were packed and ready to go, taking with us countless, wonderful memories of Ramstein. The Air Force had dispatched a large, blue station wagon to take us to Frankfurt where, after much paper exchange, we would board the jet that would transport us back to the land of my birth. I was looking forward to returning to the States, but it felt kind of like I was leaving home, to go home. I still consider Ramstein my hometown. I grew up there, I found and lost love there, I opened my mind there, and I knew friendships that closed there. It was in Ramstein that I first started to appreciate Peg and Ray Ritter as caring and courageous people, drawing me closer to my family. And the memories of those years remain fresh in my thoughts, a small tear in the fabric of time that remains open, and free, and glorious.

As Dad tossed the last suitcase into the car, another Air Force vehicle pulled up, depositing an Airman, his wife, and four kids. Through the window of the station wagon, I noticed that one of the kids, a boy about fifteen or so, was hassling his mother about something that she was frantically searching for in her purse. I rolled down the window to hear their conversation. "The key's here someplace," the mother moaned. "I'm sure they gave it to me."

These people were our successors, part of the next wave of American families to take on the trials and joys of life in a foreign land. "Look again," the boy urged, his voice filled with excitement. "I want to move my stuff into the Maid's Room right away." I knowingly smiled when I heard his words; the passion in his voice brought back memories of my own initial thrill when I first signed the lease on the Maid's Room. His story was just beginning, blank pages waiting to be filled with adventures, heartbreaks, successes and failures, and a part of me envied his forthcoming journey.

"Okay, troop," my old man cheerily announced as he slid into the front seat, next to Mom, "this is it. Texas, here we come."

As we slowly drove down the familiar road, toward the front gate of Ramstein Air Force Base, I sat quietly in the backseat, alone in my thoughts. Glancing in the rearview mirror, I noticed Mom looking back at me. "I'm a little surprised your friends didn't show up to say goodbye," she commented, without turning around.

"They didn't have to," I smiled, clutching the Maid's Room key in my hand. "I'm taking them with me."